Orchids of the British Isles

Michael Foley

Photography by

Sidney Clarke

With contributions from

Crinan Alexander,
Sidney Clarke, John Grimshaw,
Barry Tattersall, Ian Taylor

Griffin Press

In association with

ROYAL BOTANIC GARDEN EDINBURGH

Published by GRIFFIN PRESS Publishing Limited
4 Colesbourne, Cheltenham GL53 9NP, UK (www.griffinpress.co.uk)

First published in 2005.

ISBN 0 9541916 1 7

A CIP catalogue record for this book is available from the British Library.

Typeset in Optima.

General Editor, John Grimshaw.

Copy-edited, designed and typeset by Sarah Cannon Publishing Services, Oxford, UK, with art direction by Jenni Navratil. Printed by the Alden Group, Oxford, UK.

Contents

Chapter 5. Species Accounts   *continued*

Chapter 5. Species Accounts *continued*

Acknowledgements

New Taxonomic Combination

Glossary and Abbreviations

Bibliography

Index

*There be divers kindes of Fox-stones, differing very much in the shape
of their leaves, as also in floures: some have floures wherein is to be
seene the shape of sundry sorts of living creatures, some the shape and
proportion of flies, in others gnats, some humble bees, others like unto
honey Bees; some like Butter-flies, and others like Waspes that be dead;
some yellow of colour, others white; some purple mixed with red,
others of a browne over-worne colour: the which severally to distinguish,
as well as those here set downe, as also those that offer themselves dayly
to our view and consideration, would require a particular volume ...*

John Gerard, *The Herball, or Generall Historie of Plantes* (1597)

Ophrys insectifera

The photography in this book is dedicated to four friends and colleagues who freely gave their help, encouragement and enthusiasm for the project but sadly did not live to see its completion. In their company many very happy days were spent searching for wild orchids.

Mary Mendum, Patrick (Paddy) Woods, John Fisher and Herbert Weyler

A man, I trifle on thee, cares to kill,
Haunting thy mossy steeps to botanise
And hunt the orchis tribes, where Nature's skill
Doth, like my thoughts, run into phantasies,
Spider and bee all mimicking at will,
Displaying powers that fool the proudly wise
Showing the wonders of great Nature's plan
In trifles insignificant and small,
Puzzling the power of that great trifle, Man,
Who finds no reason to be proud at all.

John Clare, from 'Swordy Well'

Plate 1. The Lesser Twayblade *Neottia cordata*, growing on peat with hair moss *Polytrichum* commune at about 600 m. Cairngorm Mountains, east Inverness-shire, 4 June 2002.

Foreword

It is a great pleasure to introduce this excellent new work on the orchids of the British Isles. As the world's largest and most diverse family of flowering plants, orchids have a special fascination. Their remarkable pollination mechanisms are the most finely tuned in the plant kingdom, reflecting the mutual adaptation of the flowers and their pollinators during the course of evolution.

The native British and Irish orchids may be less flamboyant than some of their showy tropical relatives, but examined closely they are every bit as intricate and colourful. When you get down on your hands and knees to look at it my personal favourite, the Bee Orchid, rivals anything you could find in a tropical rainforest! Sidney Clarke's photographs capture this beauty perfectly, but more than this, they are the result of ten years of painstaking effort to photograph every British species and variety in the wild.

The fact that orchids are often very particular in their ecological requirements and restricted in their distribution added to the challenge. This book will make it easier to find wild orchids thanks to Michael Foley's authoritative text, which provides helpful detail regarding their biology and habitat preferences. The distribution of each species is carefully shown in the accompanying maps; additional chapters by invited experts add to the information provided. Most important of all is the emphasis given to the conservation of orchids, many of which are rare and threatened by the loss of suitable habitats.

This is a book to savour in the winter months and to inspire you to action in the flowering season! For me it is as much a milestone in the literature of orchids as V.S. Summerhayes' classic *Wild Orchids of Britain*, first published in 1951 in the New Naturalist series. I am certain it will serve as an inspiration to its readers.

Professor Stephen Blackmore
Regius Keeper, Royal Botanic Garden Edinburgh, March 2005

Plate 2 (opposite). Always a thrill to find, for many the Bee Orchid *Ophrys apifera* is the epitome of orchids. Coastal chalk grassland, Dorset, 27 June 2002.

Preface

Sidney Clarke

In 1993 the Royal Botanic Garden Edinburgh produced the book *Wild Orchids of Scotland* (by Brian Allan and Patrick Woods, with photography by Sidney Clarke), to coincide with the 14th World Orchid Conference held in Glasgow that year. Following the success of *Wild Orchids of Scotland* a further work was conceived, that would include all the wild orchids of the British Isles, and this project has now come to fruition. The aim throughout has been to produce a book that fully describes all wild orchids found in the United Kingdom and the Republic of Ireland – the geographic British Isles – and to illustrate each taxon with high-quality photographs to show their beauty, structure, habitat and identifying features.

My quest to see, study and photograph British orchids has covered many flowering seasons over a period of at least 25 years, with photography specifically for this book spanning the flowering seasons of eight of the last ten years. Such searches have involved travel from Caithness to Guernsey and from Kent to Clare in western Ireland. The task of capturing these images has been one of enormous pleasure and not a little frustration – both sensations that will be familiar to the ever-expanding community of orchid enthusiasts.

Before any serious fieldwork could commence sites for photography had to be located, flowering periods established, and access granted by conservation bodies and private landowners. The logistics were challenging; long-term planning was made virtually impossible by the fact that the majority of the taxa flower between May and July, some being at their best for as few as ten days – and that period can be earlier or later than expected depending on the weather conditions in a particular year. I am indebted to a network of friends and informants in different parts of the country who kept me advised of local orchid progress! To make the most of the short season available for photography each year a camper van became my home during the summer months, making it possible for me to eat and sleep when light or weather didn't suit photography, or occasionally just to stand by waiting for the conditions to change.

Even so, things didn't always go to plan. *Dactylorhiza incarnata* subsp. *ochroleuca*, almost extinct in Britain, was particularly difficult to capture. On two consecutive years we obtained the necessary permission to photograph it at a site in Cambridgeshire, but in the first year the single plant to appear fell victim to a slug just before flowering, and in the second year no plants appeared. The following year, to ensure that we had at least some photographs of this subspecies, a visit was made to a known site in Bavaria. While we were photographing the German

Plate 3 (opposite).
To photograph the hauntingly beautiful but elusive Ghost Orchid *Epipogium aphyllum*, one of the rarest plants of the British Isles, Sid Clarke had to travel to the Black Forest in Germany. 5 August 1998.

plants, however, *Dactylorhiza incarnata* subsp. *ochroleuca* reappeared at a previously known site in Suffolk – where we did successfully photograph it one year later! On another occasion, having allowed four days on the island of North Uist to photograph *Dactylorhiza ebudensis* we spent three days waiting for a force 10 gale to pass. Fortunately on the fourth day the storm abated to force 8, and it was possible to take the photograph on p. 249. In 2001 virtually no fieldwork was accomplished owing to foot-and-mouth disease restrictions. To complete the series, images of the British rarities *Cypripedium calceolus, Epipogium aphyllum* and *Spiranthes aestivalis* were sought in Austria, Germany and France, respectively.

Over 100,000 miles were covered in the search for the photographs in this book, and in gathering the images I gathered an equivalent store of happy memories of delightful locations, plants, and the many good friends encountered along the way.

Plate 4. Seriously threatened by habitat loss, *Dactylorhiza incarnata* subsp. *ochroleuca* survives in a couple of alkaline fens in East Anglia. West Suffolk, 10 June 2002.

Plate 5 (opposite). Incredible detail is revealed by close-up photography. 'The body of a little man without a head, with armes stretched out, and thighes stradling abroad' – Gerard's description (1597) of the labellum of 'Whitish Dogs stones', known to us as the Monkey Orchid *Orchis simia*. East Kent, 7 June 1996.

Introduction

Michael Foley

The orchid family (Orchidaceae) is one of the largest of all flowering-plant families, with approximately 20,000 species world-wide. Whilst the majority of these are found in the tropics, many growing as epiphytes on trees, around 300 – all of them terrestrial – occur in Europe. Fifty-four species are currently found in the British Isles, and these are described in full in this book.

Orchids have been known since ancient times and were mentioned in the writings of Dioscorides, the Greek herbalist of the first century AD. More recently, the herbal writers of the sixteenth century such as Turner, Gerard, de L'Écluse and de L'Obel described and illustrated many European and British species. At about the same time, the famous Swiss scientist Conrad Gesner was collecting beautifully executed water-colours of orchids and other plants, and many of these still exist in the archives of Erlangen University. In those days it was thought that the shape and appearance of a plant gave an indication of its possible medicinal value (the 'doctrine of signatures'). For instance, orchids possessing a pair of underground tubers, whose appearance suggested a pair of testicles, were thought to be of use in enhancing male virility.

When tropical orchids, with their bizarre and fabulously colourful blooms, were first discovered by European collectors they were difficult to obtain and even more difficult to cultivate. These days they are no longer so elusive but their reputation as rarities still lingers and this may account in part for the particular allure, to botanists throughout Europe, of our own native orchids. Although smaller and less flamboyant than their exotic relatives, the wild orchids of the British Isles have a similarly elusive quality, frequently growing at a site for several years only to disappear – and then subsequently reappear – for reasons which as yet remain something of a mystery. Their method of reproduction is also eccentric, requiring a partnership with a mycorrhizal fungus that provides nutrients for the embryo and young seedling. Methods of pollination are highly intricate and varied and the flowers wonderfully adapted for this process. Charles Darwin, perceiving the implication of these adaptations for his theory of evolution, studied orchid pollination in close detail, and his researches led to a greater understanding of the wide range of methods employed. Few British flowers are more exotic-looking than those of the genus *Ophrys*, which have evolved so as to mimic various insects, luring male pollinators with the expectation of mating.

Most of the species we currently recognise have been known to occur in the British Isles for centuries, with records in some cases going back over four hundred

Plate 6 (opposite). The beautiful white-flowered form of the Burnt Orchid *Neotinea ustulata* occurs occasionally among normal populations. Limestone grassland, Derbyshire, 30 May 2002.

Plate 7. *Dactylorhiza fuchsii* var. *cornubiensis*, the dark-flowered local variant of the Common Spotted-orchid. Coastal grassland, West Cornwall, 16 June 1998.

years or more. As taxonomic and systematic studies have developed, new species and subspecies have been recognised within existing groupings. This is especially so in the case of the marsh-orchids *Dactylorhiza* within which, during the last century, relationships between species have been clarified and several new taxa identified. The occurrence of incoming species, on the other hand, migrating into the British Isles, is rare and hard to prove: one possible case is that of the Lesser Tongue-orchid *Serapias parviflora*. A number of new discoveries have also been made at varietal level in the last 15 years, although there are still several schools of thought regarding the status and validity of some taxa. In continental Europe, for example, *Dactylorhiza ochroleuca* is accepted as a full species, whereas most British botanists regard it as a subspecies of *D. incarnata*. A more extreme example is that of the genus *Ophrys*, of which Europe has between 30 and 200+ species, according to different opinions.

An important development for plant systematics in recent years has been the use of modern molecular techniques, especially in studying DNA sequences. These techniques have come into widespread use in the last decade and the information they reveal has led to a major and ongoing revision of the classification of European orchids. In many cases this work has necessitated nomenclatural adjustments, so that the current scientific names of a few species may be unfamiliar to some readers. The taxonomic path we have chosen to follow in the present book reflects these changes to the traditional classification and is based on the relevant genetic work of others, especially Richard Bateman, Pete Hollingsworth and Jane Squirrell.

It should be remembered that nearly all British and Irish orchids are quite rare, and some are extremely rare. Their conservation for the future is therefore of high priority. Orchids are very sensitive to human activity and are easily damaged or disturbed. Farming practices such as ploughing, drainage, the use of artificial fert-ilisers – almost anything, indeed, that affects their habitat – are harmful and may easily lead to their eradication. When admiring plants, observers should be aware that there may be small seedlings within the immediate area that could be damaged by trampling. Orchid flowers should not be picked, nor should plants be dug up. Collection of a specimen to form the basis for an authentic scientific record should only be undertaken in the most extreme cases and where the size of the population allows. It remains a sad fact that orchids continue to be targeted by unscrupulous collectors, so in most cases we have been deliberately vague as to precise localities. Many sites for rarities are well known to the botanical community and arrange-ments for visiting them can be made with the relevant authorities. Other sites are less carefully monitored and may be sensitive to disturbance, so are best visited sparingly.

As awareness of environmental issues increases and more active efforts are made towards conservation and protection of the natural landscapes of the British Isles, the future looks brighter for many of our native orchids. We can only hope that the extraordinary diversity and beauty of the species described and illustrated in this book remain available for future generations to enjoy.

Plate 8. Orchids can flourish even in close proximity to human activity: the Early Spider-orchid *Ophrys sphegodes*, on chalk cliffs above the ferry terminal, Dover, E. Kent, 11 May 1996.

Chapter 1

The Orchid Plant

John Grimshaw

As Orchids are universally acknowledged to rank amongst the most singular and most modified forms in the vegetable kingdom, I have thought that the facts to be given might lead some observers to look more curiously into the habits of our several native species. An examination of their many beautiful contrivances will exalt the whole vegetable kingdom in most persons' estimation.

Charles Darwin, *The Various Contrivances by which Orchids are Fertilised by Insects* (1862)

It was with such characteristic modesty that Darwin introduced his great work on orchid pollination, a subject that was to him, and remains to us, a wonderful exemplar of the forces of evolution in action. *On the Origin of Species* had been published in 1859 and his book on orchids was intended as a supporting volume, detailing some of the background research that had gone into the long gestation of his theory of evolution. Since Darwin wrote *The Fertilisation of Orchids* the orchid family has been subjected to intense biological scrutiny and the many remarkable features of the life cycle of an orchid plant are now well known. Orchid biology is comprehensively reviewed in many sources, in particular Dressler (1990) and *Genera Orchidacearum* (Pridgeon *et al.* 1999, *et seq.*), as well as popular sources such as Allan & Woods (1993), Cribb & Bailes (1989), Davies *et al.* (1983), Delforge (1995) and Summerhayes (1968), all used in preparing this account.

The orchid flower

The flower, with its adaptations for pollination, is a good starting point for a discussion of a plant's life cycle, and this is perhaps especially so in Orchidaceae. Orchid flowers, however complex they may seem, all share the same basic morphology, with six **perianth segments** arranged in two whorls around the reproductive parts in the centre of the flower. The three perianth segments of the outer whorl represent the sepals, and are usually more or less identical in size and shape. The uppermost is known as the **dorsal sepal**, the other two as **lateral sepals**. In orchids the outer perianth segments are an important part of the flower, usually being as large and showy as the petals and playing an important role in attracting insect visitors.

Plate 9 (opposite).
The Early Purple Orchid
Orchis mascula is a typical
European terrestrial orchid.
Limestone grassland,
Derbyshire, 31 May 2001.

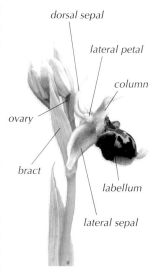

Figure 1. Parts of an orchid inflorescence. *Ophrys fuciflora.*

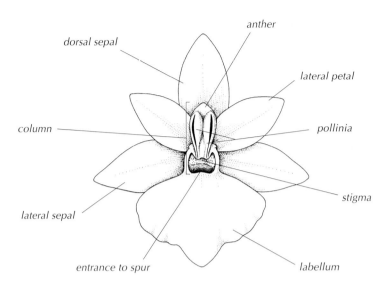

dorsal sepal

anther

lateral petal

column

pollinia

stigma

lateral sepal

labellum

entrance to spur

Figure 2 (above right). Parts of an orchid flower (generalised *Dactylorhiza*).

The three petals form the inner whorl of perianth segments. The two **lateral petals** are identical and often look rather similar to the sepals, but the lower petal is different and may be highly modified. It is known as the **labellum**, or **lip**, and is the feature that gives orchid flowers so much 'character'. The labellum is usually distinctly larger than the other two petals, with a different shape, and often a different colour, or with differently coloured markings. The lip may be lobed, and it may be spurred, the **spur** formed of a hollow process at its base. The spur may or may not contain nectar.

In the helleborines, *Epipactis* and *Cephalanthera*, the labellum is made up of two distinct portions, the **hypochile** at the base and the **epichile** forming the tip. The hypochile is usually pouched or cupped, while the epichile is a flap of tissue projecting beyond it. They are usually differently coloured. Callosities may occur on the upper surface.

In most orchids the labellum faces downwards, providing a landing platform or guide for insects. This posture occurs through a process termed 'resupination', in which the flower's pedicel twists through 180° during its development. Most orchid flowers, with the labellum in the lowermost position, are therefore **resupinate**. In

Figure 3 (right). Normal resupinate position of an orchid flower (*Corallorhiza trifida*) with labellum at the base, the ovary having twisted through 180°.

Figure 4 (far right). In the hyper-resupinate flower of *Hammarbya paludosa* the labellum is uppermost, the ovary having twisted 360°.

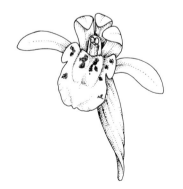

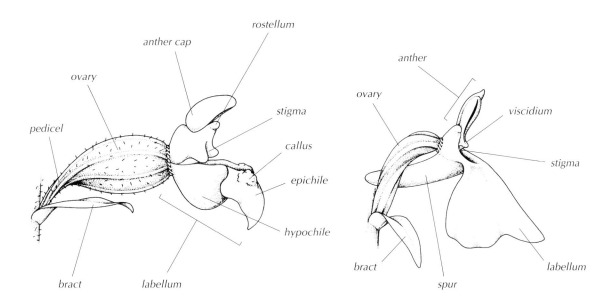

a few cases, however, the labellum points upwards and the flower appears to be upside-down. In the Bog Orchid *Hammarbya paludosa* this is because the flower is **hyper-resupinate**, having twisted through 360° during development. In the Ghost Orchid *Epipogium aphyllum* the lip is uppermost because there has been no twisting, and the flower is described as **non-resupinate**. The labellum of the Fen Orchid *Liparis loeselii* is often higher than the rest of the perianth, but this is because the flower is tipped backwards, bringing the labellum into the uppermost position.

In most plants the male and female reproductive parts are separate, but in orchids they are united in a single structure known as the **columnar gynostegium**, or **column**, formed of the anther and stigma, with the ovary below the insertion of the perianth segments at the base of the column. The column is held in the centre of the flower, immediately above the labellum. At its apex is the single modified **anther** (two in *Cypripedium*), with a staminate portion of two locules producing one or two **pollinia**, each a mass of pollen grains held together in groups of four (tetrads). Pollinia sometimes have a 'stalk' or **caudicle** at their base that connects them to the sticky surface known as the viscidium (see below). The whole assemblage is sometimes termed a **pollinarium**.

Figure 5 (above left). Side-view of an *Epipactis* flower, with sepals and lateral petals removed.

Figure 6 (above right). Side-view of a *Dactylorhiza* flower, with sepals and lateral petals removed.

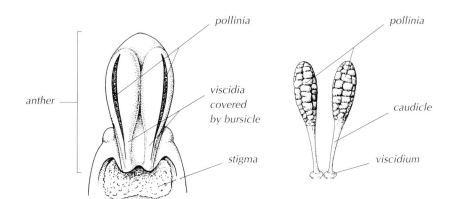

Figure 7 (far left). Column of a *Dactylorhiza*, showing the juxtaposition of the anther and the stigma.

Figure 8 (near left). Detail of the structure of the pollinaria of a *Dactylorhiza*.

Plate 10. Following fertilisation the ovary swells to form a capsule containing many thousands of seeds. *Ophrys sphegodes*, East Sussex, 17 May 1989.

The **stigmatic surface** is found at the base of the column. It is usually a depression or flat area, and is sticky with an exudation of sugars and amino acids. Above it, derived from the median lobe of the stigma, is the **rostellum**. This is a projection of tissue above the stigmatic surface that has a remarkable double function: by forming a barrier between pollinia and stigma it prevents (or reduces the chance of) self-fertilisation, but in many cases it is also involved in pollen transfer. The upper surface of the rostellum produces the sticky **viscidium**, which is held in various ways. In many European orchids the viscidium is attached to the ends of the caudicles of the pollinia and is removed with them when touched by the pollinator. In some genera such as *Orchis* and *Dactylorhiza* the viscidium and pollinia are covered by a membrane termed the **bursicle**, which is ruptured when the pollinator makes contact. In others the viscidium is merely a sticky substance that must be picked up by the insect before the pollinia can be removed, while in *Neottia* the viscidium holds its glue under pressure until contact is made, then squirts it out onto the insect. There is no rostellum in *Cypripedium* or *Cephalanthera*, but in *Cephalanthera* the median lobe of the stigma produces a sticky substance that facilitates the collection and transfer of pollen.

The **ovary**, lying behind the perianth, is also often the 'stalk' of the orchid flower, connecting it to the main stem. It is cylindrical or somewhat rounded, usually with strong ridges that mark the sutures that will eventually open to shed the seed. Sometimes, however, the ovary is held on a distinct **pedicel**, or the ovary and pedicel may intergrade almost imperceptibly.

Pollination

Figure 9. Adaptations for pollination: the long proboscis of a skipper butterfly probes the spur of a *Gymnadenia* flower for nectar (note the pollinia attached to the proboscis), while the stiff labellum supports the insect. The scent and bright colour of the flower attract such diurnal pollinators.

The function of an orchid flower is to achieve the transfer of pollen from the anther of one flower to the stigma of another: it is both an advertisement and a precision mechanism for pollen transfer and reception.

As an advertisement the flower must catch the attention of and attract its pollinators, and it is here that we see most clearly the evolutionary process at work, resulting in the beautiful and extraordinary flowers we enjoy. Each species of orchid has a favoured pollinator or small group of pollinators and the flowers are adapted to attracting precisely these and conscripting them into carrying pollen. Other insects may also visit the flower. These are not likely to be beneficial to the orchid, but occasionally their visits may result in chance acts of cross-pollination within the species, or with a neighbouring plant of a different species to create a hybrid.

Adaptations for attracting pollinators take three principal forms: **'normal' attraction**, through the provision of a reward in the form of nectar; **visual mimicry** or deception, in which the flowers look as if they offer a reward, but do not; and **sexual mimicry**, in which a pollinator is lured to a flower in the expectation of mating. In all cases a combination of floral shape and coloration are involved to bring the insect into contact with both pollen and stigma, the floral parts being placed so as to achieve this easily with the preferred pollinator but less easily with other visitors. Further adaptations function to minimise the chance of self-fertilisation:

for example, the anthers and stigma may mature at different times; or there may be a delay, once the pollinia have attached to the insect, before they move into the position most likely to bring them into contact with the stigma. Specific pollination mechanisms are discussed in detail in the individual species accounts (*Chapter 5. Species Accounts*), but an overview is also given here.

Nectariferous species

The highly fragrant nectar-producing species of orchid such as the fragrant-orchids *Gymnadenia*, the butterfly-orchids *Platanthera* and the Pyramidal Orchid *Anacamptis pyramidalis* are visited by moths and butterflies that probe with their probosces to reach the nectar in the long spurs of the flowers. Brightly coloured flowers are associated with diurnal pollinators, while the creamy-white of the butterfly-orchids makes them visible to night-flying moths. Similarly, the shape of the labellum is important. The lingulate labellum of *Platanthera* offers little support, and these flowers are

Plate 11. Hovering insects may also effect pollination: a Hummingbird Hawk-moth *Macroglossum stellatarum* at a Chalk Fragrant-orchid *Gymnadenia conopsea*. Oxfordshire, 24 June 2003.

Figure 10. Adaptations for pollination: only a large insect such as a wasp can depress the epichile of the labellum of an *Epipactis helleborine* flower to reach the nectar secreted in the hypochile and bring the insect's head into contact with the pollinia and stigma. Wasps are attracted to the subtle colouring and musty scent, while the flowering period of August coincides with their peak abundance.

visited by hovering moths. In contrast, the stiff-textured, outward-facing labella of *Gymnadenia* and *Anacamptis pyramidalis* offer a 'landing pad' for butterflies, although the flowers are also visited by diurnal hovering moths. In these cases the pollinia become attached to the insect's proboscis or head.

Other nectariferous species provide their nectar in different parts of the flower. The helleborines *Epipactis* secrete nectar on the 'floor' of the hypochile where it is accessible to pollinating wasps that have the strength to pull down the epichile. In delving into the flower the wasp's head receives pollen from the anthers, and then deposits it onto the stigma. In the twayblades *Neottia* the nectar is secreted in a groove in the labellum, for collection by flies and ichneumon wasps.

Visual mimicry

A number of brightly coloured orchids with obvious spurs, including *Orchis* and some species of *Anacamptis* and *Dactylorhiza*, offer no reward to their pollinating insects and attract them solely by deception. The flowers look to the insects as if they should contain nectar – often because their appearance is suggestive of truly nectariferous plants such as clover-like legumes – and the insect attempts to reach the nectar it expects to find in the spur. In so doing it comes into contact with pollinia and stigma in the usual way. Markings on the labellum may mimic the honey-guides found in other flowers, and in some species there are structures that look like abundant pollen. In the British and Irish orchid flora this is perhaps most evident in the yellow-coloured ridges on the epichile of the three species of *Cephalanthera*, which resemble masses of pollen. Some visitors may also obtain some reward from the stigmatic exudate.

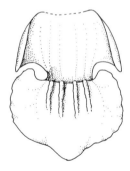

Figure 11. Adaptations for pollination: the ridges and yellow coloration on the labellum of *Cephalanthera longifolia* mimic the appearance of abundant pollen, deceiving potential pollinators into visiting the flower.

Plate 12. *Cephalanthera longifolia*, Assynt, Sutherland, 30 May 2004.

Plate 13. The hairy labellum of an *Ophrys* flower fools male insects into attempting to copulate with the female insect it mimics. *Ophrys sphegodes*, coastal chalk grassland, Dorset, 9 May 1996.

Sexual mimicry

The most remarkable means by which orchids attract pollinators is by mimicking a female insect, to lure in males hoping to mate. The attraction may be achieved through visual stimuli alone, but may also involve the production of odours that mimic the pheromones emitted by female insects. Sexual mimicry is known in many genera of orchids around the world but in few is it as marked as in the European *Ophrys*. In flowers of this genus the labellum mimics the appearance of females of hymenopteran insects so accurately that in conjunction with the production of pheromone-like odours it can stimulate the male insect to attempt copulation. This act, known as **pseudocopulation**, brings the insect's head (or in some cases abdomen) into contact with the pollinia or stigma, and may continue for several minutes, presumably as the male insect attempts to stimulate a reaction from the 'female'. Within *Ophrys*, selection pressure to meet the requirements of insect pollinators has led to a great adaptive radiation of species and varieties, especially in the Mediterranean basin, with most species apparently having very specific pollinators. Despite this, however, relatively few flowers may be fertilised and go on to produce seed.

Plate 14. The best of both worlds: although adapted for pollination by pseudo-copulation the Bee Orchid *Ophrys apifera* is most frequently self-pollinated, as the pollinia descend on long caudicles to touch the stigmatic surface. Limestone grassland, North Somerset, 28 June 1996.

In all cases where orchids mimic another flower, or an insect, their success depends on attracting naive pollinators that have not yet learned the features that will lead them to a real reward. Attracting early-emerging males is important for *Ophrys*, and many Mediterranean species flower in early spring, while species that mimic other flowers often open before the majority of their models.

Self-fertilisation and cleistogamy

Despite the extreme adaptations for attracting pollinators in the genus *Ophrys* it is in *Ophrys apifera*, the Bee Orchid, that we find the most conspicuous example in the British Isles of self-fertilisation. This obviously greatly vexed Darwin, who assumed that the species was doomed to extinction through the ill-effects of inbreeding. In *O. apifera* the long caudicles dry out after the flower opens and detach the pollinia from their original positions, effectively lowering them from the column towards the stigma. Seed-set is consequently high, but mutations are often preserved through inbreeding and local variants can develop and become established.

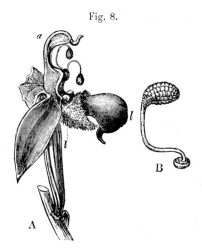

Fig. 8.

B

A

OPHRYS APIFERA, OR BEE OPHRYS.

a. anther.
l. l. labellum.
A. Side view of flower, with the upper sepal and the two upper petals removed. One pollinium, with its disc still in its pouch, is represented as just falling out of the anther-cell; and the other has fallen almost to its full extent, opposite to the hidden stigmatic surface.
B. Pollinium in the position in which it lies embedded.

Plate 15. Charles Darwin's meticulous observations of orchid flowers and their pollinators contributed to his theory of evolution. The self-pollination of the Bee Orchid puzzled and worried him. This engraving from his book *The Fertilisation of Orchids* shows the pollinia descending on their long caudicles towards the stigma.

This is also the case in *Epipactis*, where several taxa lack a rostellum or viscidium and are readily self-fertilised by their own pollen falling onto the stigma, and here again populations of plants with distinct morphologies have developed in some areas. In both these cases cross-fertilisation is possible but appears to be rare.

A few orchids are **cleistogamous** – a state in which the flower is self-pollinated while still in bud. In the British Isles this is most marked in *Epipactis leptochila* var. *cleistogama*; the Dense-flowered Orchid *Neotinea maculata* is probably also at least partially cleistogamous.

Orchid seeds

Successful pollination leads quickly to the fertilisation of the ovules in the ovary and rapid withering of the flower, the mission of which has been accomplished. The ovary swells and develops into a capsule containing the seeds. At maturity the capsule dries and dehisces, releasing the seeds through the slits that develop as the valves open. Orchid seeds are tiny and extremely numerous: counts indicate that in

Dactylorhiza each capsule can contain as many as 2000–5000 seeds, and in Ophrys 10,000–15,000. Tiny and dust-like (0.1–0.25 mm in length), each seed is composed of a **testa** (seed coat) and an undifferentiated **embryo** consisting of 100–200 cells. Most orchid seeds are very similar to each other, as may be seen from the three scanning electron micrographs in Plate 16 (left), differing principally in small details of the architecture of the testa.

Seeds as light as these are easily carried on the wind. Most probably come to rest within a few metres of the parent plant, but if conditions are right they can be carried long distances. It is impossible to be sure quite how far they travel, but colonisation by the Military Orchid *Orchis militaris* of a site in Suffolk, and the arrival of species of tongue-orchid *Serapias* in the Channel Islands and Cornwall, are indicative of journeys of many hundreds of kilometres. The occurrence of Irish Lady's-tresses *Spiranthes romanzoffiana* on the western fringes of the British Isles, directly to windward of its populations in North America, suggests that its seed may have been blown across the Atlantic (although the feet of migratory birds have also been suggested as potential vectors). This dispersibility of orchid seed means that it is not impossible for species to 'turn up' in unusual sites. Sadly though, suitable orchid habitat is currently rare in the British Isles, and gene flow between populations may now be very limited.

Plate 16. Minute and dust-like, containing only an embryo within a reticulate testa, orchid seeds are all very similar: (from top) *Ophrys apifera*; *Epipactis palustris*; *Dactylorhiza purpurella* (all at magnification 32×).

Germination and establishment: the role of mycorrhiza

On landing, orchid seed is easily washed into the soil by rain. Lacking food reserves it is incapable of germination by itself, leading to perhaps the most remarkable part of an orchid's life history: the intimate relationship between the seedling and a **mycorrhizal fungus**. 'Mycorrhiza' is a compound word formed from the Greek words

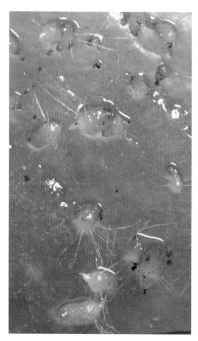

Phases in the development of orchid seedlings, as grown artificially *in vitro*: (1) protocorms shortly after germination (Plate 17, left), *Dactylorhiza purpurella*; (2) protocorms producing their first shoots (Plate 18, right), *Satyrium carneum*.

for 'fungus' and 'root', and is used to describe cases where there is a close relationship between a plant and a fungus, leading to benefit for one or both partners. Mycorrhizal associations are common and many plants are dependent on their fungal symbiont for successful growth, as the fungus provides the plant with phosphates and other essential nutrients in higher concentrations than could be supplied by the roots alone. The fungus benefits, in return, from the carbohydrates produced by the plant's photosynthesis.

In orchids the role of mycorrhiza is rather different, and at least in the early stages the benefit is all towards the orchid; it is not clear whether there is any advantage to the fungus. The orchid seed needs energy to germinate and this is provided by the mycorrhizal fungus. The seed coat is penetrated by a fungal hypha, which also invades the embryo. To prevent annihilation by the fungus the embryo controls this invasion with endogenous fungicides that limit the penetration to a small area of the embryo. Carbohydrates and other nutrients begin to flow into the orchid cells from the fungus, which is connected to a vast ramification of mycelium breaking down organic matter in the soil, or directly to other green plants. The embryo begins to swell, and germination can be said to have begun. The cells proliferate to create a small, white, rounded body called the **protocorm**, from which fine root-hairs extend into the soil. The young plant may develop for some time in this way, gradually fattening up on the mycorrhizal food supply. A growing point will then develop and eventually form a shoot, from the base of which the roots emerge, and the plant will reach the surface for the first time. The first aerial organ is usually a small green leaf, which enables the start of normal photosynthesis and the plant's production of its own carbohydrates. From then on, in most species, the importance of the fungus wanes and the orchid plant increases in size in the normal way through incremental expansion of its photosynthetic capacity. Older works, such as Summerhayes (1968), suggest that a period of many years may elapse between germination and first flowering, but it is now becoming apparent that these estimates were far too long and that many species can flower in three to five years from seed, or even faster, especially when grown *in vitro*.

In many species of orchid the extent to which adult plants are involved with a mycorrhizal partner is unclear, although most do retain fungal hyphae within their roots. Some orchids, however, remain dependent on mycorrhizae for their entire life span, as they lack chlorophyll and are therefore unable to photosynthesise. These have traditionally been known as 'saprophytes', implying that they exist on dead material only. The more accurate term, which we use here, is **mycoheterotroph**, indicating that the fungus derives its nutrients from several sources: living plants as well as decaying matter. In the British Isles three species are obligate mycoheterotrophs: the Bird's-nest Orchid *Neottia nidus-avis*, the Ghost Orchid *Epipogium aphyllum* and the Coralroot Orchid *Corallorhiza trifida*. In addition, plants of some *Epipactis* species are occasionally found that lack chlorophyll

Phases in the development of orchid seedlings: (3) young plant producing its first true leaves and roots and beginning to form a tuber (Plate 19, left), *Anacamptis laxiflora*; (4) young plant with small tubers (Plate 20, right), *Ophrys tenthredinifera*. In their early stages orchid seedlings are indistinguishable.

Plate 21. *Epipogium aphyllum* is totally dependent on its mycorrhizal fungus for nutrients, which may come from fungal breakdown of organic material in the soil or from other plants with a mycorrhizal association. Buckinghamshire, 14 July 1987.

and appear to be truly dependent on their mycorrhizae in the same way.

Several species of fungus form mycorrhizal associations with orchids, but they are usually asexual and almost impossible to identify with any accuracy. Recent research suggests that the suite of fungi involved in orchid germination are different from those involved in mycorrhizal relationships with adult plants (Bateman 2001). Although the relationship between orchid and fungus is often called symbiotic, it is not clear what benefit if any is received by the fungus, and it is difficult to escape the conclusion that this is a parasitic relationship rather than a mutually beneficial one.

Horticulturists were long baffled as to how to get orchid seeds to germinate, although it was known that scattering the seeds around the roots of an established plant gave the best chance of success. The role of mycorrhizae was discovered and elucidated early in the twentieth century, by Bernard, Burgeff and others, and in the early 1920s Knudson grew the first orchid seedlings without mycorrhizae, culturing the seed on plates of sugar and nutrient-rich agar jelly in sterile conditions. With refinements this is still the method orchid growers use to raise seedling orchids, producing vast numbers of plants for commercial horticulture, mostly of showy tropical species and hybrids, although many temperate terrestrial species also thrive in sterile media. Some European orchids, however, do not respond well to this regime, and require a mycorrhizal fungus for successful growth. This must be isolated from the roots of mature plants and carefully cultured so that the seeds can be sown on agar plates containing both nutrients and the fungus (Clements *et al.* 1985, Mitchell 1989, Rasmussen 1995).

The mature orchid plant

Once it has become photosynthetic and less dependent on its mycorrhizal associations the orchid grows much like any other herbaceous or geophytic plant, increasing in size each year until it is large enough to flower. Each species has a distinct growth cycle during which new shoots and roots form, usually in the period during and after flowering.

In the case of **tuberous species** such as *Dactylorhiza*, *Ophrys* and *Orchis*, among many others, the shoot grows each year from the mature tuber that was formed in the previous season, using stored starch as its energy source. Tubers vary in shape from rounded (e.g. *Anacamptis*, *Himantoglossum*, *Orchis*, *Ophrys*) to flattened with finger-like processes (e.g. *Dactylorhiza*, *Gymnadenia*) to narrow and pointed (e.g. *Spiranthes*). As the shoot develops the old tuber withers, and simultaneously a new tuber is formed by the active shoot of the current year. At flowering time, therefore, both the old and the new tubers are usually visible, although the older one is often

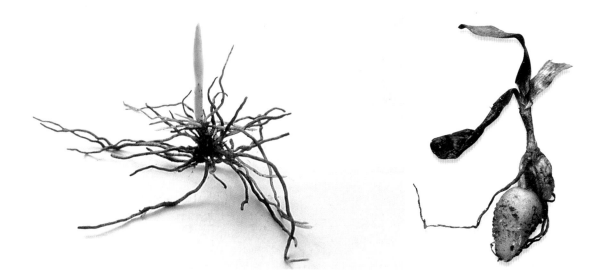

almost completely withered. Following flowering and seed production the tuber becomes dormant – an important adaptation allowing it to withstand summer heat and drought. With falling temperatures and the return of rain in the autumn the tuber produces a new shoot with roots at its base. In some species of the British Isles, including Autumn Lady's-tresses *Spiranthes spiralis*, the Man Orchid *Orchis anthropophora*, the Lizard Orchid *Himantoglossum hircinum*, the Green-winged Orchid *Anacamptis morio*, and all four species of *Ophrys*, the leaves are produced in autumn and are active throughout the winter, but in most the shoot emerges in late winter and early spring, growing as warmth and daylight increase. Flowering occurs in early summer, and the cycle is repeated.

The growth cycle in **rhizomatous species** is similar, but the rhizome perennates from year to year, senescing gradually with the ageing of the plant. The rhizome is usually a more or less thickened horizontal stem, being extended by the development of a new shoot. The roots emerge from the new extension growth but may persist for several years. Rhizomatous orchids may develop extensive systems of roots and long subterranean stems, as in the case of the Marsh Helleborine *Epipactis palustris*. In others such as the helleborines *Cephalanthera*, other *Epipactis* species and the twayblades *Neottia* the shoots may be shorter, resulting in a tighter clump. In a few mycoheterotrophic species (the Ghost Orchid *Epipogium aphyllum* and Coralroot Orchid *Corallorhiza trifida*) the rhizome is a complex structure resembling coral and bearing no roots at all, all nutrients being supplied by the mycorrhizal fungus on which the plant depends. In the Birds-nest Orchid *Neottia nidus-avis* the roots are reduced and congested on the short rhizome, aptly suggesting the common name.

Extremely common in tropical orchids, **pseudobulbs** (swollen leaf bases attached to a rhizome that act as food storage organs, with a bud at their base from which the current year's shoot grows) are formed by only two orchids found in the British Isles, the Fen Orchid *Liparis loeselii* and the Bog Orchid *Hammarbya paludosa*.

The leaves of an orchid plant are all borne from the stem, but may be arranged in various ways. In the British and Irish orchid flora the leaves are all simple, with entire margins and parallel veins, but some are distinctly keeled while others have conspicuous veins. The lowermost leaves are often reduced and somewhat scale-

Plate 22 (above left). In a rhizomatous orchid, such as this *Neottia ovata*, annual new growth extends the rhizome, which slowly decays from the rear. Roots are produced from the base of the new shoot, as in a tuberous orchid, but may survive for several seasons. Garden specimen, March 2005.

Plate 23 (above right). A plant of *Ophrys tenthredinifera* after the year's growth has been completed: note the withered tuber from the previous season and the plump fresh one formed in the current year. Garden specimen, May 1998.

Plate 24. In *Orchis mascula* the lower basal leaves emerge in late winter and form a spreading rosette, while erect basal leaves surround the developing inflorescence later in spring. East Kent, 27 April 1982.

like, serving as sheaths to protect the developing shoot; they are usually not visible on the undisturbed growing plant. In rosette-forming (**rosulate**) species the basal foliage leaves are borne on the lower, subterranean part of the stem and expand just above the ground. In some cases such as *Ophrys* and *Spiranthes spiralis* they make a rosette closely appressed to the surface, while in others such as some *Orchis* species they form an erect tuft. The tight-rosette form is most often seen in species where the basal leaves emerge in autumn and are active through the winter, growing in short turf. The basal leaves of the spotted- and marsh-orchids *Dactylorhiza* form a loose, upright rosette at the base of the stem. Other tuberous species may not have a basal rosette at all, as for example the fragrant-orchids *Gymnadenia* and the Pyramidal Orchid *Anacamptis pyramidalis*, the lower leaves being attached to the above-ground part of the stem.

In rosulate species the above-ground stem may or may not bear leaves: in *Orchis* the stem is leafless but sheathed at the base by erect basal leaves. Most other genera have true stem- or **cauline** leaves, which reduce in size towards the inflorescence, sometimes becoming almost indistinguishable from the bracts subtending the flowers. Some tuberous species have spotted foliage, but the extent and intensity of spotting is often quite variable between individuals in a population. The purpose of such spotting is not clear but it may mimic insect or gastropod damage, encouraging potential predators to move on to a less 'affected' specimen.

In rhizomatous species the leaves are always borne on the aerial part of the stem, although at the earlier stages of growth they may appear to form a rosette. On the stem the leaves may be arranged in opposite pairs (e.g. the twayblades *Neottia*) or alternately on each side (e.g. *Cypripedium, Cephalanthera, Epipactis*). The leaves are often conspicuously ribbed with prominent veins. In mycoheterotrophic species the leaves are reduced to small scales on the stem. Most of our orchids are hairless (**glabrous**) but a few have glandular hairs on the stem, and there may be hair-like papillae on the labellum.

Vegetative reproduction and longevity

Some terrestrial orchids (by no means all) can increase vegetatively, through the production of adventitious buds from the stem and the subsequent development of a shoot. In tuberous species this vegetative reproduction – leading to clumps that are recognisably of the same clone and that may persist for several years – is most likely to occur in optimal conditions, and is perhaps more often seen in gardens than in the wild. A few species, such as the Musk Orchid *Herminium monorchis*, produce stolons that develop a tuber at their tips and thus form a new plant some distance from the original shoot, probably leading to the development of a diffuse clonal colony over time. *Hammarbya paludosa* is again unique in British orchids in producing masses of tiny bulbils on its leaf margins, that detach and may eventually develop into flowering plants.

Orchids have a reputation for being erratic in their appearance, being found in large numbers in some years but far fewer in others. This may be because individual plants sometimes expend more energy in flowering and seeding than they have built up in their tubers, resulting in fewer plants of flowering size for the following season, and occasionally even the death of a plant. This is particularly the case for the Bee Orchid *Ophrys apifera*, where self-fertilisation usually leads to heavy and therefore energetically expensive seed-set. Only the most detailed of long-term observations can monitor such fluctuations, but studies of this kind have been conducted for some species, including *Anacamptis morio*. In one population of *A. morio* more than 40 per cent of the plants usually flowered each year, and some individuals survived and flowered for years in succession (Wells *et al.* 1998).

Some species are able to survive for long periods in poor conditions – as for example when a tree or scrub canopy develops over them, reducing light to sub-optimal levels; they may then reappear as mature, flowering plants if the canopy reopens. In such cases it could be that the plants return for a while to dependency on mycorrhizal fungi for nutrition. Individual orchid plants can be genuinely long-lived; the single surviving native plant of Lady's-slipper *Cypripedium calceolus* in the Yorkshire Dales has been watched devotedly by conservationists since 1930!

Plate 25. The overwintering rosette of *Spiranthes spiralis* is closely pressed to the soil surface, helping to protect it from damage by frost or grazing animals. Herefordshire, December 2004.

Chapter 2

Orchid Taxonomy and Classification

John Grimshaw

Orchid enthusiasts cannot have failed to notice how, over the years, the names of the plants they enjoy have changed. Almost every flora and reference work uses a different taxonomy for them. In preparing *Orchids of the British Isles* we also have adopted the most recent nomenclature and classification – a system now underpinned by molecular studies as well as by traditional morphological comparison.

Some of the revised names and generic concepts applied here may seem odd to some readers, especially when invisible molecular evidence of differences appears to overrule conspicuous morphological similarities. Amendment of generic boundaries is nothing new, however, and earlier generations would find most of our 'familiar' names equally strange. Take, for instance, the inconspicuous and scarce Small White Orchid: now known as *Pseudorchis albida*, this plant has in previous times been placed in the genera *Satyrium*, *Entaticus*, *Bicchia*, *Habenaria*, *Gymnadenia*, *Platanthera* and *Leucorchis*. Even our abundant spotted- and marsh-orchids have undergone switches between genera. Victor Summerhayes, in his *Wild Orchids of Britain* – that great New Naturalist volume that has been the foundation of the enthusiasm of so many orchid-lovers – included them in *Orchis*. Summerhayes' book was first published in 1951; the nomenclatural transition to *Dactylorhiza* (via *Dactylorchis*) was accomplished soon afterwards, and is now fully accepted. Name changes can, however, be irritating for the layperson, so the aim of this chapter is to explain how botanical names arise and how they become altered through the processes of taxonomy and classification.

Taxonomy

Taxonomy, the process of naming objects, is founded on the recognition of distinct entities. Its development is impelled by the need for accurate communication, and in the process a classification often develops. We use taxonomies for almost everything in everyday life. As I write I am sitting on a four-legged wooden object, and my keyboard rests upon another: a chair and a table. They have similarities, but also differences. Further differentiation tells us more – the

Plate 26 (opposite). Recognition of plants for medicinal purposes was the foundation of botanical taxonomy: the herbalist John Gerard said that the Common Twayblade *Neottia ovata* was 'good for greene wounds, burstings, and ruptures'. Old chalk-pit, N. Hampshire, 21 May 2002.

Plate 27. A plant with a nomenclatural past: *Pseudorchis albida*, Roxburghshire, 29 June 2000.

chair may be a dining chair, or a collapsible chair; furniture *aficionados* may well be able to add much additional detail – 'an oak carver by Thompson *c.*1930' conveys a succinct description of that particular object. The same system of hierarchical taxonomy is applied in botany, giving us the means to communicate effectively about the identity of a particular plant.

As European savants began to recognise plants, often during the course of investigations into their medicinal properties, they described and named them on the basis of their main features, usually employing the academic lingua franca of Latin to do so. The knowledge these early observers gained was disseminated by means of the numerous herbals written during the sixteenth century, many of which achieved a surprisingly wide circulation. Later works, becoming more botanical than medicinal in character, adopted and further developed the Latin nomenclature. The early descriptive names were often long and cumbersome: *Orchis alba bifolia minor*

CHAP. 118.   *Of Birds nest.*

1 *Satyrium abortinum, siue* Nidus auis.
Birds nest.

¶ *The Description.*

1 Birds Nest hath many tangling roots platted or crossed one ouer another very intricately, which resembleth a Crowes nest made of stickes; from which riseth vp a thicke soft grosse stalk of a browne colour, set with small short leaues of the colour of a dry Oken leafe that hath lien vnder the tree all the winter long. On the top of the stalke groweth a spikie eare or tuft of floures, in shape like vnto Maimed Satyrion, whereof doubtlesse it is a kinde. The whole plant, as well sticks, leaues, and floures, are of a parched browne colour.

‡ I receiued out of Hampshire from my often remembred friend Master *Goodyer* this following description of a *Nidus auis* found by him the twenty ninth of Iune, 1621.

¶ *Nidus auis flore & caule violaceo purpureo colore;*
an Pseudoleimodoron Clus. Hist. Rar. plant.
pag. 270.

This riseth vp with a stalke about nine inches high, with a few smal narrow sharpe pointed short skinny leaues, set without order, very little or nothing at all wrapping or inclosing the stalke; hauing a spike of floures like those of *Orobanche*, without tailes or leaues growing amongst them: which fallen, there succeed small seed-vessels. The lower part of the stalke within the ground is not round like *Orobanche*, but slender or long, and of a yellowish white colour, with many small brittle roots growing vnderneath confusedly, wrapt or folded together like those of the common *Nidus auis*. The whole plant as it appeareth aboue ground, both stalkes, leaues, and floures, is of a violet or deepe purple colour. This I found wilde in the border of a field called Marborne, neere Habridge in Haliborne, a mile from a towne called Alton in Hampshire, being the land of one *William Balden*. In this place also groweth wilde the thistle called *Corona fratrum*. Ioh. *Goodyer*.

¶ *The Place.*
This bastard or vnkindely Satyrion is very seldome seene in these Southerly parts of England.
It

Plate 28. An early representation and description of a British orchid: *Neottia nidus-avis*, in the second edition of Gerard's *Herball*, prepared by Thomas Johnson (1633). Appended to Gerard's description by Johnson is a note by the Hampshire botanist John Goodyer (of *Goodyera* fame) describing a mysterious purple-flowered plant that he thought to be similar to the Bird's-nest Orchid.

calcari oblongo (literally 'the smaller two-leaved white orchid with an oblong spur') was the name coined by Caspar Bauhin, in his *Pinax theatri botanici* of 1623, for the plant we now know as *Platanthera bifolia*. Bauhin's *Pinax* was in effect a concordance of the different names each plant had been given to date, covering some 6000 species, and is thus a work of extreme importance. Its conclusions were largely adopted by the great English botanist John Ray (1627–1705), and later by the founder of modern taxonomy, Linnaeus himself (Arber 1986). Ray has been described as the father of British natural history – his *Catalogus Plantarum Angliae* of 1670, and its later incarnation as *Synopsis methodica Stirpium Britannicarum* (first edition 1690), being the first attempt at a catalogue of the English flora. Each entry gives a plant's accepted Latin name, any synonymy, and an English name: for our current example *Orchis alba bifolia minor calcari oblongo* the English name 'lesser Butter-fly orchis' is used, almost exactly as it is today (Lesser Butterfly-orchid). Ray

STIRPIUM BRITANNICARUM. 385

§. Calceolus Mariæ *Ger.* 359. Helleborine flore rotundo feu Calceolus *C. B. Pin.* 187. Elleborine major feu Calceolus Mariæ *Park.* 217. Damafonii fpecies quibufdam feu Calceolus D. Mariæ *J. B. III.* 518. *Ladies-Slipper.* In fome Woods in *Lancafhire,* and in *Helks* Wood by *Ingleborough* in *Yorkfhire.*

Floris labellum calopodii figura, colore flavo, fufficit ad hunc a reliquis difcriminandum.

§. 1. Bifolium majus feu Ophris major quibufdam *J. B. III.* 533. Bifolium fylveftre vulgare *Park.* 504. Ophris bifolia *Ger.* 326. *C. B. Pin.* 87. *Common Twayblade.* In fylvis & dumetis, nec rarius in pratis & pafcuis.

Hujus notæ funt folia bina Plantaginea; flores in fpica herbacei Orchidum fimiles, calcaribus carentes, utriculis brevioribus quam Orchidum infidentes.

2. Bifolium minimum *J. B. III.* 534. Ophris minima *C. B. Pin.* 87. *Pr.* 31. *The leaft Twayblade.* I have found it on feveral Moors and Heaths in *Derbyfhire, Yorkfhire,* and *Northumberland*; in *Yorkfhire* not far from *Almondbury,* and on *Pendle*-Hill in *Lancafhire* near the Beacon; (Juxta lacum uno milliari *Kaghlaia* diftantem, occidentem verfus, folo putrido mufcofo nafcitur copiofe; D. *Richardfon.*) Icon *J. Bauhini* hanc fpeciem optime reprefentat. Folia triangula funt feu cordata.

3. Bifolium paluftre *Park.* 505. *defcr.* Orchis bifolia minor paluftris *Pluk. Alm.* 270. *f.* 247. *f.* 2. *Marfh Twayblade.* Found by Mr. *Dent* and Mr. *Dale* in company, on the boggy and fenny Grounds near *Gamlingay* in *Cambridgefhire*; by *Parkinfon* on the low wet grounds between *Hatfield* and St. *Albans,* and in divers places in *Romney*-Marfh; (by Mr. *Dubois* at *Hurfthill, Tunbridge-wells*; Mr. *Doody.*)

A bifolio vulgari differt parvitate fua, & quod interdum etiam trifolium fit, virore infuper & glabritie foliorum, florum fpica multo minore, tandem radicibus reptatricibus.

Plate 29. Pre-Linnean nomenclature as used by John Ray in his *Synopsis methodica Stirpium Britannicarum*, the first British flora (third edition, 1724). Much of the description is contained in the name, conveyed in the then universal language of Latin, while his notes on localities are in English.

Plate 30. *Platanthère à deux feuilles* – or Lesser Butterfly-orchid? The binomial *Platanthera bifolia* is internationally recognisable. Coastal grassland, North Uist, Outer Hebrides, 15 June 1990.

also tells us that the plant grows in meadows, and flowers in June. In other cases he gives further information about localities where he or others had observed the plant.

Modern nomenclature officially begins with Carl von Linné (1707–1778), the Swedish botanist most frequently known by his latinised name, Linnaeus. Linnaeus's work revolutionised the classification and description of plants, his most important contribution being the system of binomial nomenclature that we still use, based on the combination of generic and specific names. Linnaeus recognised that the lengthy descriptive names in use at the time were unhelpful for rapid communication, and in his *Species Plantarum* (1753) adopted the scheme of providing a single descriptive epithet for each species within a genus. Thus for the Lesser Butterfly-orchid, which fell within his concept of the genus *Orchis*, the specific epithet *bifolia* stood duty for the full descriptive name; *Orchis bifolia* was therefore the binomial that facilitated communication about the plant. Although Linnaeus seems to have regarded binomials as merely a shorthand for the 'correct', lengthier names, the binomial system came to be adopted universally for its simplicity. Supporting each binomial was a description providing the details necessary to characterise each species. Modern taxonomic practice still requires a description in Latin to validate the first publication of a new plant taxon, and a 'type' specimen must be nominated and deposited in a recognised herbarium as a permanent voucher and taxonomic 'yardstick'.

The publication of *Species Plantarum* is taken as the beginning of our current system of plant taxonomy, its binomials superseding all previous nomenclature (although Linnaeus and others did adopt many elements of older names). Many of the names in *Species Plantarum* have in their turn been superseded as the science of the systematics of plants has progressed. In the British orchid flora, for example, very few Linnean binomials have survived unscathed. What has continued, however, is the principle established by Linnaeus of an immutable specific name, enabling a validly published species to be tracked through the literature no matter how frequently its generic assignment has been altered.

In formal usage the author of the specific epithet is always indicated, often by means of an abbreviation of that person's name: for example, two binomials established by Linnaeus (always abbreviated simply to 'L.') are *Cypripedium calceolus* L. and *Orchis militaris* L. The case of *Pseudorchis albida* is slightly more complicated in that the specific epithet was established by Linnaeus within his genus *Satyrium* – *Satyrium albidum* L. – but a series of other authors have since placed the plant in different genera, for different reasons: thus *Orchis albida* (L.) Scop.; *Habenaria albida* (L.) R. Br.; *Gymnadenia albida* (L.) Rich.; *Entaticus albidus* (L.) Gray; *Platanthera albida* (L.) Lindl.; *Peristylus albidus* (L.) Lindl.; *Leucorchis albida* (L.) E. Mey.; *Bicchia albida* (L.) Parl.; we now know it as *Pseudorchis albida* (L.) Á. & D. Löve, although its nomenclature is still the subject of debate. Throughout this sequence the stability of the name *albidum* given by Linnaeus is clearly demonstrated (the name changes its gender – *albidus, albida, albidum* – to reflect that of each genus) and the author of each new combination is also clearly identified, again using a standard form or abbreviation of their name(s).

In the case of *Pseudorchis albida* the majority of name changes resulted from the plant being transferred from one genus to another to reflect, as will be discussed below, the different approaches of the various systematists involved, but some (*Entaticus*, *Bicchia* and *Leucorchis*) were the result of errors of taxonomy. Many of the older synonyms have long been forgotten by all but the most dedicated taxonomists, and in this book we have chosen to omit all synonyms except those that have been in use in the past few decades. For those interested in the changing taxonomy of British orchids, an extensive synonymy is presented by Sell & Murrell (1996) in their *Flora of Great Britain and Ireland, Volume 5.*

The naming of plants is strictly governed by the International Code of Botanical Nomenclature, which sets out the 'rules and regulations' botanists must follow when publishing a new name, whether as an entirely new epithet or as a consequence of a systematic rearrangement. The aim of the Code is to promote stability and continuity in plant nomenclature, and thereby to avoid confusion. An infraction of the Code that results in the rejection of a published name means further change is required to achieve a valid name, and such changes are particularly irritating. A recent case in the British orchid flora involves the plant now known as *Dactylorhiza ebudensis* (Wief. ex R.M. Bateman & Denholm) P. Delforge. This was twice (1976, 1979) invalidly published as *D. majalis* subsp. *scotica* E. Nelson, through failure to follow the requirements of the Code, so *D. majalis* subsp. *occidentalis* var. *ebudensis* Wief. ex R.M. Bateman & Denholm (1995) was the first validly published epithet (Wiefelspütz's own first publication of this name in 1977 having been invalid) (Lowe 2003). The epithet *scotica* lingers on, however, in various combinations, causing ongoing confusion in the literature (e.g. Sell & Murrell 1996, Lang 2004).

Plate 31. A recent discovery with a long list of synonyms: the Hebridean Marsh-orchid *Dactylorhiza ebudensis*. Wet machair, North Uist, Outer Hebrides, 14 June 1990.

Classification

In biological science, classification, or systematics, is the act of interpreting relationships between organisms. As is usually the case with interpretations, opinions can differ, and successive systematic botanists have had their own views of the relationships between members of the family Orchidaceae, based on concepts current at the time and on the availability of supporting data.

It will perhaps be useful here to provide working definitions of the various taxonomic ranks that botanists use. Such definitions are notoriously difficult, but an explicit framework is essential.

The key starting point is the **species**, as this is the fundamental unit for evolutionary studies and recognition of plants in the field, as well as for practical considerations such as conservation. A species is often defined as a group of organisms that closely resemble each other and are reproductively isolated (i.e. are able to interbreed within that group, but not outside it). In other words, the populations of individuals that make up a species are more closely related to each other than they are to populations of other species. A species will have several reliable diagnostic characters, so that when all its attributes are compared a clear distinction can be made between it and any other similar species. Ideally, a species should be recognised on the basis of a wide, objective sampling and comparison of as many characters as possible (morphological and, if feasible, molecular) from both it and its nearest allies, building up a complete picture that highlights clearly the discontinuities between them (e.g. Bateman 2001).

Typically, several closely related species form a **genus** – each species being distinct within the genus, but more closely related to others within it than to species in other genera. In the same way, **families** of flowering plants are made up of related genera: the family Orchidaceae encompasses almost 800 genera, containing in total about 20,000 species, all sharing some fundamental similarities that enable them to be placed within the family. Within Orchidaceae the genera are grouped into five **subfamilies**, then many **tribes** and **subtribes**, reflecting their morphological and molecular similarities and differences (see Table 1, and the full classification of Orchidaceae of the British Isles, pp. 29–31). The generic relationships within Orchidaceae are currently under intense systematic scrutiny, and for a full exposition of subfamilial, tribal and generic affinities the reader is referred to the ongoing six-volume work *Genera Orchidacearum* (Pridgeon *et al.* 1999, *et seq.*).

Plate 32 (below left). A hierarchical infraspecific taxonomy should be informative about a plant's relationships. A representative specimen of the widespread *Dactylorhiza fuchsii* in its typical subspecies *fuchsii*. Chalk downland, Dorset, 7 June 2003.

Plate 33 (centre). The Hebridean variant of *Dactylorhiza fuchsii* differs from typical plants in several morphological characters and occurs in a definable geographical area, justifying its recognition as subsp. *hebridensis*. Vatersay, Outer Hebrides, 16 July 2003.

Plate 34 (right). Occasional variants that do not occur in recognisable populations should be thought of as forms, rather than varieties. Many have, however, been described at varietal level, as in the case of *Dactylorhiza fuchsii* subsp. *fuchsii* var. *rhodochila*. Chalk downland, Wiltshire, 20 June 2003.

TABLE 1. TAXONOMIC HIERARCHY

FAMILY	Orchidaceae
Subfamily	Orchidoideae
Tribe	Orchideae
Subtribe	Orchidinae
GENUS	*Dactylorhiza*
SPECIES	*fuchsii*
Subspecies	*fuchsii*
Variety	*okellyi*
Form	(none described)

Figure 12. Occurring as a recognisable population in limited areas, but inter-grading with normal plants, the pale-flowered *Dactylorhiza fuchsii* subsp. *fuchsii* var. *okellyi* is appropriately regarded as a variety.

The species is often itself subdivided into infraspecific taxa, at the diminishing ranks of subspecies (abbreviated to 'subsp.'), variety (or *varietas*, 'var.') and form (or *forma*, 'f.'). These are often rather contentious and their delimitation can be particularly subjective. Bateman's (2001) useful definition of **subspecies** is that it has the principal characters of its species, with significant definable morphological differences, but with some overlap of characters when compared objectively. Geographical or habitat differentiation is often used to justify the use of subspecific rank. A **variety** should have several diagnostic characters, but they are usually not clearly discriminating and there will be considerable overlap with other varieties. A **form** usually has few, but distinctive, defining characters, and seldom occurs in pure populations.

These guidelines are clear, but unfortunately they are often not applied. Orchids are perceived as 'special', charismatic plants and have an enthusiastic following among both amateur and professional botanists, and this emphasis seems sometimes to cloud taxonomic judgements. In recent decades there has been a trend, especially among Continental botanists, to accord even minor variants full specific status, which a more objective analysis would perhaps not allow. Bateman (2001) rather aptly calls this 'literative speciation' – a proliferation on paper rather than in nature – and it leads to an undesirable artificial flattening of the taxonomic hierarchy. In the British Isles the rank of variety has been widely used, often legitimately for populations of recognisably similar plants but also indiscriminately for minor variants that would be far more appropriately considered as forms; examples of this include albinos and other colour variants occurring within a normal population. Morphological freaks (e.g. plants with inverted or peloric flowers) have usually been recognised as such in the British flora and have not been accorded formal taxonomic recognition, although they may be of considerable evolutionary significance (Bateman & Rudall 2005, in press). In this book we have minimised the creation of new taxonomic combinations and have usually retained taxa at their published rank, but the useful distinction in importance between variety and form should be borne in mind throughout.

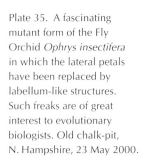

Plate 35. A fascinating mutant form of the Fly Orchid *Ophrys insectifera* in which the lateral petals have been replaced by labellum-like structures. Such freaks are of great interest to evolutionary biologists. Old chalk-pit, N. Hampshire, 23 May 2000.

The characters systematists have chosen to use to delimit different genera have varied greatly over the years and have often been based on somewhat subjective concepts of the relative importance of one character over another. Linnaeus, for example, chose spur length as a primary character, with very curious results. His genus *Ophrys* is a case in point: it contained terrestrial orchids lacking a spur and so encompassed the modern genera *Neottia, Liparis, Hammarbya, Corallorhiza* and *Herminium* as well as *Ophrys* itself. The Linnean genus *Satyrium* had short spurs,

Ophrys ovata

Plates 36 and 37 (right, opposite). The Common Twayblade *Neottia ovata*, illustrated and described in William Curtis's *Flora Londinensis* (Fascicle 3, Issue 30, 1780), one of the finest botanical works ever produced in Britain. Curtis uses the Linnean name *Ophrys ovata*, but the elements of a modern botanical description are all present. The artist is unknown but may have been William Kilburn.

while *Orchis* had longer spurs. Later botanists adopted different characters, such as the presence or absence of bursicles, or other small floral distinctions, and rather missed the broader picture by focusing in this way on a small and 'preordained' set of characters; this process is well reviewed, for *Orchis* in particular, by Bateman *et al.* (1997). The broad pattern of generic distinctions that we are familiar with today was gradually worked out, but the classification of orchid genera remained 'artificial' rather than 'natural'.

OPHRYS OVATA. TWAYBLADE.

OPHRYS *Lin. Gen. Pl.* GYNANDRIA DIANDRIA.

Nectarium fubcarinatum.

Raii Syn. Gen. 29. HERBÆ RADICE BULBOSA PRÆDITÆ.

OPHRYS *ovata* bulbo fibrofo, caule bifolio, foliis ovatis, nectarii labio bifido. *Lin. Syft. Vegetab.* p. 667. Sp. Pl. 1342. Fl. Suec. n. 808.

EPIPACTIS foliis binis ovatis, labello bifido. *Haller. hift.* 1291. t. 37.

OPHRYS ovata, *Bauhin. Pin.* 87. *Ger. emac.* 402.

BIFOLIUM fylveftre vulgare *Parkins.* 504. *Raii Syn.* 385. Common Twayblade.

Fl. Dan. t. 137. *Hudfon Fl. Angl. ed.* 2. p. 388. *Lightfoot Fl. Scot.* p. 523.

RADIX perennis, fibrofa, fibris plurimis, teretibus, cylindricis, contortis.

ROOT perennial, fibrous, fibres numerous, round, cylindrical, matted together.

SCAPUS pedalis et ultra, folidus, teres, villofus, fubvifcidus, foliolis paucis perbrevibus, alternis, acuminatis, vaginantibus inftructus.

STALK a foot or more in height, folid, round, villous, flightly vifcid, and furnifhed with very fhort, alternate, pointed fheathing leaves.

FOLIA bina, prope terram, inferiore bafi fua fuperioris bafin ambiente, ovata, mucronata, quinquenervia.

LEAVES growing in pairs, near the ground, the lower one by its bafe furrounding the bafe of the upper one, ovate, pointed, with five ribs.

FLORES herbacei, fpicati, laxe et diftincte infidentes.

FLOWERS of a greenifh colour, growing in a fpike, fitting loofely and diftinctly.

SPICA prælonga, angufta.

SPIKE very long and narrow

Fig. 1. ad 12. exhibent partes fructificationis ficut per lentem apparent.

Fig. 1. to 12. exhibit the parts of the fructification as they appear through a magnifier.

Fig. 1. ad 6. Flos antice vifus.

Fig. 1. to 6. a flower feen in front.

Fig. 1. 4. 5. PETALA exteriora latiora, 2. 3. interiora anguftiora.

Fig. 1. 4. 5. the outer broadeft PETALS, 2. 3. the inner and more narrow ones.

Fig. 6. *Labellum* NECTARII bifidum, in fitu naturali fæpius inflexum.

Fig. 6. the *Lip* of the NECTARY, which in its natural fituation is generally bent inward.

Fig. 7. *Squama* fuperior, *fig.* 10. *Squama* inferior, (fuftentaculum Halleri) inter quas theca ftaminum quafi in forcipe continetur.

Fig. 7. the fuperior *Squama*, *fig.* 10. the inferior *Squama* (the fuftentaculum of Haller) between which the cafe containing the ftamina is held as in a pair of forceps.

Fig. 12. Theca ftaminum, cum ftaminibus inclufis.

Fig. 12. the Cafe of the ftamina, with the ftamina enclofed.

Fig. 8. Theca ftaminum, demiffis ftaminibus, *fig.* 9.

Fig. 8. the Cafe of the ftamina, the ftamina having fallen out, *fig.* 9.

Fig. 15. STAMINA cum ANTHERIS bilamellofis, flavis, feorfim exhibitis.

Fig. 15. the STAMINA with the ANTHERÆ compofed of two lamellæ of a yellow colour fhewn by themfelves.

Fig. 11. Stigma.

Fig. 11. the Stigma.

Fig. 15. PERICARPIUM nat. magnitud.

Fig. 15. SEED-VESSEL of its natural fize.

To render the characters of this genus, which are very difficult of inveftigation, eafy to the Botanic Student, they are reprefented in a magnified ftate, and particularly referred to.

It will be feen on comparing, how very different they are from thofe of the Orchis.

This fpecies of Ophrys is the moft common of the whole genus, and may be found in moft of the woods about London, particularly fuch as have a moift foil, as about Shooter's-hill, and fometimes it is found in Meadows and on Heaths.

A variety with three leaves is now and then met with.

It flowers in May and June.

Natural classification

Contemporary systematics has as its aim the production of classifications that are 'natural', reflecting genuine evolutionary relationships, rather than 'artificial', cobbled together on the basis of predetermined similarities or dissimilarities. The modern approach is to look for genealogical rather than convergent similarities; in other words, similarities that are believed to reflect a shared ancestry, rather than those that do not. In pursuing this aim the contemporary botanist has the assistance of powerful new technical and conceptual methods, including analysis of molecular data and use of the cladistic approach (see below) to reconstruct evolutionary history. A particularly clear exposition of the application of modern methodology to orchid classification is given by Bateman (2001).

Molecular analysis of evolutionary relationships

The assumption that overall morphological similarity between plants is equivalent to closeness of relationship is long-standing, but had never been strictly testable (Chase 1999, Bateman 2001). New techniques for analysing molecular data, however, have enabled more objective testing of relationships. The twin strands of deoxyribose nucleic acid (DNA), the genetic material of heredity, consist of a series of paired bases occurring in a sequence that can now easily be read. Comparison of similarities and differences in sequences from two or more individuals reveals the closeness of the relationship of the taxa under study, enabling a systematic judgement to be made. Certain regions of the genome in the nucleus, in plastids and in mitochondria (organelles transmitted through the maternal line only) are particularly suitable for this kind of analysis: the ITS (internal transcribed spacer) region of nuclear ribosomal DNA is one such region that can be compared across a wide range of taxa, as can the rbcL, matK and trnl sequences of plastid DNA. Three different sources of DNA, then, are available for comparison and testing, and the more marker sequences that can be used in any given analysis the more reliable the evidence will be. ITS and plastid sequencing have been the foundation for much of the recent work that has been done on the phylogeny of terrestrial orchids (e.g. Pridgeon *et al.* 1997, Bateman *et al.* 1997, 2003).

The value of DNA for phylogenetic research is that any mutations are permanently recorded in these genetic 'annals', and can therefore be used to observe the pathways of evolutionary change. Molecular information is not, however, the sole factor to be considered; it remains only part of the suite of characters that make up the defining points of a taxon, and a full assessment of morphology should be combined with molecular data in the delimitation and identification of species.

Cladistic analysis

Modern systematics makes heavy use of the principles of cladistics – an approach that utilises a wide set of data to generate branching tree-like diagrams known as **cladograms** to summarise, for a given set of species, hypotheses (derived analytically from the data) about the relationships among them (Kitching *et al.* 1998, Skelton & Smith 2002). A cladogram is made up of pairs of 'sister-groups', each containing

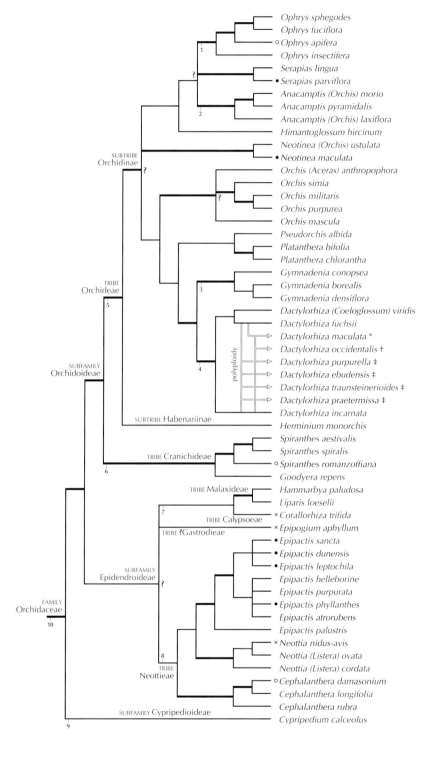

Figure 13. Evolutionary tree showing the relationships of all British and Irish orchid species; a grafted aggregate phylogeny based on several more focused analyses. Thick branches denote the more reliable relationships.

× obligate mycoheterotrophs ('saprophytes')

• obligate self-pollinators

○ facultative self-pollinators

* *Dactylorhiza maculata* is an autotetraploid, probably derived from *D. fuchsii.*

† *Dactylorhiza occidentalis* is a polyploid derivative of *D. incarnata* and *D. maculata.*

‡ Other polyploid *Dactylorhiza* are hybrids of *D. fuchsii* and *D. incarnata.*

Numbers indicate sources of component cladograms:

1. Soliva *et al.* (2001),
2. Bateman & Hollingsworth (2004),
3. Bateman *et al.* (in prep.),
4. Pillon *et al.* (subm.),
5. Bateman *et al.* (2003),
6. Salazar *et al.* (2003),
7. Salazar *et al.* (in prep.),
8. Bateman *et al.* (2005),
9. Cox *et al.* (1997),
10. Dressler (1993), Cameron *et al.* (1999), Freudenstein & Rasmussen (1999).

one or more species that are hypothesised to have diverged from a single ancestor. It thus resembles a family tree. Each lineage derived from a single ancestor in the evolutionary sequence is known as a **clade**, and should contain both the ancestor and all its surviving descendant species. Such a clade is known as **monophyletic**, having only one evolutionary origin (although divergence may have since occurred

From Bateman 2005 (in press), reproduced by kind permission of Prof. Richard Bateman.

Plate 38. Variants such as this *Anacamptis pyramidalis* with an enlarged labellum ('var. *emarginata*') may be the starting point for a new evolutionary pathway. The longer, broader labellum also suggests the connection between *A. pyramidalis* and other *Anacamptis* species formerly placed in *Orchis*, such as *A. papilionacea*. N. Hampshire, 14 July 1998.

in the descendants), and is thus truly 'natural'. Monophyletic groups are now used as the basis for classification, as they are believed to reflect the course of evolution.

Another important concept is that of **paraphyly**, where analysis shows that a group of taxa are descended from a common ancestor but systematists have excluded some of these descendants from the group on account of perceived differences. In the British orchid flora, to maintain *Dactylorhiza* and *Coeloglossum* as separate genera would be to create a paraphyletic situation in *Dactylorhiza*, as the cladogram analysing the ITS sequences of the two groups clearly demonstrates that they share a common ancestry (Bateman *et al.* 2003). The relatively trivial differences between them, of flower colour and size of spur, can be explained as the result of divergence through adaptive change associated with shifts to different pollinators.

The third state is a **polyphyletic** group, in which the species in question are derived from several ancestors in their evolutionary past, and so are held together as a group only by superficial morphological similarities. Neither paraphyletic nor polyphyletic groups are recognised by cladistic analysis. They are artificial systematic constructs that hinder evolutionary studies and natural classification, and for this reason we should not continue to recognise them as groups, however familiar they may have become (Bateman 2001). Within the European terrestrial orchid flora the principal example of a polyphyletic genus was *Orchis* in its earlier broad sense. Recent cladistic analysis of this group and related taxa revealed that the broad genus *Orchis* encompassed species of several different evolutionary origins and was therefore unacceptably polyphyletic (Pridgeon *et al.* 1997, Bateman *et al.* 1997). The cladogram (largely based on ITS sequences, though generally well supported by morphological characters as well) revealed that species traditionally classified as *Orchis* in fact fall into three clades. That containing *O. mascula* – the type species of the genus *Orchis* – and related species retains the generic name *Orchis*; all its members share a diploid chromosome number of 2n = 42. Within this genus are smaller clades of more closely related species, the indisputably closely related 'anthropomorphic' species *O. militaris*, *O. purpurea* and *O. simia* being linked together in one such group (see Figure 13). Other '*Orchis*' species, however, were shown to be more closely related to the formerly monospecific genera *Anacamptis* and *Neotinea* and so have been incorporated into these genera, resulting in the name changes that currently appear so unfamiliar to some: *Orchis morio* L., for example, has become *Anacamptis morio* (L.) R.M. Bateman, Pridgeon & M.W. Chase. Members of *Anacamptis* all have the diploid chromosome number of 2n = (32–)36, whereas in *Neotinea* 2n = 42; the distinction made on the basis of molecular data is therefore supported by an additional physical difference widely recognised as an important taxonomic character. The morphological dissimilarity of *Anacamptis pyramidalis* to its 'new' relations can be explained by evolutionary divergence through adaptation to different pollinators – summer-flying butterflies in the case of *A. pyramidalis*, spring-flying bees for *A. morio*.

Orchid taxonomy and systematics remain in an exciting state of flux. If history repeats itself, developments in systematic concepts and techniques are likely to lead to still more reclassifications and changes of name, as species delimitations and relationships between genera are elucidated further.

Orchidaceae of the British Isles

Family Orchidaceae

Subfamily Cypripedioideae
  1. **Cypripedium** L.
    1.1. **C. calceolus** L. Lady's-slipper Orchid

Subfamily Epidendroideae

Tribe Neottieae

  2. **Cephalanthera** Rich.
    2.1. **C. rubra** (L.) Rich. Red Helleborine
    2.2. **C. longifolia** (L.) Fritsch Narrow-leaved Helleborine
    2.3. **C. damasonium** (Mill.) Druce White Helleborine

  3. **Neottia** Guett.
    3.1. **N. cordata** (L.) Rich. Lesser Twayblade
    3.2. **N. ovata** (L.) Bluff & Fingerh. Common Twayblade
    3.3. **N. nidus-avis** (L.) Rich. Bird's-nest Orchid

  4. **Epipactis** Zinn.
    palustris group
    4.1. **E. palustris** (L.) Crantz Marsh Helleborine
    helleborine group
    4.2. **E. atrorubens** (Hoffm. ex Bernh.) Besser Dark-red Helleborine
    4.3. **E. helleborine** (L.) Crantz Broad-leaved Helleborine
      4.3a. **E. helleborine** var. **helleborine**
      4.3b. **E. helleborine** var. **youngiana**
          (A.J. Richards & A.F. Porter) Kreutz Young's Helleborine
    4.4. **E. purpurata** Sm.* Violet Helleborine
    4.5. **E. leptochila** (Godfery) Godfery Narrow-lipped Helleborine
    4.6. **E. dunensis** (T. & T.A. Stephenson) Godfery Dune Helleborine
    4.7. **E. phyllanthes** G.E. Sm. Green-flowered Helleborine
    4.8. **E. sancta** (P. Delforge) P. Delforge & A. Gévaudan Lindisfarne Helleborine

Tribe ?Gastrodieae

  5. **Epipogium** Gmelin ex Borkh.
    5.1. **E. aphyllum** Sw. Ghost Orchid

Tribe Malaxideae

  6. **Liparis** Rich.
    6.1. **L. loeselii** (L.) Rich. Fen Orchid
      6.1a. **L. loeselii** var. **loeselii**
      6.1b. **L. loeselii** var. **ovata** Ridd. ex Godfery

  7. **Hammarbya** Kuntze
    7.1. **H. paludosa** (L.) Kuntze Bog Orchid

Tribe Calypsoeae

  8. **Corallorhiza** Ruppius ex Gagnebin
    8.1. **C. trifida** Châtel. Coralroot Orchid

Subfamilial taxonomic ranks, species and principal variants (adapted from Bateman 2005, in press). Asterisks (*) indicate where nomenclatural priority is a subject of debate.

Subfamily Orchidoideae

Tribe Cranichideae

Subtribe Goodyerinae

9. **Goodyera** R. Br.

9.1. **G. repens** (L.) R. Br. Creeping Lady's-tresses

Subtribe Spiranthinae

10. **Spiranthes** Rich.

10.1. **S. romanzoffiana** Cham. Irish Lady's-tresses

10.2. **S. spiralis** (L.) Chevall. Autumn Lady's-tresses

10.3. **S. aestivalis** (Poir.) Rich. Summer Lady's-tresses (extinct)

Tribe Orchideae

Subtribe Habenariinae

11. **Herminium** L.

11.1. **H. monorchis** (L.) R. Br. Musk Orchid

Subtribe Orchidinae

Orchis clade

12. **Orchis** L.

militaris group

12.1. **O. anthropophora** (L.) All. Man Orchid

12.2. **O. simia** Lam. Monkey Orchid

12.3. **O. militaris** L. Military Orchid

12.4. **O. purpurea** Huds. Lady Orchid

mascula group

12.5. **O. mascula** (L.) L. Early Purple Orchid

Platanthera clade

13. **Pseudorchis** Seguier

13.1. **P. albida** (L.) Á. & D. Löve* Small White Orchid

14. **Platanthera** Rich.

14.1. **P. bifolia** (L.) Rich. Lesser Butterfly-orchid

14.2. **P. chlorantha** (Custer) Rchb.* Greater Butterfly-orchid

Gymnadenia clade

15. **Gymnadenia** R. Br.

15.1. **G. conopsea** (L.) R. Br. Chalk Fragrant-orchid

15.2. **G. borealis** (Druce) R.M. Bateman, Pridgeon & M.W. Chase
Heath Fragrant-orchid

15.3. **G. densiflora** (Wahlenb.) A. Dietr.* Marsh Fragrant-orchid

Dactylorhiza clade

16. **Dactylorhiza** Neck. ex Nevski

incarnata group

16.1. **D. incarnata** (L.) Soó Early Marsh-orchid

16.1a. **D. incarnata** subsp. **incarnata**

16.1b. **D. incarnata** subsp. **ochroleuca** (Wüstnei ex Boll) P.F. Hunt & Summerh.

16.1c. **D. incarnata** subsp. **coccinea** (Pugsley) Soó

16.1d. **D. incarnata** subsp. **pulchella** (Druce) Soó

16.1e. **D. incarnata** subsp. **cruenta** (O.F. Müll.) P.D. Sell

Dactylorhiza clade   *continued*

   16. **Dactylorhiza** Neck. ex Nevski   *continued*

   viridis group

      16.2. **D. viridis** (L.) R.M. Bateman, Pridgeon & M.W. Chase* Frog Orchid

   fuchsii group

      16.3. **D. fuchsii** (Druce) Soó Common Spotted-orchid

         16.3a. **D. fuchsii** subsp. **fuchsii**

         16.3b. **D. fuchsii** subsp. **hebridensis** (Wilmott) Soó

   maculata group

      16.4. **D. maculata** (L.) Soó Heath Spotted-orchid

   majalis (*s.l.*) group

      16.5. **D. praetermissa** (Druce) Soó Southern Marsh-orchid

      16.6. **D. traunsteinerioides** (Pugsley) Landwehr Narrow-leaved Marsh-orchid

      16.7. **D. ebudensis** (Wief. ex R.M. Bateman & Denholm) P. Delforge Hebridean Marsh-orchid

      16.8. **D. purpurella** (T. & T.A. Stephenson) Soó Northern Marsh-orchid

         16.8a. **D. purpurella** var. **purpurella**

         16.8b. **D. purpurella** var. **cambrensis** (R.H. Roberts) R.M. Bateman & Denholm

      16.9. **D. occidentalis** (Pugsley) P. Delforge Irish Marsh-orchid

Neotinea clade

   17. **Neotinea** Rchb. f. (*s.l.*)

   maculata group

      17.1. **N. maculata** (Desf.) Stearn* Dense-flowered Orchid

   ustulata group

      17.2. **N. ustulata** (L.) R.M. Bateman, Pridgeon & M.W. Chase Burnt Orchid

Himantoglossum clade

   18. **Himantoglossum** Koch (*s.l.*)

      18.1. **H. hircinum** (L.) Spreng. Lizard Orchid

Anacamptis clade

   19. **Anacamptis** Rich. (*s.l.*)

   laxiflora group

      19.1. **A. laxiflora** (Lam.) R.M. Bateman, Pridgeon & M.W. Chase Jersey Orchid

   pyramidalis group

      19.2. **A. pyramidalis** (L.) Rich. Pyramidal Orchid

   morio group

      19.3. **A. morio** (L.) R.M. Bateman, Pridgeon & M.W. Chase Green-winged Orchid

Serapias clade

   20. **Serapias** L.

      20.1. **S. parviflora** Parl. Lesser Tongue-orchid

Ophrys clade

   21. **Ophrys** L.

   insectifera group

      21.1. **O. insectifera** L. Fly Orchid

   apifera group

      21.2. **O. apifera** Huds. Bee Orchid

   fuciflora–sphegodes group

      21.3. **O. fuciflora** (Crantz) Moench (*s.s.*)* Late Spider-orchid

      21.4. **O. sphegodes** Mill. (*s.s.*) Early Spider-orchid

Chapter 3

Distribution and Ecology of
Orchids in the British Isles

Michael Foley

General distribution

A glance at the distribution maps for the orchids in this book will be sufficient to show that most have a limited, or at least well-defined area of occurrence in the British Isles. These distributions reflect the habitat preferences that characterise our native orchids, sometimes so strongly that they are an unofficial taxonomic character. For example, the Chalk Fragrant-orchid *Gymnadenia conopsea* occurs on dry chalk and limestone soils and the Marsh Fragrant-orchid *G. densiflora* in damp calcareous grassland, while the Heath Fragrant-orchid *G. borealis* tends to be found in more acidic conditions. Requirement for a particular soil type is one obvious factor in distribution, but others may be whether a plant needs dry or wet ground conditions, for example, or the presence or absence of shade; whether it is able to compete with other accompanying species, or tolerates ground disturbance, or even whether it prefers higher or lower altitudes. In consequence, most wild orchids are confined to particular habitats, and some have a very restricted range indeed. A few species are more tolerant, and range more widely, but even these will be found only in suitable habitats.

The varied geology and geography of the British Isles therefore has a fundamental effect on the distribution of our orchids. For example, areas of high alkalinity where the soil is derived from chalk or limestone, such as the Downs and the Chilterns of southern England, have their own characteristic orchid flora, usually comprising species preferring close-grazed grassland or woodland conditions. Plants favouring such calcareous soils are known as 'calcicoles'. The presence of calcium in the soil layer can, however, have an adverse affect on the uptake of certain essential mineral elements, making it hard or even impossible for some plants ('calcifuges'), including some orchids, to survive. As a general rule, acidic soils are most frequent on the higher ground in the north and west of the British Isles, and it is here that many calcifuge species may be found, in boggy conditions, wet meadows or hill pastures. The same species may also occur in locations outside their main range but where similar conditions prevail – proving the rule that such plants are sitespecific in their habitat requirements.

By contrast, some orchid species are largely limited to the lightly vegetated depressions in coastal sand dunes, especially where alkalinity is high because of the

Plate 39. Orchids are found throughout the British Isles, wherever suitable habitat occurs: *Ophrys sphegodes* on coastal chalk grassland, Dorset, 18 April 2002.

Plate 40. *Anacamptis laxiflora*, wet pasture, Guernsey. A species at the edge of its range in northern Europe. 11 May 2001.

Plate 41. Threatened by habitat destruction, *Herminium monorchis* survives on ancient chalk-workings. N. Hampshire, 2 July 1999.

presence of crushed-shell sand. Since these features occur only along limited parts of the coast, the distribution of such species is inevitably restricted.

Despite all this, some orchid species have a much wider tolerance of ecological variation and so occur over a much wider range of habitats. A few are even able to exist occasionally in conditions apparently quite different to those in which they are 'normally' found. In these instances the geographical distribution of the plant is less easy to predict and may be determined by opportunism or the effect of climate, rather than by habitat. The fine discrimination some orchids show in favouring one habitat over another can be clearly revealed in some areas with complex microtopography. One such area is the Burren, Co. Clare, in the Republic of Ireland, where the famous limestone pavement is often overlaid by patches of acidic peat. This peaty soil is home to the Heath Spotted-orchid *Dactylorhiza maculata* and to Heather *Calluna vulgaris*, both well-known calcifuges, while adjacent turf, perhaps only centimetres away, is home to calcicolous plants such as the Early Purple Orchid *Orchis mascula* and – Burren specialities – the Dense-flowered Orchid *Neotinea maculata* and the Spring Gentian *Gentiana verna*.

As well as being determined by natural phenomena, orchid distribution in the British Isles has been influenced greatly by human activity, leading in many cases to local extirpations from sites that were naturally ideal. This may be due to direct pressure on the orchids themselves, as in the case of the Lady's Slipper *Cypripedium calceolus*, harried almost to extinction for the sake of its horticultural desirability, or Summer Lady's-tresses *Spiranthes aestivalis*, unnecessarily collected by botanists from a naturally dwindling population and now extinct in Britain. In most cases, however, losses are not species-specific, and most frequently they come about through habitat change as patterns of land-use shift. This is no new phenomenon. Matthew Arnold, in his elegiac *Thyrsis* (1867), bemoaned how hillsides had been destroyed by ploughing: 'Where thick the cowslips grew, and, far descried, High tower'd the spikes of purple orchises … Down each green bank hath gone the ploughboy's team.' Such destruction continues with more modern equipment and areas of orchid habitat continue to become smaller and more isolated, increasing still further the likelihood of population loss. The distribution maps reproduced later in this book (see *Chapter 5. Species Accounts*), which show both modern and former sites for all species, reveal this trend only too clearly. Threats to orchids, and options available for conserving them, are discussed in greater detail in *Chapter 6. Approaches to the Conservation of British and Irish Orchids.*

Ecology

All British orchids are perennial plants which in order to germinate their seed are dependent on infection by an associated mycorrhizal fungus (see *Chapter 1. The Orchid Plant*), and this association continues to be necessary, to a greater or lesser extent, throughout the life of the plant. Most species are slow to reach maturity, taking several years to develop from the seedling stage to an adult flowering plant, although having achieved this they may flower repeatedly for several years. Others, such as the Bee Orchid *Ophrys apifera*, tend to flower just once, using up their nutritional resources in doing so. Owing to this long period of development – perhaps as long as ten years in some species – and in consequence of the plants' partial reliance on the fungal associate, any disturbance of the root system (by ploughing for example, or excessive trampling, or more insidiously by interference through the application of fertilisers and herbicides) can harm orchids, adversely affecting their development and in many cases eradicating them. A long period will then ensue before they are able to re-establish themselves, if indeed they ever do.

Another factor affecting orchid ecology is the availability or otherwise of light to the growing plant. Some species thrive in the open where the light is strong but are lost if conditions become more shaded, or at least develop only vegetatively. In the latter case a spectacular display of flowering can sometimes occur immediately after coppicing or woodland clearance, when the light available to long-dormant plants is suddenly improved; but it is uncertain for how long individual species can survive in a permanent vegetative state. Other species such as the Bird's-nest Orchid *Neottia nidus-avis* prefer, by contrast, to occupy the deepest, darkest recesses of woodland and react adversely to any increase in the light that reaches them, after felling, for example, or wind damage.

Plate 42. *Cephalanthera damasonium* × *C. longifolia* hybrid (*C.* ×*schulzei*), found with its parent species in deciduous woodland, Hampshire, 22 May 2002.

Associated plant species are another part of the equation. In good quality habitat plant species exist 'in balance', each occupying its own niche in time and space. This balance can easily be disturbed by a change in management, or invasion by a vigorous species. Grazing by herbivores is often an essential element in habitat maintenance, and if it ceases grasses and other plants may become too vigorous, outcompeting and eventually even eliminating orchids and other sensitive species. Seasonality of grazing is important too; sheep and cattle are often partial to orchid flowers in summer, while winter-growing species may be damaged by trampling when in leaf. Increased fertility, usually through the application of inorganic fertilisers (either directly or as run-off from treated fields), is another adverse factor often mentioned in this book. The result is usually to promote vigorous growth in grasses that then outcompete most other plants, including orchids, eventually causing great loss of biodiversity. In addition the soil chemistry is altered, which may in turn affect the sensitive interaction between orchid roots and their mycorrhiza.

The National Vegetation Classification

The National Vegetation Classification (NVC) was originally commissioned by the Nature Conservancy Council (now known as English Nature and Scottish Natural Heritage) in an attempt to provide a detailed systematic classification of the various types of vegetation present in Great Britain and Northern Ireland. Carried out by a team of workers under the direction of Dr John Rodwell of Lancaster University, the project reviewed published ecological literature and also surveyed a large number and very wide range of habitats. In each of these the occurrence and frequency of the various component species was recorded and analysed. The survey was comprehensive, not restricted to the more interesting habitats and the rarer species but rather including man-made sites, farmland and afforested areas, and all widely occurring 'common' species. More than 30,000 localities were examined, and when all the data were processed a set of discrete, recognisable plant communities and sub-communities were identified and named, their names relating to the most characteristic species present within them (for example, the *Fagus sylvatica – Mercurialis perennis* woodland community, W12). This classification has rapidly become an accepted means of habitat identification and is now widely used by ecologists, conservation agencies, the Forestry Commission, the National Trust, the RSPB, Defra and many industrial developers. Named NVC communities are often mentioned in this book. Many species of orchid are only found in a limited number of such communities, so by identifying these the possible presence of a particular species may be predicted. More detailed information on the NVC system can be obtained by consulting *British Plant Communities* (Rodwell 1991–2000).

Habitats of British orchids

Woodland habitats

Beechwood

This type of woodland is most frequent in southern parts of England, usually occurring on slopes over chalk or limestone, sometimes with deep humus resulting from fallen, rotting leaves that have accumulated beneath the trees. Mature trees of Beech *Fagus sylvatica* create a dense canopy, effectively shading the ground and excluding most plants. In consequence ground cover is sparse, often comprising Dog's Mercury *Mercurialis perennis*, Sweet Woodruff *Galium odoratum* and brambles *Rubus fruticosus* agg. Several species of orchids grow in such areas of reduced competition. Beech woodland especially is the home of two of our rarest orchids, the Red Helleborine *Cephalanthera rubra* and the mycoheterotrophic Ghost Orchid *Epipogium aphyllum*, the latter being extremely rare. Both can be shy flowerers, especially so the *Epipogium* which, at its very few known sites, is only found where the light is at its weakest. Another mycoheterotrophic orchid, *Neottia nidus-avis*, is

also found in similar conditions to the *Epipogium*
but can tolerate more light and is not restricted to
Fagus sylvatica – *Mercurialis perennis* woodland.
Beech woodland is also the preferred habitat of
yet another mycoheterotroph, this time not an
orchid – the Yellow Bird's-nest *Monotropa hypopitys*. The Narrow-leaved Helleborine *Cephalanthera longifolia*, a more widespread plant, also
shows a preference for beechwoods but occurs
in stronger light, as do the Lady Orchid *Orchis
purpurea*, the Broad-leaved Helleborine *Epipactis
helleborine*, the Violet Helleborine *E. purpurata*,
and sometimes other species of *Epipactis*. These
orchids usually prefer the margins of the woodland, or partial clearings within it.

Other deciduous woodland

It is generally true that old semi-natural woodlands,
often referred to as 'ancient woodlands', contain a
wider, more interesting orchid flora than those more
recently established. Woodlands of Ash *Fraxinus
excelsior* and Hazel *Corylus avellana* on clay or
limestone can be home to the commoner species,
especially *Orchis mascula*, the Greater Butterfly-
orchid *Platanthera chlorantha* and the Common
Twayblade *Neottia ovata*, which often grow in a

Plate 43. The Violet
Helleborine *Epipactis
purpurata* can form robust
clumps. Roadside verge,
edge of deciduous woodland
on chalk, Chilterns, Oxfordshire, 4 August 1996.

ground flora dominated by *Mercurialis perennis*, Ivy *Hedera helix* and sparse bramble
Rubus fruticosus agg. Oak *Quercus* and Birch *Betula* woods usually exist over more
acidic substrates and in consequence the associated orchid flora is less diverse,
although the species mentioned above may sometimes be found, as may the calcifuge Lesser Twayblade *Neottia cordata*. In contrast, however, currently regenerating, less natural mixed woodlands may also contain interesting species. Some
within the central industrial belt of Scotland, which have developed over disused
spoil-heaps of coal mines, are favoured by Young's Helleborine *E. helleborine* var.
youngiana and other species of *Epipactis*, and some woodlands over heavy-metal
contaminated soils in northern England are similarly favoured by both the commoner and the rarer species of *Epipactis*.

Light coppiced hazel woodland

Another type of woodland habitat, also loosely described as deciduous woodland,
is the hazel coppice. Here the trees are of smaller stature and the canopy is less
dense, allowing appreciable levels of light to filter through to reach the ground
flora. Light availability is greatest in spring before the leaves develop in the canopy,
so early-flowering species are favoured. Light is further increased in any areas cleared

by renewed coppicing and this can stimulate plants that have long been dormant, whereupon species such as *Orchis mascula, Neottia ovata, Platanthera chlorantha* and the Common Spotted-orchid *Dactylorhiza fuchsii* may suddenly reappear in flower. In southern Britain hazel coppices can also be home to species more frequently found in other habitats, including *Cephalanthera longifolia*, the Fly Orchid *Ophrys insectifera* and the Lady Orchid *Orchis purpurea*; even the Man Orchid *Orchis anthropophora*, more commonly a plant of open grassland, may sometimes be found.

Coniferous woodland

There are two types of coniferous woodland habitat for orchids in the British Isles, one comprising the relatively restricted native pinewood of Scots Pine *Pinus sylvestris*, the other more widespread forestry plantations, often of alien species. The former now survives only as scattered remnants in northern Scotland, the largest tracts being on Deeside and Speyside, with one especially extensive area at Rothiemurchus. This is the natural home of Creeping Lady's-tresses *Goodyera repens*, which can form large colonies, even in poor light, loosely rooted in the mossy carpet and decaying pine needles of the forest floor, often in association with species of winter-

Plate 44. *Goodyera repens* growing in Scots Pine *Pinus sylvestris* plantation, Roxburghshire, 22 July 1989.

green *Orthilia secunda* and *Pyrola* spp. As a result of pines being planted outside this area, however, using stock from the old pinewoods, *Goodyera repens* has become well established much further south, especially in Cumbria and on the Norfolk coast, having been transferred with the soil around seedling roots. Other orchids occurring in pinewoods, although not limited to them, are the Coralroot Orchid *Corallorhiza trifida* and the Lesser Twayblade *Neottia cordata*. Ultimately, however, planted pines develop into dense stands from which light is progressively excluded, with the result that this habitat becomes unsuitable for most species, even *Goodyera repens*. Along the margins and woodland rides of sparser, older conifer plantations, such as exist on the coastal sands of southern Lancashire, the Dune Helleborine *Epipactis dunensis* and the Green Helleborine *E. phyllanthes* thrive.

Grassland habitats

The calcareous grasslands of the British Isles hold perhaps the largest variety of our orchid species, and this is a very important habitat. Acidic grasslands, more frequent in the north, also have particular species that are mostly restricted to such conditions.

Plate 45. *Dactylorhiza fuchsii* subsp. *fuchsii* in base-rich grassland, Midlothian, 6 July 1990.

Calcareous grassland

The well-grazed but otherwise undisturbed chalk downland of southern England is particularly rich in orchid species. Since the mid-twentieth century, however, much of the grazing – essential for the maintenance of competition- and shade-free conditions – has been reduced or even discontinued. Large areas of this habitat have also been converted to other use, so that the best orchid populations are now found only in well-managed locations, often where there is legal protection. Short *Festuca*-dominated turf over chalk and also, in some cases, over limestone, has a rich herb flora in which species of milkwort *Polygala*, thyme *Thymus*, gentian *Gentiana* and *Gentianella*, and Kidney Vetch *Anthyllis vulneraria* are frequent components. When such habitat has remained unploughed for generations it is the natural home of the Green-winged Orchid *Anacamptis morio*, the Musk Orchid *Herminium monorchis*, the Burnt Orchid *Neotinea ustulata*, the Early and Late Spider-orchids *Ophrys sphegodes* and *O. fuciflora*, the Bee Orchid *O. apifera* and the Monkey Orchid *Orchis simia*. Steep unploughable banks and the sides of ancient earthworks usually remain free of disturbance over very long periods and are especially favoured habitats for these species. Some of the above orchids also occur further north,

Plate 46. Orchids are frequently found in species-rich chalk downland: *Gymnadenia conopsea*, Dorset, 27 June 2002.

but are usually less abundant there. The Pyramidal Orchid *Anacamptis pyramidalis*, the Common Spotted-orchid *Dactylorhiza fuchsii*, the Frog Orchid *Dactylorhiza viridis*, the Chalk Fragrant-orchid *Gymnadenia conopsea* and the Common Tway-blade *Neottia ovata* are common wherever there is habitat of this type.

Most of these species have their own fairly specific period of flowering, *Anacamptis morio*, *Ophrys sphegodes* and *Orchis mascula* being amongst the earliest. In the south of England *Neotinea ustulata* is either spring- or summer-flowering, and whilst the two forms invariably occur in separate populations they can appear in close proximity to each other under seemingly very similar ecological conditions. Later-flowering orchids of grazed calcareous grassland include *Herminium monorchis*, *Ophrys apifera*, *O. fuciflora*, *Orchis anthropophora* and *O. simia*, whilst Autumn Lady's-tresses *Spiranthes spiralis* makes its appearance in August and September. Some species of grazed calcareous turf, such as *S. spiralis* and *Ophrys apifera*, may also be visible in winter, as rosettes of leaves held close to the ground.

Lowland meadows

Unimproved lowland meadows are now a highly threatened habitat, being especially subject to changes in management and the application of fertilisers. Many of the best surviving examples are now protected in some way, with appropriate management regimes in place. Diversity of plants can be high and such sites can contain a rich array of orchids, particularly where there is calcareous soil. Many of the commoner species will be represented, especially *Dactylorhiza fuchsii,* and in damper areas the Early Marsh-orchid *Dactylorhiza incarnata* may be found. Regeneration of plants from seed will, however, be restricted unless these meadows are mown late in the season. In especially favoured localities, downland orchids such as *Anacamptis morio* and *Neotinea ustulata* may be found growing in quite tall vegetation, but if this surrounding growth becomes excessive or too persistent the orchid plants' long-term survival may be jeopardised, hence the need for active management.

Upland meadows, pastures and moorland

Upland meadows and pastures – a special feature of northern England, though they also exist in parts of Wales, Scotland and Ireland – can be rich in a more limited range of orchid species. Conditions may vary from strongly base-rich, especially where there are areas of flushing, through neutral to acidic. Owing to the altitude and to the moister climate, fodder grasses develop later in these situations than elsewhere, so that the orchids have the opportunity to flower and set seed before the farmer takes his crop for the first time in mid-summer. The fields are often small and uneconomical to work intensively, and the absence of artificial fertilisers is another factor that helps orchids to flourish. Many such areas have, however, been 'improved', with consequent loss of species diversity. Typical habitat is often damp, with a range of *Dactylorhiza* species present, especially the Heath Spotted-orchid *D. maculata,* the Northern Marsh-orchid *D. purpurella* and two of the subspecies of *D. incarnata*, subsp. *incarnata* and subsp. *pulchella*. More rarely, in similar habitats, the Heath Fragrant-orchid *Gymnadenia borealis* and the Lesser Butterfly-orchid *Platanthera bifolia* may be found. In just a few places in northern England, but more frequently in Scotland, these upland pastures are the principal home of the Small White Orchid *Pseudorchis albida*.

Plate 47. The Lesser Twayblade *Neottia cordata,* in typical habitat of sparse vegetation of *Calluna,* bryophytes and lichens on peat, *c.*600 m, Cairngorm mountains, east Inverness-shire, 2 June 2002.

The large tracts of moorland found in the north and west of the British Isles are essentially acidic, so that Purple Moor-grass *Molinia caerulea*, Deergrass *Trichophorum cespitosum*, heaths *Erica* spp. and Heather *Calluna vulgaris*, and cottongrasses *Eriophorum angustifolium* and *E. vaginatum* are frequent. Here the orchid flora is poorer, *Dactylorhiza* species being most typical and widespread, especially *D. maculata*, but with *Gymnadenia borealis* and *Platanthera bifolia* sometimes also present. One rather rare orchid, the Lesser Twayblade *Neottia cordata*, especially favours these conditions but is often inconspicuous amongst the mosses beneath heaths and Heather.

Dune grassland and machair

Dune systems are usually calcareous, as a result of overlying a crushed-shell sand substrate. Other than in damp depressions or 'slacks' amongst the dunes themselves (see below) the well-drained sandy ground means that conditions are generally dry. *Anacamptis morio, A. pyramidalis, Dactylorhiza fuchsii* and *Ophrys apifera* can occur amongst the short turf of the more stabilised areas. On the south coast of England the rare Lizard Orchid *Himantoglossum hircinum* also occupies such a habitat. In some parts the Creeping Willow *Salix repens* may be frequent, and growing amongst this populations of the Coralroot Orchid *Corallorhiza trifida* can sometimes be found.

Plate 48. A local endemic, *Dactylorhiza ebudensis* is found only in wet machair on North Uist, Outer Hebrides. 14 June 1990.

The machair of north-west Scotland, and in particular of the outer Hebridean islands, is a similar habitat. Here the main features are not the dunes themselves but the large flattish or gently sloping areas of short species-rich turf lying over the rich shell-sand base, from which taller competing vegetation is absent. In such places orchids may be extremely abundant – especially *Dactylorhiza* species, including the Frog Orchid *D. viridis*. *Dactylorhiza fuchsii* subsp. *hebridensis* may occur in large populations, and on North Uist, very locally, the much rarer Hebridean Marsh-orchid *D. ebudensis* is also found.

Wet habitats

Fens

Where alkaline water deriving from soluble calcareous rocks has lain over peat for long periods, fen vegetation can develop. Typically this comprises species of sedge *Carex*, horsetails *Equisetum* and rushes *Juncus*, interspersed with herbaceous flowering plants which can include Marsh Marigold *Caltha palustris*, Meadowsweet *Filipendula ulmaria*, Yellow Iris *Iris pseudacorus* and Bogbean *Menyanthes trifoliata*. Again this is usually a species-rich habitat, and is a favoured locality for several of the rarer species of marsh-orchid, especially the Narrow-leaved Marsh-orchid *Dactylorhiza traunsteinerioides*, which is almost entirely restricted to these areas. Another rarity is *D. incarnata* subsp. *ochroleuca* which has only ever been positively recorded from a few localities in the East Anglian fens, where it is particularly susceptible to loss through drying-out of the ground. More common orchids of the fens are *D. incarnata* subsp. *incarnata* and subsp. *pulchella*, as well as the Southern Marsh-orchid *D. praetermissa*. In East Anglia may be found another rarity, the Fen Orchid *Liparis loeselii* var. *loeselii,* growing rooted amongst the mosses in *Juncus*-dominated reed beds, and needing surrounding vegetation to be well cut back if it is not to be lost through overcrowding.

Bogs

In contrast to fens, bogs develop where acid water has lain for long periods over peat. This habitat is distinctly acidic and is usually dominated by *Sphagnum* mosses, but also supports such species as the Round-leaved Sundew *Drosera rotundifolia*, bladderworts *Utricularia* spp., and the Butterwort *Pinguicula vulgaris*. Here the orchid flora is much more restricted but at least one species, the Bog Orchid *Hammarbya paludosa* – a very small plant growing loosely rooted in the *Sphagnum* cover – is found nowhere else. On drier raised areas *Dactylorhiza maculata, Neottia cordata* and *Platanthera bifolia* may sometimes be found. In better-drained soils a heathland vegetation will develop, dominated by ericaceous species such as Heather *Calluna vulgaris* and Bell Heather *Erica cinerea*, and under these conditions a few orchid species may occur, *Dactylorhiza maculata* and *Neottia cordata* being those most frequently found.

Plate 49. *Dactylorhiza traunsteinerioides* ('*D. lapponica*'), in a typical bog community with *Drosera anglica*, W. Ross, 7 July 1998.

Marshes

Marshes develop in areas where the soils are much less peaty and the water is closer to neutral. Typical of this habitat are Cuckooflower *Cardamine pratensis*, rushes *Juncus* and Ragged-Robin *Lychnis flos-cuculi*, and here particularly the commoner species of *Dactylorhiza* are most at home. In the southern half of England *D. praetermissa* is especially frequent in these situations but further north it is effectively replaced by *D. purpurella*. Two local taxa, *D. purpurella* var. *cambrensis* and the Irish Marsh-orchid *D. occidentalis*, have this as their main habitat, as does the Marsh Helleborine *Epipactis palustris*. Marshy conditions around lake margins in parts of Ireland and Scotland support the rare Irish Lady's-tresses *Spiranthes romanzoffiana*.

Dune slacks

Dune slacks are another important orchid habitat. These are depressions in the dunes that approach the water-table and may become flooded in winter, drying out in summer. They are therefore very different to the surrounding raised dry sand-hills dominated by Marram *Ammophila arenaria*. The slacks are especially base-rich

Plate 50. The hollows, or 'slacks' between sand dunes are often damp, affording suitable conditions for the Marsh Helleborine *Epipactis palustris*. Lancashire coast, 5 July 2000.

where there is a high calcareous content resulting from the crushed marine shells from which the dunes are formed. Creeping Willow *Salix repens*, a mat-forming shrub, can cover large areas. The lowest parts are usually moist, and here may be found small herbs such as the Bog Pimpernel *Anagallis tenella*, the Marsh Pennywort *Hydrocotyle vulgaris* and the Round-leaved Wintergreen *Pyrola rotundifolia*. Various species of *Dactylorhiza*, especially *D. incarnata* subsp. *incarnata*, *D. incarnata* subsp. *coccinea* and *D. purpurella*, and also *Epipactis palustris*, may be found here in vast numbers. A less frequent dune-slack plant is *E. dunensis*, which also occurs in slightly drier areas. The very local Lindisfarne Helleborine *E. sancta* is another orchid restricted to such a habitat, and *Liparis loeselii* var. *ovata* is found in a few similar places in south Wales.

Other habitats

Limestone pavement

Plate 51. The 'grikes' of limestone pavement are the favoured habitat of the Dark-red Helleborine *Epipactis atrorubens*: north Lancashire, 26 June 1998.

This is particularly a feature of northern England, parts of north Wales, north-west Scotland and western Ireland, in the latter case most famously in the Burren, Co. Clare. Several orchid species find an acceptable habitat in the grikes and fissures of the pavement or in the associated more shattered limestone clitter. In the Burren the Dense-flowered Orchid *Neotinea maculata* is a celebrated speciality, growing in short turf over the limestone. More widespread but largely restricted to pavements and to limestone cliffs is the Dark-red Helleborine *Epipactis atrorubens*, which is relatively frequent in certain parts of northern England in association with Angular Solomon's-seal *Polygonatum odoratum* and species of fern such as the Rigid Buckler-fern *Dryopteris submontana* and Hart's-tongue *Phyllitis scolopendrium*. The Common Spotted-orchid *Dactylorhiza fuchsii* and the Early Purple Orchid *Orchis mascula* can also be found on limestone pavement. As discussed above, pockets of acidic soil may occur overlying the limestone and here apparently anomalous calcifuge species can appear, scarcely separated from the surrounding calcicoles.

Plate 52. *Anacamptis pyramidalis*, roadside verge, East Gloucestershire. Such verges may be the only refuges for orchids in areas of intensive farming. 25 June 2004.

Man-made habitats (chalk-pits, quarries, mining waste, road verges)

The disused chalk-pits of southern England may contain species typical of the adjacent chalk downland. One such pit in Suffolk is of considerable importance as it contains the largest British population of the very scarce Military Orchid *Orchis militaris*. Another artificial habitat is among the debris and broken fragments of abandoned limestone quarry floors, sometimes favoured by *Dactylorhiza fuchsii* and the Bee Orchid *Ophrys apifera*. The 'hills and holes' of former heavy-metal workings, as in Derbyshire or at Barnack in Cambridgeshire, are usually species-rich. At the Barnack site a large population of the Man Orchid *Orchis anthropophora* has been known almost since records began, and in similar places in Derbyshire the Frog Orchid *Dactylorhiza viridis* and the Burnt Orchid *Neotinea ustulata* may grow in the short-grazed stony turf. Some of the larger mining tips of the central industrial belt of Scotland support good colonies of Young's Helleborine *E. helleborine* var. *youngiana*, as do others in Northumberland where lead and zinc have been extracted. In some parts of southern Lancashire alkaline waste tips have been landscaped and grassed over and have subsequently been found to generate an interesting flora of the commoner orchid species.

Perhaps the most widespread of all orchid habitats is also a man-made one. A wide range of species can develop along the verges of roads, especially where sympathetic management and conservation measures have been put into practice. Most frequent here are the widespread *Dactylorhiza fuchsii* and the Common Twayblade *Neottia ovata*, but others such as *Dactylorhiza viridis*, *Ophrys apifera* and the Fly Orchid *O. insectifera* (usually more at home in light scrubland) may also be found. *Anacamptis pyramidalis* and some of the marsh-orchids are also to be seen on roadside verges, sometimes in large, conspicuous colonies.

Chapter 4

Identifying Orchids

Crinan Alexander

Identifying orchids in the British Isles is generally not too difficult, and in most cases a name can be discovered by referring to the illustrations in books such as this one. Molecular techniques are valuable for systematic studies but are not yet useful for recognition of plants in the field, and for this morphology remains paramount. Fortunately the majority of our native orchids are easily distinguished on sight, using reliable morphological characters. The key given below (pp. 50–53) provides an accurate means of identifying most British orchids to genus level using obvious features of the plant.

For identification to species level it may be necessary to compare the plant in question against illustrations and descriptions as given in *Chapter 5. Species Accounts*. Habitat and distribution can be useful diagnostic features, and may indeed be an important means of distinguishing between plants, as in the case of the three species of *Gymnadenia*, the Chalk, Heath and Marsh Fragrant-orchids. In other cases, such as the rather similar Heath and Common Spotted-orchids *Dactylorhiza maculata, D. fuchsii,* habitats are usually quite separate but may occasionally overlap, and here more critical observation is needed. More rarely, an anomaly in habitat or range may be discovered, and the possibility of this should be borne in mind. With luck, however, the beginner will become familiar with orchids in their typical and most frequent habitats before encountering them in more unusual sites. It should also be remembered that orchids, like other plants, respond to their environment and may look slightly different in different habitats.

Plate 54. Colour variants can present identification problems. This hyperchromic *Dactylorhiza maculata* f. *concolor* (Vermeul.) Landwehr is identifiable by its central labellum lobe being much smaller than the lateral lobes. Acid heathland, New Forest, S. Hampshire, 17 June 2003.

Plate 53 (opposite). A normal plant of the Heath Spotted-orchid *Dactylorhiza maculata*: its association with acid soil is an important identification character for this species. Peaty pocket on limestone pavement, Burren, Co. Clare, 3 July 2002.

Colour variations

Mutations causing colour variations may lead to some difficulties with identification, but variant plants usually occur in populations of otherwise normal individuals. **Albinism** is the most frequent colour variation and tends to result in a flower lacking any reddish pigment, as can be seen in many of the illustrations in this book (see Plates 6, 168, 169, 174, 193, 202, 208, 216, 246, 294). Green pigments, if present in the flower, are not usually affected, so albinism may produce a white and green flower; indeed the whole plant may be paler green than normal. In less extreme cases pigmentation may be reduced, resulting in a paler flower than usual, sometimes more yellow or paler pink in appearance. More rarely, in a condition known as **hyperchromism**, colour is enhanced, giving darker flowers than usual (see, for example, Plates 34, 54, 229, 264, 265). Variants of this kind have often been described as varieties, but in view of their sporadic occurrence among populations of normal plants the rank of forma is more appropriate.

Morphological freaks

Teratological mutants or **terata** (from Greek *teras*, 'monster') – more colloquially known as 'freaks' – are usually quickly recognisable as such. They are rare and will seldom be met with. One of the more frequent examples is when one or more flowers in an inflorescence are inverted (non-resupinate), with the lip uppermost.

Plate 55. An abnormal plant of *Platanthera chlorantha*. Unimproved pasture, Kinross-shire, 7 July 2002.

Plate 56. A variant of *Ophrys sphegodes* with enlarged petals. Such occasional mutations in a population of normal plants should not cause identification problems. Kent, 5 May 2004.

Other mutations involve the duplication or reduction of floral parts, and again this may affect only one or two flowers in each inflorescence. The term **peloric** is sometimes used to describe cases when the normal symmetry of the flower is affected.

Hybrids

Hybrids are likely to be the worst problem for those trying to identify orchids. In Orchidaceae hybridisation is frequent. In tropical orchids horticulturists have artificially created many thousands of hybrids, some involving several genera. In nature, if the intimate relationship between orchid and pollinator breaks down and cross-fertilisation occurs by chance, orchids seem often to lack the genetic barriers to hybridisation that occur in most other families. Most orchids of the British Isles, however, do not hybridise readily. The exception to this is the genus *Dactylorhiza*, whose species have a strong tendency to hybridise, sometimes with closely related genera. Hybrids within and between other genera of British and Irish orchids have been recorded but only on very rare occasions, and they are not likely to be found in the field. Some, indeed, are unlikely ever to recur in the British Isles, as po:v4°ations of the parent plants are no longer in contact.

Plate 57. The parentage of hybrids often has to be deduced from nearby plants. *Dactylorhiza incarnata (s.l.)* × *D. traunsteinerioides* (*D. ×dufftii*), marshy loch margin, W. Ross, 23 June 1996.

The range of variation evident in hybrids is not easily described, but they can usually be recognised by having a suite of characters unlike those of either parent alone, sometimes being intermediate between the parents, in other cases having one or two anomalous features that suggest hybridity. Such plants may be the result of a backcross of a hybrid to a parent (frequent in *Dactylorhiza*). In all instances where a hybrid is suspected, care must be taken to ensure that the differences are not merely due to minor mutations within one of the putative parents.

Epipactis and *Dactylorhiza*

The two largest genera of British and Irish orchids, and the most problematic as far as identification is concerned, are *Epipactis* and *Dactylorhiza*, and separate keys are provided for these in the generic descriptions later in this book (*Chapter 5. Species Accounts*). Both are often said to be 'taxonomically difficult', probably because they are evolving rapidly, with the result that individuals and populations do not always fall into neat taxonomic units. In *Dactylorhiza*, where hybridisation is frequent, hybrids may in some populations have largely or entirely replaced one or both parents. In such cases an educated guess will be needed to untangle the parentage, perhaps based on considerations of habitat and information about possible parental species in the area.

In *Epipactis* hybrids are uncommon but complications for identification arise from the frequency with which self-pollination occurs. This can result in the establishment of geographically restricted, morphologically distinct 'races' through inbreeding in local variants. In some cases, such as the Dune Helleborine *Epipactis dunensis* and the Lindisfarne Helleborine *E. sancta*, there is a recognisable genetic distinction between these plants and their closest relatives; in other species however, and particularly in *E. phyllanthes*, there appear to be few genetic differences between morphologically distinct entities.

Key to orchid genera of the British Isles

1a. Plant producing fully developed green leaves 2

1b. Plant never producing fully developed green leaves; stem and
　　　bracts white to yellowish green or brown, sometimes pale green 24

2a. Base of labellum expanded into hollow spur 3

2b. Base of labellum not expanded into hollow spur 13

3a. Labellum 'man-like' with four major lobes and distinct, though
　　　much smaller, central lobe
　　　　　　　.............. *Orchis* (*simia, militaris, purpurea*) pp.158, 162, 167

3b. Labellum not distinctly four-lobed; if weakly so,
　　　then not 'man-like' 4

4a. Spur to 3 mm long 5

4b. Spur more than 3 mm long 8

5a. Labellum with two spreading lateral lobes attached near base,
　　　shorter than the simple or bifid middle lobe 6

5b. Labellum with two or three more or less equal lobes 7

6a. Middle lobe of labellum ribbon-like and twisted,
　　　3–5 cm long .... *Himantoglossum* p.271

6b. Middle lobe of labellum not ribbon-like,
　　　less than 1 cm long .... *Neotinea* p.261

7a. Flowers greenish yellow to brown or red ...... *Dactylorhiza* (*viridis*) p.219

7b. Flowers white or yellow .... *Pseudorchis* p.177

8a.   Spur slender and curved, more than 6× longer than widest point 9

8b.   Spur broad and straight, less than 6× longer than widest point 11

9a.   Labellum narrow, unlobed, not wavy-edged;
        flowers white to cream .... *Platanthera* p.181

9b.   Labellum clearly lobed, or broad and wavy-edged;
        flowers pink to red or magenta 10

10a. Labellum with two pale spreading
        keels at base .... *Anacamptis* (*pyramidalis*) p.279

10b. Labellum without keels at base .... *Gymnadenia* p.191

11a. At least the lower bracts usually green;
        labellum three-lobed, middle lobe often
        triangular, smaller than side lobes ..... *Dactylorhiza* (not *viridis*) p.201

11b. All bracts red to brown; labellum shallowly
        bifid or with a large middle lobe 12

12a. Labellum marked with a few dark longitudinal
        stripes; petals not strongly veined inside .... *Orchis* (*mascula*) p.171

12b. Labellum marked with many dark spots; petals
        strongly veined inside .... *Anacamptis* (*morio, laxiflora*) pp.276, 284

Plate 58. A potentially confusing *Epipactis lepto-chila* with labellum slightly broader than normal. Other key characters confirm its identity as this species. Roadside verge in deciduous woodland on chalk, Bucking hamshire, 29 July 2002.

Plate 59 (above). The brightly coloured flowers of *Dactylorhiza incarnata* subsp. *coccinea* are unique amongst British orchids. Wet calcareous machair, North Uist, Outer Hebrides, 14 June 2000.

13a. Some flowers in each spike with labellum at side or top 14
13b. All flowers with labellum at bottom 15

14a. Flowers usually fewer than 10 per spike,
         loosely arranged; labellum trough-like, crenate .... *Liparis* p.119
14b. Flowers usually more than 15 per spike,
         densely arranged; labellum ± flat, lanceolate .... *Hammarbya* p.125

15a. Labellum strikingly different from other perianth
         segments in shape and size, hanging well clear of
         flower, sometimes inflated, hairy/velvety in places
         and resembling an insect's abdomen 16
15b. Labellum generally similar to other perianth segments,
         if different in colour or shape then not hanging well
         clear of flower 20

16a. Perianth segments, other than labellum, strongly connivent,
         forming a hood over the column 17
16b. Perianth segments, other than labellum, not connivent 18

17a. Labellum 'man-like' with four narrow major lobes and
         a distinct though small central lobe ...... *Orchis* (*anthropophora*) p.154
17b. Labellum broadly three-lobed .... *Serapias* p.289

18a.   Labellum inflated and sac-shaped, yellow .... *Cypripedium* p.59

18b.   Labellum flat or undulating, red, brown,
           green or purple, rarely yellow 19

19a.   Labellum with two parallel, linear or
           strap-shaped lobes; leaves two, subopposite,
           sessile, just above ground level,
           broadly ovate-elliptic to orbicular .. *Neottia* (*cordata, ovata*) pp.76, 78

19b.   Labellum with three or four broad lobes,
           hairy/velvety in places and resembling
           an insect's abdomen; leaves not as above .... *Ophrys* p.293

20a.   Flowers in one to three spirals 21

20b.   Flowers evenly dispersed or concentrated on one side of spike 22

21a.   Basal leaves conspicuously net-veined;
           labellum narrowly triangular, acute, entire .... *Goodyera* p.133

21b.   Leaves not conspicuously net-veined;
           labellum broadest at apex, frilled .... *Spiranthes* p.137

22a.   Leaves two (to three to four), basal; labellum three-
           lobed, not transversely constricted, entire .... *Herminium* p.149

22b.   Leaves three to many, cauline; labellum transversely
           constricted into distinct basal and apical portions,
           toothed, crenate or wavy 23

23a.   Flowers stalked, spreading to pendent .... *Epipactis* p.83

23b.   Flowers sessile, erect to ascending .... *Cephalanthera* p.65

24a.   Spur to 5 mm long, or longer; labellum and spur
           at top of flower .... *Epipogium* p.113

24b.   Spur absent; labellum at bottom of flower 25

25a.   Leaves well developed, standing out from stem
           (chlorotic varieties of usually green species) .... *Epipactis* p.83

25b.   Leaves not well developed, vestigial or sheathing stem 26

26a.   Flowers 2–8(–15) per spike; labellum white
           to pale greenish yellow, maroon at base;
           stem and bracts yellowish or brown .... *Corallorhiza* p.129

26b.   Flowers 20 or more per spike; labellum white
           to pale brown, not marked with maroon;
           stem and bracts yellow to brown .... *Neottia* (*nidus-avis*) p.80

Chapter 5

Species Accounts —
The Orchids of the British Isles

Michael Foley

This chapter gives detailed accounts of all the orchids native to Britain, Ireland and the Channel Islands. The descriptions have been compiled from personal observations and the published literature (e.g. Summerhayes 1968, Lang 1980, 1989, Davies *et al*. 1983, Sell & Murrell 1996, Stace 1997). Use of technical vocabulary is unavoidable in a work of this kind but terms that might be unfamiliar to the general reader are explained in a glossary (pp. 375–378). All measurements are given in metric units, and where dimensions are stated as a formula (e.g. 25 × 5 mm) the first figure indicates length and the second width.

As explained in *Chapter 2. Orchid Taxonomy and Classification*, nomenclature in this book follows the most recent generic revisions. The citation of authorities for plant names uses the forms recommended by Brummitt & Powell (1992).

Plate 60 (opposite). Variation in colour and size must always be borne in mind when identifying plants: a pale-flowered *Anacamptis morio*. Grassy hillside, East Kent, 22 May 1994.

Distribution maps

The maps we have used are taken, with permission, from the *New Atlas of the British and Irish Flora* (2002) compiled by C.D. Preston, D.A. Pearman and T.D. Dines. This monumental collaborative work presents the most accurate picture available of the distribution of British and Irish plants and we are proud to be able to reproduce here the maps for Orchidaceae.

Each dot on the map represents a 10 × 10-km square (hectad) within which the species in question has been recorded, and the dots are colour-coded to indicate the date of the record.

- present as a native plant between 1987 and 1999
- present as a native plant between 1970 and 1986, but not recorded as either a native or an introduction since then
- present as a native before 1970, but not recorded as either a native or an introduction since then; *or* records undated

- present as an introduction between 1987 and 1999
- present as an introduction between 1970 and 1986, but not recorded as either a native or an introduction since then
- present as an introduction before 1970, but not recorded as either a native or an introduction since then; *or* records undated

Sample map, showing in this case the distribution of *Anacamptis pyramidalis*. The Channel Islands are included inset into the main map (bottom left); similarly, Orkney and Shetland (top right).

Since the *New Atlas* was published in 2002 there have been some changes to the taxonomy of mapped taxa, and maps in this book have been amended accordingly. Our maps for *Epipactis dunensis* (p.105) and *E. sancta* (p.110) are derived from the previously published map for *E. leptochila*. The map for *E. leptochila* has been correspondingly amended (p.101) by removing records for the two segregate taxa. Similarly, following the recognition of separate allotetraploid taxa in *Dactylorhiza* the records in the *New Atlas* map for '*Dactylorhiza majalis*' have been reallocated to the currently accepted *Dactylorhiza occidentalis* (p.258), *D. ebudensis* (p.248) and *D. purpurella* var. *cambrensis* (p.254) to produce new maps for these three taxa. The *New Atlas* maps for '*D. traunsteineri*' and '*D. lapponica*' have been combined, to illustrate the distribution of *D. traunsteinerioides* (p.245), and two Irish localities have been added for *D. incarnata* subsp. *cruenta* (p.218).

TABLE 2. NUMBERS AND NAMES OF THE VICE-COUNTIES OF THE BRITISH ISLES

ENGLAND

1. W. Cornwall
2. E. Cornwall
3. S. Devon
4. N. Devon
5. S. Somerset
6. N. Somerset
7. N. Wiltshire
8. S. Wiltshire
9. Dorset
10. Isle of Wight
11. S. Hampshire
12. N. Hampshire
13. W. Sussex
14. E. Sussex
15. E. Kent
16. W. Kent
17. Surrey
18. S. Essex
19. N. Essex
20. Hertfordshire
21. Middlesex
22. Berkshire
23. Oxfordshire (Oxon)
24. Buckinghamshire
25. E. Suffolk
26. W. Suffolk
27. E. Norfolk
28. W. Norfolk
29. Cambridgeshire
30. Bedfordshire
31. Huntingdonshire
32. Northamptonshire

33. E. Gloucestershire
34. W. Gloucestershire
36. Herefordshire
37. Worcestershire
38. Warwickshire
39. Staffordshire
40. Shropshire (Salop)
53. S. Lincolnshire
54. N. Lincolnshire
55. Leicestershire
56. Nottinghamshire
57. Derbyshire
58. Cheshire
59. S. Lancashire
60. W. Lancashire
61. S.E. Yorkshire
62. N.E. Yorkshire
63. S.W. Yorkshire
64. Mid-W. Yorkshire
65. N.W. Yorkshire
66. Co. Durham
67. S. Northumberland
68. Cheviot
69. Westmorland
70. Cumberland

WALES

35. Monmouthshire
41. Glamorgan
42. Breconshire
43. Radnorshire
44. Carmarthenshire
45. Pembrokeshire

46. Cardiganshire
47. Montgomeryshire
48. Merioneth
49. Caernarvonshire
50. Denbighshire
51. Flintshire
52. Anglesey

ISLE OF MAN

71. Isle of Man

SCOTLAND

72. Dumfriesshire
73. Kircudbrightshire
74. Wigtownshire
75. Ayrshire
76. Renfrewshire
77. Lanarkshire
78. Peeblesshire
79. Selkirkshire
80. Roxburghshire
81. Berwickshire
82. E. Lothian
83. Midlothian
84. W. Lothian
85. Fife
86. Stirlingshire
87. W. Perth
88. Mid Perth
89. E. Perth
90. Angus
91. Kincardineshire
92. S. Aberdeen

93. N. Aberdeen
94. Banffshire
95. Moray
96. Easterness
97. Westerness
98. Main Argyll
99. Dunbarton
100. Clyde Isles
101. Kintyre
102. S. Ebudes
103. Mid Ebudes
104. N. Ebudes
105. W. Ross
106. E. Ross
107. E. Sutherland
108. W. Sutherland
109. Caithness
110. Outer Hebrides
111. Orkney
112. Shetland

CHANNEL ISLANDS

S. Channel Islands

IRELAND

1. S. Kerry
2. N. Kerry
3. W. Cork
4. Mid Cork
5. E. Cork
6. Co. Waterford
7. S. Tipperary

8. Co. Limerick
9. Co. Clare
10. N. Tipperary
11. Co. Kilkenny
12. Co. Wexford
13. Co. Carlow
14. Laois
15. S.E. Galway
16. W. Galway
17. N.E. Galway
18. Offaly
19. Co. Kildare
20. Co. Wicklow
21. Co. Dublin
22. Meath
23. Westmeath
24. Co. Longford
25. Co. Roscommon
26. E. Mayo
27. W. Mayo
28. Co. Sligo
29. Co. Leitrim
30. Co. Cavan
31. Co. Louth
32. Co. Monaghan
33. Fermanagh
34. E. Donegal
35. W. Donegal
36. Tyrone
37. Co. Armagh
38. Co. Down
39. Co. Antrim
40. Co. Londonderry

Vice-counties

Some of the sites mentioned in the species accounts are described with reference to vice-counties. These are geographical areas used for biological recording of the distribution of plant and animal species in Britain and Ireland. They are based on former administrative counties but their boundaries, unlike those of current administrative districts, have been stable for over a hundred years.

A NOTE ON FLOWERING TIMES

We believe that the flowering periods given in this book are indicative of the main season in which each species flowers, but latitude and seasonal climatic conditions may lead to variation. In recent decades the flowering times of many species have become earlier as climate change has shifted Spring forwards, and this trend seems likely to continue.

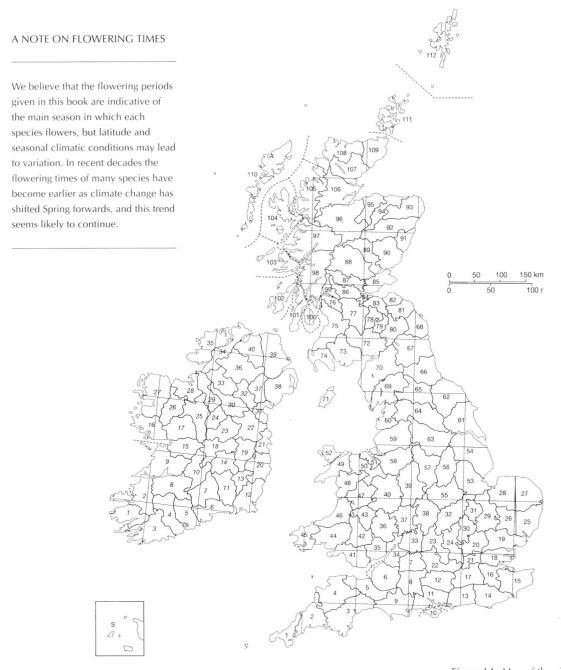

Figure 14. Map of the vice-counties of the British Isles.

1.1. *Cypripedium calceolus* L.

Lady's-slipper Orchid

Perennial rhizomatous herb with fibrous roots; *stems* to 50 cm, glandular-pubescent, erect, leafy above; *leaves* four to five, to 20 × 9 cm, green, ovate, veined, and partially folded; *inflorescence* one- or two- (to three-)flowered; *bracts* erect, 1–6 cm long; *flowers* showy; *perianth segments* maroon, the outer dorsal segment erect, the laterals fused to form a syn-sepalum to 5 × 1.8 cm; *inner perianth segments* free, slightly twisted, 4–6 cm long; *labellum* inflated, to 3 × 3 cm, bright yellow and slipper-shaped, glabrous externally, hairy within; *column* short-stalked; *anthers* two; *stigma* ± papillose; *capsule* cylindrical to ellipsoidal; *flowering* May to June (to July); 2n = 22.

The rarest, and by far the most distinctive of all British orchids, the Lady's-slipper Orchid *Cypripedium calceolus* is perhaps also the most threatened. Historically known in Britain from only a few areas of northern England, during the last half of the twentieth century it became reduced to a single plant in the Yorkshire Dales, where it has survived only through rigorous protection. Much earlier it was far more abundant, to the extent that in the eighteenth century it was sold at local markets for home decoration, and dug up for use as a garden plant. Such depredations inevitably took their toll and it quickly came close to extinction. Fortunately, following recent work at the Royal Botanic Gardens, Kew, using the surviving Dales plant and cultivated ones of known wild British origin, a method has been found to cultivate seedlings successfully *in vitro* (Fisher 1987, Ramsay & Stewart 1998). A reintroduction programme has been developed and it is hoped that such seedlings will eventually lead to the species becoming re-established at many of its former extinct sites. Early indications are that this is proving successful (see *Chapter 6. Approaches to the Conservation of British and Irish Orchids*).

The genus *Cypripedium* comprises more than 40 species, whose collective range covers much of the temperate region of the northern hemisphere; many of these are narrow endemics (Cribb 1997). Whilst *C. calceolus* is known only from the Old World, it is very wide-ranging. Mainly a boreal plant, it occurs from the Pyrenees northwards to Britain and Scandinavia, across Europe including the Alps and the Balkans, and eastwards through central Asia to China and Japan. It is scarce, and threatened in many countries, but in others good populations can still be found.

The generic name, coined by Linnaeus, was derived from a reference to Cyprus, the supposed birthplace of Venus or Aphrodite, and the Greek *pedilon*, 'shoe', i.e. 'lady's slipper'. The Latin epithet *calceolus* means a small shoe. Legend has it that Venus lost her slipper in the woods; when a shepherdess attempted to pick it up it vanished, but a slipper-shaped flower was left in its place. The earliest definite British record for this orchid appears to be that of John Parkinson (1629), of plants at Helks Wood near Ingleborough, Yorkshire, from where his lady correspondent

Plate 61 (opposite).
The sole surviving native Lady's-slipper Orchid *Cypripedium calceolus* has been protected at its Wharfedale site since 1930: a flagship for conservation. 1 June 1978.

Thomasin Tunstall – 'a great lover of these delights', who lived near Hornby Castle – had 'often' sent him roots for his London garden. This locality and others were well known in the eighteenth century, as were the merits of the orchid as a garden plant, with the result that populations were frequently ravaged by collectors. An example of this is provided by Curtis (1941), who reproduces a letter written in 1781 to the eighteenth-century botanist William Curtis, the author of *Flora Londinensis*, stating 'Mr Birkeck [quoted as being a respectable Quaker businessman in Settle] bought 10 Lady's Slippers on market day from a man who had brought about 40 to sell.' A similar situation apparently existed at Ingleton, where plants also went on sale. Despite this, the Lady's-slipper Orchid survived in the nearby Helks Wood into the late-eighteenth century, until it was searched for 'in vain … a gardener of Ingleton having eradicated every plant for sale' (Lees 1888). This is now one of the areas where a reintroduction is being attempted. Judged by this information and other contemporary references, the plant must at one time have been frequent at Helks Wood and have provided quite a spectacle. Additional evidence of its horticultural popularity and its consequent decline in nature can be gained from the large number of nineteenth-century herbarium specimens originating from private gardens, most if not all of which must have originally been uprooted from the wild.

A painting dated 1797 of a plant transplanted into cultivation from this same Ingleborough locality has recently been identified by Cribb (1997), although the earliest coloured illustrations published in Britain appear to be those in the *Gardeners Dictionary* (Miller 1758) and *English Botany* (Sowerby 1790). The sixteenth-century Swiss botanist and naturalist Conrad Gesner was the first to describe a *Cypripedium*, and also the first to produce a water-colour painting of plants of *C. calceolus*, from near Geneva. Gesner's life was cut short by plague and his painting (reproduced in Cribb 1997) was unfortunately not published for another two centuries. His original illustration is nowadays preserved in Germany, in the archives of Erlangen University.

The historical British range of the Lady's-slipper Orchid is restricted to small parts of Derbyshire, Cumbria, Co. Durham and North Yorkshire. A planted specimen grows at a site in north Lancashire (it was vandalised in 2004 but has survived), and it has also been erroneously recorded from Northumberland. It is not known in Ireland. In Derbyshire it was recorded on the wooded limestone cliffs near Matlock until at least 1864, but by the turn of the century it was considered to have been long since extinct (Linton 1903). An early record for Co. Durham is for 1777, but by the middle of the following century it was under severe threat at its few known localities in the wooded magnesian limestone denes such as at Castle Eden Dene. It seems that cultivated stock was later introduced there in an attempt to ensure the plant's survival, but it became extinct in the county early in the twentieth century. The last record appears to have been made in 1926, but this may not refer to genuinely wild stock. In Cumbria there is doubt as to whether the orchid was ever native in the north of the county but it was certainly known on the southern limestones. It was recorded there (at Scout Scar) in 1860, and probably lingered on elsewhere in the south into the twentieth century. In the wooded gills of Yorkshire there were two main centres. An extensive one in the Craven area stretched from Ingleborough eastwards to upper Wharfedale and then north to Wensleydale, where there were two separate populations. The other centre was in the upper Rye valley around Helmsley. Particularly in the former area there were several localities, but all were systematically plundered by collectors, so that only a few plants survived at the beginning of the twentieth century. One of the Ingleborough localities was the famous Helks Wood where *C. calceolus* was first noted, in 1629. Other than the single surviving plant in the Yorkshire Dales, the most recent British record was near Leyburn, Wensleydale, but this population became extinct in 1956 when the last plant was dug up. Although unscrupulous collecting for home and garden decoration caused by far the greatest loss, the trend towards less coppicing in recent times probably also played a part in its demise, as its woodland habitat became overgrown. What are thought to be offspring of native plants still survive on some private estates, including Sizergh Castle in Cumbria and Bolton Abbey in Yorkshire. An isolated plant of uncertain origin known to have been present adjacent to the golf course at Silverdale, Lancashire for at least 80 years was partially dug up in 2004, with much ensuing publicity. In March 2005 it was announced that this plant has produced several shoots and is expected to recover.

In Britain *C. calceolus* is restricted to lime-rich soils. Populations are, or rather were, on the carboniferous, oolitic and magnesian limestones of northern England, where the favoured habitat was partially shaded or north-facing slopes, lightly wooded scree, or open deciduous woodland, with *Corylus*, *Fraxinus* or *Quercus*. It is also recorded as favouring the *Sesleria albicans – Galium verum* (CG9c) community of the NVC classification. At its only surviving British site other plants with a

Plate 62. The maroon and yellow flower of *Cypripedium calceolus* is immediately recognisable. Grassy clearing in *Picea abies* forest, southern Black Forest, Baden-Württemberg, Germany, 26 May 1999.

Plate 63. A once and future sight in northern England? A mass of *Cypripedium calceolus,* Vorarlberg, in the Austrian Alps, 6 June 1999.

very restricted local distribution, such as *Epipactis atrorubens, Polemonium caeruleum* and *Polygala amarella,* occur nearby. Elsewhere in Europe its habitat is more varied, including both coniferous as well as deciduous woodland, scrub, shaded limestone pavement and alpine meadows. In the colder climates of northern Eurasia it tends to grow in calcium-rich, spring-fed fens and wet grassland.

Fertilisation is effected by small bees of the genus *Andrena.* Detailed work in Sweden (Nilsson 1979) has shown these to be attracted by flower colour and fragrance and not, as had earlier been thought, by nectar in the lip of the flower. Once inside the lip the bees are unable to escape by their entry route, but those that are of just the right size can, by using the stigma as support, bend down the lip and pass under the anthers, receiving pollen, before exiting through holes in the base of the lip. They are then free to visit other flowers and so achieve cross-pollination. A limited amount of viable seed can also be produced by selfing. Since the work of Charles Darwin (1862) there has been much speculation on the mechanism of pollination of the genus *Cypripedium;* a useful review of this is given by Nilsson (1979).

Experimental work in Germany has shown that from seed sown in a natural environment, flowering can be achieved within five years (Cribb 1997). In 1993 a laboratory-grown seedling that had been re-established at an undisclosed wild site in the north of England flowered for the first time 11 years after planting (Lindop 1996), and a second reintroduced plant has since also flowered. Seedlings have been introduced at other sites in the north of England but it is expected to be several more years before they flower, assuming that the conditions are suitable. The survival rate of reintroduced seedlings is apparently rather low, and they are especially prone to attack by slugs.

Plate 64 (opposite). A detailed study of the floral parts of *Cypripedium calceolus* by Franz Bauer (1758–1840), one of the most talented botanical artists of all time. For more of his orchid paintings, see Stewart & Stearn (1993).

The Lady's-slipper Orchid is instantly recognisable in the field by its large, showy flowers and bright yellow lip, and cannot be confused with any other British orchid or plant. On certain days during the spring reintroduced plants that have yet to flower (see above) can be seen in their natural surroundings at the Helks Wood site, where access is by public footpath.

Morphological variation appears to be unknown in England but in larger populations elsewhere more than 10 variants have been formally described. Hybrids are also unknown in Britain.

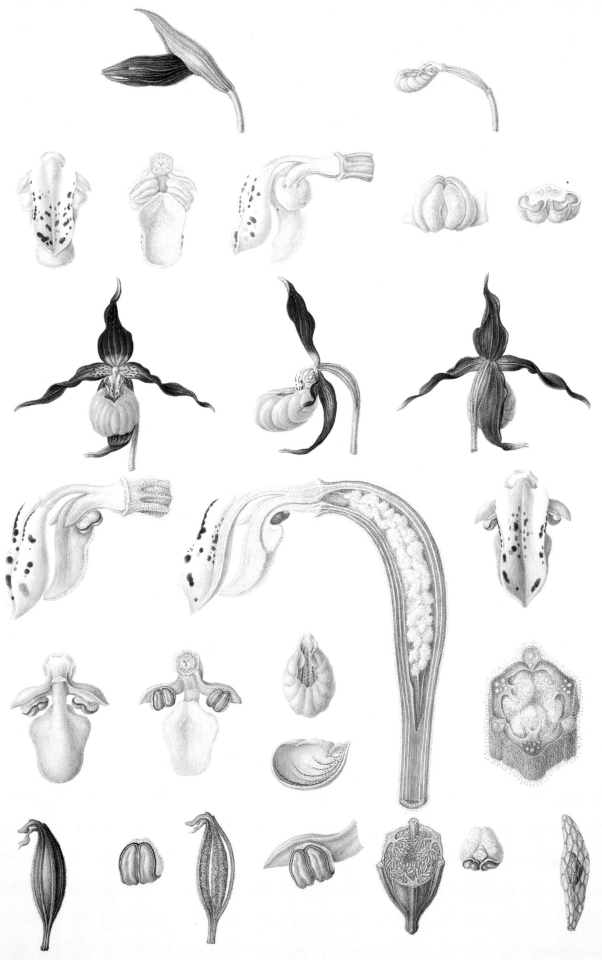

2. *Cephalanthera* Rich.

Helleborines

Perennial herbs with fibrous roots and short, creeping rhizomes; *stem* leafy; *leaves* cauline, flat, unspotted; *inflorescence* usually rather lax; *bracts* leafy towards the base of the inflorescence; *flowers* few, large, ± sessile, lacking scent; *perianth segments* subequal, ± connivent; *labellum* bipartite, divided into a suberect basal hypochile and a forward-pointing, ± ovate distal epichile; *spur* absent; *column* long, erect; *anthers* hinged; *pollinia* two; *stigma* rounded; *rostellum* absent; *ovary* ± subsessile.

Plate 65 (opposite).
A magnificent clump of the Narrow-leaved Helleborine *Cephalanthera longifolia*, growing in mixed deciduous woodland on limestone, Argyll. 20 May 1989.

Plate 66. The White Helleborine *Cephalanthera damasonium* lacks the elegance of *C. longifolia*, having short leaves and flowers that often remain closed. Old chalk-pit, North Hampshire, 22 May 1997.

This genus comprises about 14 species variously distributed in temperate areas of the northern hemisphere, in Europe, North Africa, western Asia, and eastwards through the Himalayas into China and Japan; in the New World it is represented by a single mycoheterotrophic (saprophytic) species in the north-western USA and British Columbia. In Britain only three species occur, two of which are local or have a relatively restricted distribution; the third, *Cephalanthera rubra,* is very rare. The generic name derives from the Greek words *kephale,* 'head', and *anthera,* 'anther', and is descriptive of the single stamen present in this rather primitive group.

Unlike most other orchids *Cephalanthera* has an uncomplicated method of pollination, whereby visiting insects pressing against the stigma pick up from it a sticky substance, to which the pollinia then adhere. When the next flower is visited parts of the pollinia are detached from the insect's body by the stigma, and cross-pollination is effected. Self-pollination and vegetative propagation can also occur. Several hybrids are known, but that between *C. damasonium* and *C. longifolia* is the only one reported from the British Isles.

Plate 67. The deep red-pink flowers of *Cephalanthera rubra* open more widely than those of other *Cephalanthera* species. N. Hampshire, 4 June 1996.

2.1. *Cephalanthera rubra* (L.) Rich.

Red Helleborine

Perennial herb; *stem* to *c.*45 cm, glabrous below, glandular above, normally solitary; *leaves* dark green, to 15 × 2 cm, lanceolate to oblong-lanceolate, ± acute; *inflorescence* a lax spike; *bracts* elliptic to linear-lanceolate, acute, to 45 × 4 mm; *flowers* two to seven (to eighteen), large, rose-pink, opening fairly wide, scentless; *outer perianth segments* to 25 × 5 mm, pink, linear-lanceolate, subpatent; *inner perianth segments* similar, connivent; *labellum* to 17 mm, erect; *hypochile* saccate, white with yellow ridges; *epichile* ovate-elliptic, white with reddish margins near apex; *spur* absent; *column* violet-rose, erect; *anther* broad with papillae; *pollinia* two; *ovary* to 15 mm, subsessile, cylindrical with short glandular hairs; *flowering* June to July; 2n = 48.

A very rare plant in the British Isles, *Cephalanthera rubra* has always had a restricted range here, and is now known from only three British localities. It is unrecorded further north than Gloucestershire, where formerly there were at least seven separate sites, but now reduced to one. Other records, confirmed or otherwise, are from Buckinghamshire, Hampshire, Kent, Somerset and Sussex. There is also an isolated Somerset record for 1836 in the Quantocks. Today the plant is known only from single localities in two of these areas, Buckinghamshire and Hampshire. The first authenticated British record appears to have been made in 1797 at Hampton Common, Gloucestershire by a Mrs Smith, although the Revd W. Lloyd Baker (1752–1830) claimed to have found the plant some time before. The epithet *rubra*, 'red', refers to the colour of the flowers.

The Red Helleborine is widely distributed throughout Europe, northwards to Finland, eastwards into western Asia through Turkey, and as far east as Iran. It is very rare in many countries and is often legally protected. In mainland Europe it is a plant of open, light deciduous woodland or localities where there is an ample penetration of dappled light, such as shaded road verges. It is frequently found over calcareous substrates but is not restricted to these, and usually occurs as scattered individuals or in small populations. In Britain it favours sloping *Fagus* woodland, always over calcareous substrates; this is broadly described as the *Fagus sylvatica – Mercurialis perennis* community (W12) of the NVC system. The plant is intolerant of competition and is only found

where the ground flora is sparse. Associates include *Anemone nemorosa, Campanula trachelium, Carex flacca, Hedera helix, Mercurialis perennis, Prunella vulgaris* and *Viola riviniana*. Under adverse conditions, such as dense ground cover, it can apparently remain for long periods as an underground rhizome, maintained in the vegetative state by its mycorrhizal associate. This explains how it can reappear after some considerable time, when conditions change, at sites where it had previously been thought lost. However, a sustained departure from the ideal balance of adequate light and minimum ground competition will have been a major factor in its eventual extinction at many former localities.

The single extant Gloucestershire site is in a nature reserve north of Painswick, at the foot of sloping *Fagus* woodland over the oolitic limestone, where the few surviving plants are protected by a cage. It was first recorded there in 1864. A new locality was found in 1962 at two adjacent sites, near Wotton-under-Edge, but no plants have been seen there since 1978. Other than the above, this was the last recorded site in the county. At Stanley Wood, near Stroud, once considered the strongest Gloucestershire population, there were 40 plants in 1936, but after tree-felling a few years later the species was lost. Up to 60 plants have been recorded in the past at a single Gloucestershire site.

Plate 68. One of the rarest British orchids, the Red Helleborine *Cephalanthera rubra* is the subject of stringent conservation measures. Deciduous woodland on chalk, Buckinghamshire, 16 June 1997.

The Buckinghamshire site may now hold the strongest British population, having had up to twelve plants in flower during the 1990s. It is situated in a similar habitat, on a west-facing chalk slope in *Fagus* woodland. It was first recorded in 1955 by H.V. Hawkins, when there were three flowering plants, but in the following year eleven were found, and in 1959 four. Although vegetative plants were often present, a period of 25 years then elapsed before the next flower was found in 1984, and since then flowering has occurred almost annually. In 2000 there were four plants in flower, with six additional

vegetative shoots. This improvement is probably due to reduced tree cover following felling and gale damage over the past dozen years or so.

In Hampshire a single flowering plant was found in 1986 (Rose & Brewis 1988), and this was the first fully confirmed record for the county. An earlier record in 1926 at a different locality, by E.M. Williams, was surrounded by secrecy, and that site has never been refound. The new plant grew in deep shade in woodland over chalk, along with several non-flowering shoots. Growth appears to have been stimulated by improved lighting after trees were felled higher up the slope. Subsequent flowering has been fairly regular, with the occasional blank year. Further excessive thinning of the tree canopy has since allowed competing vegetation to become established, and this is likely to be to the detriment of the plant.

To see the Red Helleborine it is best to contact the local conservation group in one of the three counties where it is extant. It is readily identified by its relatively large rose-pink flowers. Confusion with the smaller and much deeper-red flowered *Epipactis atrorubens*, a plant of quite different distribution and habitat, is unlikely. Variants and hybrids are unrecorded in Britain.

Pollination appears to be by bees or hoverflies, but owing to the small size of the few British populations the likelihood of this being effective is currently minimal. At

Plate 69. With 18 flowers, this is an unusually large inflorescence of *Cephalanthera rubra*. Deciduous woodland on chalk, Buckinghamshire, 16 June 1997.

the Buckinghamshire site plants are handpollinated annually, but the seed is usually found to be infertile. Work in Sweden has suggested that some species of *Campanula* have the same pollinators as *Cephalanthera rubra*. Seed production was found to be reduced in *C. rubra* in the absence of bees of the genus *Chelostoma*, which are known to visit both *Campanula* and *Cephalanthera rubra* (Nilsson 1983). *Campanula trachelium* is present at the Buckinghamshire site, and *Chelostoma* bees have been observed on *Cephalanthera rubra* in Hampshire. The significance of this is not clear, but it is possible that in British populations there is a common pollinator of both the orchid and the *Campanula*. Recent genetic analysis indicates that the three extant populations are of independent origins, with the Gloucestershire plants showing the closer connection to Continental material (A. Showler, pers. comm. 2005). A period of up to 10 years is thought to be required between germination and flowering. Propagation can also be by vegetative means, from root buds on rhizomes which have maintained an independent existence underground in the absence of any leafy shoots. In Britain *Cephalanthera rubra* is a shy flowerer but this may partly be governed by the condition and management of its habitat.

2.2. *Cephalanthera longifolia* (L.) Fritsch

Narrow-leaved Helleborine

Perennial herb, usually single-stemmed, sometimes clump-forming; *stem* to 60 cm; *leaves* bright green, alternate, two-ranked, to 20 × 2.5 cm, linear-lanceolate, acute tipped; *inflorescence* a lax spike; *bracts* small, pointed, larger below; *flowers* 5–15(–20), large, pure white, ± sessile, partially opening, scentless; *outer perianth segments* 10–15 mm, lanceolate, acute-tipped; *inner perianth segments* shorter, broader, more obtuse; *labellum* shorter still; *hypochile* white, blotched with orange at the base; *epichile* cordate distally, wider than long, with a few orange basal ridges, tip downturned; *column* erect; *anther* whitish with stigma below; *pollinia* two; *ovary* to 15 mm, cylindrical, twisted, glabrous; *flowering* May to June; 2n = 32.

The distribution pattern of the genus *Cephalanthera* as a whole is largely exemplified by that of the Narrow-leaved Helleborine *C. longifolia*, which occurs throughout much of Europe, southern Scandinavia, North Africa, and from western Asia to China. The specific epithet *longifolia* is a clear reference to the shape of the leaves.

The first British record for *C. longifolia* was given by Christopher Merrett (1666) from Helks Wood, near Ingleborough – the same locality where the Lady's-slipper Orchid *Cypripedium calceolus* was first found. A slightly later record for the same area was that of Ray (1696).

Although *Cephalanthera longifolia* is appreciably more widespread in the British Isles than its close relative *C. damasonium* it has undergone a decline during the past century (Lang 1980). It is still locally frequent in woodlands in the south of England but becomes increasingly rare to the north. Several populations occur in Wales, and it is also fairly frequent in western Scotland, from Arran northwards to the Lochinver area of Sutherland. The greatest losses seem to have been in central and northern England. In Cumbria only three populations remain, where in the nineteenth century there were more than ten, and in the Durham denes the plant was not recorded in the twentieth century; in North Yorkshire it is apparently also extinct. In Ireland it formerly occurred in 15 counties; now, however, it is very local following a severe decline, with only seven localities recorded since 1970, though some of these apparent losses may be due to under-recording. Throughout the plant's range in

Plate 70. The horizontally borne, pure-white flowers and long narrow leaves are good recognition characters for *Cephalanthera longifolia*. Assynt, West Sutherland, 3 June 2002.

Plate 71. The Narrow-leaved Helleborine *Cephalanthera longifolia*. birch (*Betula* sp.) woodland on limestone, Assynt, West Sutherland, 3 June 2002.

the British Isles changes in woodland management, especially disturbance and reduced coppicing, are probably important contributors to its decline.

The Narrow-leaved Helleborine is a lowland plant occupying a typical habitat of *Fagus* woodland over lime-rich substrates, especially chalk and limestone, but can also thrive in *Quercus* and *Fraxinus* woods. It requires a reasonable amount of light, and is usually found where there is broken tree cover, or where the canopy is thin but with light ground vegetation. It also inhabits ravines and rocky outcrops, as well as woodland margins and rides. A reduction in light intensity will result in diminished vigour, and where the tree cover becomes too dense populations will be eliminated. Conversely, although the plant does tolerate some ground cover, too open a habitat will allow competing vegetation to take over, and again it will be under threat. Many of its former localities in the north of England were those also occupied by the now almost extinct *Cypripedium calceolus*; as for that plant, collecting will have contributed to its loss. The chalk hangers of southern England are a particularly favoured habitat and in Hampshire, where it is more plentiful than anywhere in the British Isles, it is considered to be locally frequent or even abundant. In Scotland it is mainly found in deciduous woodland or scrub over limestone or calcareous schists. The sole locality on the Isle of Skye, now thought to be lost, was amongst *Corylus* scrub, and the plant also occurs in *Corylus/Betula* woodland in Assynt, Sutherland. In Ireland it exhibits a much wider habitat tolerance, in some cases favouring wet woodlands and scrub over acidic substrates (Curtis & McGough 1988). Other unusual Irish habitats include blown coastal sand overlying peat, whilst in the Burren it is known from limestone pavement. It is possible that the latter site is a relic of a former wooded area. In its typical habitats in mainland Britain associates include *Ajuga reptans, Epipactis helleborine, Mercurialis perennis, Sanicula europaea* and *Viola riviniana*.

Perhaps the best place to see *Cephalanthera longifolia* is in the wooded hangers north of Petersfield, Hampshire. It is most easily differentiated from the White Helleborine *C. damasonium* by its narrower, two-ranked leaves, its much smaller bracts, and its shorter, denser flower spike, the flowers of which open wider and are pure white. Morphological variants appear to be unknown in the British Isles but the hybrid with *C. damasonium* (*C. ×schulzei* Camus, Bergon & A. Camus) has been found in Hampshire growing with both parents. First discovered in the 1970s, in woodland near West Meon, Hampshire, it is intermediate between the parents in both leaf and flower characters.

Cross-pollination is the norm and is achieved by bees of the genera *Andrena* and *Halictus*, and by other hymenoptera; but seed production is limited. The plant is a long-lived perennial which appears to reproduce infrequently from seed, but can increase vegetatively. At any one site the number of flowering plants may fluctuate greatly from year to year, potentially giving a false impression of abundance.

2.3. *Cephalanthera damasonium* (Mill.) Druce

White Helleborine

Perennial herb with a short rhizome; *stem* to 60 cm, erect or flexuous, with three to five cauline leaves; *leaves* to 10 × 3 cm, ovate-elliptic below, oblong-ovate to lanceolate above, strongly parallel-veined, dull or grey-green; *inflorescence* a ± lax spike; *bracts* linear to ovate-elliptic, the lowest ± leaf-like; *flowers* (one to) three to twelve, large, cream-white, tinged orange on the labellum, only partly opening, scentless; *outer perianth segments* to 29 mm long, entire or minutely toothed; *inner perianth segments* shorter, rounded at the apex; *labellum* shorter still; *hypochile* saccate, cream with a deep orange blotch; *epichile* ± cordate, broader than long, to 12 mm long, finely crenate and with several orange-yellow keels on inner surface; *spur* absent; *column* slender, to 10 mm long; *anther* semi-ovoid, obtuse with minute papillae; *pollinia* two; *ovary* sessile, glabrous, 15–30 mm long; *flowering* May to June; 2n = 32, 36.

In the British Isles the White Helleborine *Cephalanthera damasonium* is mainly restricted to southern England, where it is found as far west as Somerset and south Devon; it also has an isolated locality in South-East Yorkshire. Outside Britain it is widely distributed through western, central and southern Europe, and eastwards into Israel, the Caucasus and Iraq; it has a southerly limit in North Africa, and is found as far north as south-east Sweden.

Plate 72. The creamy-white flowers of *Cephalanthera damasonium* are held upright and do not open widely.
N. Hampshire, 22 May 1997.

It is much the commonest of the three British species of *Cephalanthera*, but still quite local, although where it does occur it can do so in large numbers. In mainland Europe it occupies quite a wide range of habitats but in Britain it is a plant of lightly shaded *Fagus* woodland over dry, lime-rich soils with a sparse ground flora, as found in the beech hangers of the Downs and Chilterns. It is a component of the *Fagus sylvatica – Mercurialis perennis* (W12) community of the NVC system, and is also recorded from the *Sanicula europaea* (W12b) and *Taxus baccata* (W12c) sub-communities. It favours relatively bare ground, and may be accompanied by other orchids such as *Epipactis* spp., *Neottia nidus-avis* and *Ophrys insectifera*. Occasionally it may grow out in the open on north-facing slopes, or even in hedgerows.

Populations tend to be stable, the main threat to them lying in adverse changes to the ground cover, or destruction of their favoured woodland habitat. The Yorkshire population, which occurs at the southern end of the chalk Wolds, is well separated from the main distribution area of the plant, but the habitat there appears to be quite natural and the population is no doubt native. It may be that the

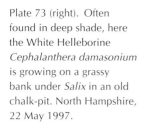

presence in that area of a slightly more continental climate allows the plant to persist so far north. It is perhaps significant that another orchid with a rather similar southerly British distribution, the Monkey Orchid *Orchis simia*, has also occurred as an isolated population within this general area (see p.159).

The first British record for *Cephalanthera damasonium* appears to be that of John Ray in 1670 (Ray 1670), in woods at Stokenchurch in Oxfordshire. The specific name *damasonium* is of classical Greek origin and was originally given by Pliny (AD 23–79) to the genus that includes the Starfruit (*Damasonium alisma*), which has leaves that are similar in shape to those of *Cephalanthera damasonium*. In appearance *C. damasonium* differs from its nearest relative the Narrow-leaved Helleborine *C. longifolia* in its more creamy, less widely opening flowers, and in having fewer, rather broader leaves. It is not a difficult plant to find, and is perhaps most easily seen in the beech woodlands that occur on calcareous hills throughout much of southern England.

Self-pollination is the usual mode of reproduction, although cross-pollination can be effected by visiting insects. The plant differs from the other two British species of *Cephalanthera* in that when the anther inclines forward on entry of an insect the bases of the pollinia become immediately attached to the stigma, resulting in self-pollination. (In the other two species the anther has an elastic hinge, so is able to retract to its original position, thus reducing the likelihood of self-pollination.) This method is very efficient, and large amounts of seed are produced. A period of up to 10 years has been suggested (Summerhayes 1968) as being necessary for flowering plants to develop from seed. In adverse flowering conditions the plant is also able to increase by the production of underground root buds.

Plants of *C. damasonium* with double labella have been found in Britain, but no other variants appear to have been recorded. The hybrid with *C. longifolia* (*C. ×schulzei*) has been found in Hampshire (see p.70, above).

Plate 73 (right). Often found in deep shade, here the White Helleborine *Cephalanthera damasonium* is growing on a grassy bank under *Salix* in an old chalk-pit. North Hampshire, 22 May 1997.

Plate 74 (opposite). The bright yellow colouring on the labellum of *Cephalanthera damasonium* suggests an abundance of pollen, deceiving insects into visiting the flower. N. Hampshire, 31 May 2002.

3. *Neottia* Guett.

Including *Listera* R. Br. ex W.T. Aiton

Twayblades, and Bird's-nest Orchid

Perennial herbs, shortly rhizomatous with numerous roots, green and leafy or ± leafless and lacking chlorophyll; *leaves* two, ± opposite and placed in the lower half of the stem, when green; or more numerous but scale-like, when yellowish-brown; *inflorescence* a lax, spike-like raceme; *flowers* shortly pedicellate, inconspicuous, yellow-green to reddish- or yellowish-brown; *perianth segments* ± of equal length, patent; *labellum* > 2 × length of other segments, deeply divided into two lobes, with a nectar channel; *spur* and *viscidia* both absent.

The close relationship between plants of the mycoheterotrophic genus *Neottia* (*sensu stricto*) (*c.*10 species, found from Europe through Asia to Japan) and the twayblades (green, leafy members of *Listera* (*s.s.*), 20–40 species, in temperate Eurasia and North America) has long been recognised (see e.g. Dressler 1990), and at earlier times morphological taxonomists even included the twayblades within *Neottia*. Recently, Bateman and his colleagues at Edinburgh and elsewhere have shown by molecular analysis that *Neottia* and *Listera* are indeed so closely related that they cannot be maintained as separate genera, and they have again combined the two, under the earliest name, *Neottia* (Bateman 2005, in press; Bateman *et al.* 2005, in press). The change will be unpalatable to many who are familiar with the living plants, but a comparison of the flowers of the Common Twayblade '*Listera*' *ovata* and the Bird's-nest Orchid *Neottia nidus-avis* will reveal their close similarity. The absence in the latter of chlorophyll and leaves is a red herring that has obscured, for those seeking differences rather than similarities in systematics, the closeness of the relationship. Bateman *et al.* (2005, in press) point out that the mycoheterotrophs of the narrowly defined genus *Neottia* could comparatively easily be derived from a leafy ancestor,

Plate 75 (opposite). The Bird's-nest Orchid *Neottia nidus-avis* with Ivy *Hedera helix*; deciduous woodland on chalk, South Hampshire, 22 May 2002.

A comparison of the flowers of the mycoheterotrophic *Neottia nidus-avis* (left) and those of the normal green *N. ovata* (right) shows their close similarity. *N. nidus-avis* (Plate 76), edge of deciduous woodland, Perthshire, 2 June 2003; *N. ovata* (Plate 77), grassy hillside, Roxburgh-shire, 25 June 2002.

and that genera containing both leafy and mycoheterotrophic species are by no means unusual in the Neottieae. For example, *Cephalanthera damasonium* is closely related to the achlorophyllous *C. austiniae* (A. Gray) A.A. Heller of western North America, and several species of *Epipactis* are known to produce long-lived achlorophyllous, mycoheterotrophic individuals (see pp. 94, 100).

The pollination mechanism in *Neottia* is relatively simple, and elegant. Insects alight on the labellum and follow the nectar channel upwards to the point where the lip bends inwards under the column; in doing so they touch the rostellum, which projects just above. As the insect contacts this a droplet of adhesive is rapidly exuded so that the pollinia (positioned just above the rostellum) become cemented to the insect's head or back. In other plants where the flowers are more mature the rostella will have curved upwards, leaving the stigma exposed. When the insect alights on the flowers of one of these and follows the labellum's nectar groove upwards, its attached pollinia make contact with the stigma, and pollination is achieved. Small insects crawling over different flowers on the same plant may effect self-pollination in a similar way.

Plate 78. The Lesser Twayblade *Neottia cordata* in sparsely vegetated moorland with bryophytes and lichens, *c.* 600 m. Cairngorm mountains, east Inverness-shire, 20 May 2000.

3.1. *Neottia cordata* (L.) Rich.

Syn. *Listera cordata* (L.) R. Br.

Lesser Twayblade

Perennial herb with a short creeping rhizome; *stem* 6–10(–25) cm, solitary, pale green, sometimes reddish, erect, somewhat pubescent above; *leaves* two, spreading, subopposite, positioned about the middle of the stem, ± ovate, shiny green above, paler below, entire, with wavy margins; *inflorescence* a short, lax raceme with up to twenty flowers; *bracts* very small, triangular-ovate, acute; *flowers* very small, greenish-red; *outer perianth segments c.* 2.5 mm, greenish, oblong, obtuse at apex, spreading; *inner perianth segments* similar to the outer, green, but reddish on inside; *labellum c.* 4 mm, reddish, usually pendulous, divided to about the middle into two linear diverging lobes, toothed on each side of the base; *spur* absent; *column* very short, hooded to protect the oblong anther; *stigma* reniform; *ovary* globose, pale green, with reddish ridges; *flowering* May to July (to October); 2n = 38, 40, 42.

A much smaller plant than its close relative the Common Twayblade *Neottia ovata*, the Lesser Twayblade *N. cordata* is rather inconspicuous. In the British Isles it is essentially a plant of Scotland and northern England, southwards to the north Midlands, but it does occur in Wales and in part of the West Country; it is also quite widespread in Ireland. There was one isolated occurrence in Sussex that has not been confirmed recently, although this may have been a casual introduction. It is also widespread but local throughout much of the rest of Europe, including Iceland.

In Scandinavia it is found as far north as latitude 71°, and it occurs eastwards through the Caucasus, Russia, northern Asia, North America and Greenland; it is therefore a circumpolar plant.

For the record, the former generic name – *Listera* – honours Martin Lister (1639–1712), the English scientist and naturalist, and friend of John Ray. The specific name *cordata* derives from the heart-shaped (cordate) base of the leaves. The earliest known British record was from 'neer the Beacon on Pendle Hill in Lancashire', given by Christopher Merrett in his *Pinax Rerum naturalium Britannicarum*, published in 1666. Merrett's name for the plant was *Bifolium minimum*, which aptly describes it, and distinguishes it from the much more frequent *N. ovata*, referred to by him as '*Bifolia vulgare ...*' or 'Ordinary Twayblade'. The habitat on Pendle Hill – heather moorland over peat on acidic gritstone – is a typical one for the plant, and must have remained virtually unchanged since Merrett's time. However the plant has not been seen there in recent years, although it could still persist.

The Lesser Twayblade is a small insignificant plant which can easily be overlooked, the more so as it often grows amongst bilberry (*Vaccinium myrtillus*), with whose leaves it can easily be confused, especially when not flowering. Perhaps the most likely way to see it is by searching carefully amongst heather in its typical habitat, particularly in the north of Scotland.

It occupies a much more specific habitat than does *N. ovata*, and is almost always found over acidic substrates in moist, shady localities, often amongst and beneath heather on moorland, or in shady woodland, especially under pine, birch and alder. It is frequently associated with *Sphagnum* and other mosses, preferring the damp conditions in which they grow. It has also been recorded on limestone pavement, but there the microhabitat is likely to have been acidic drift soil. Within the NVC system it is noted from quite a wide range of acidic communities. Typical associates, apart from ericaceous plants and mosses such as *Sphagnum* spp., may include *Anemone nemorosa*, *Galium saxatile*, *Oxalis acetosella*, *Potentilla erecta*, *Pyrola media* and *Vaccinium myrtillus*. At present it does not appear to be unduly threatened except at low-altitude localities, where woodland clearance and man-made incursions such as roadwidening will adversely affect it.

Fertilisation is carried out by small flies, in the manner described in the generic account above (p. 76). There is good seed-set, but self-pollination may also occur. In

Plate 79 (below left).
A strongly red-pigmented plant of *Neottia cordata*. Cairngorm mountains, east Inverness-shire, 2 June 2002.

any given population non-flowering plants probably predominate. *Neottia cordata* can also reproduce vegetatively, and produces root buds more frequently than does *N. ovata*. These form on the swollen parts of the underground root system, where food is stored after production by the mycorrhizal fungus (Summerhayes 1968). The buds send up aerial shoots, which later detach into separate plants; these are then able to flower within as little as three years. In Britain hybrids appear to be unknown, and no varieties have been described.

Plate 80 (above right).
Sharp eyes are often needed to spot *Neottia cordata* in its typical habitat of moss below heather. West Inverness-shire, 16 June 1990.

3.2. *Neottia ovata* (L.) Bluff & Fingerh.

Syn. *Listera ovata* (L.) R. Br.

Common Twayblade

Plate 81. The Common Twayblade *Neottia ovata* can be found throughout the British Isles. These are short plants on dry coastal machair, West Sutherland, 21 July 2000.

Perennial herb with a short, creeping rhizome; *stem* 20–75 cm, solitary, pale green, erect, somewhat pubescent above; *leaves* two, green, spreading, subopposite, positioned just above middle of stem, broadly ovate-elliptical, entire, sessile; *inflorescence* a lax, many-flowered raceme; *bracts* small, green, ovate-lanceolate; *flowers* yellow-green, inconspicuous; *outer perianth segments* 5–6 mm, greenish, ovate, obtuse at apex, ± connivent; *inner perianth segments* of similar length to the outer, yellow-green, oblong; *labellum* 7–15 mm, green, deeply divided at the apex into two linear, yellow-green lobes, sometimes with an intermediate tooth; *spur* absent; *column* short, arching over the ovate anther; *stigma* positioned on the front of the column just below the rostellum; *ovary* ± globose, green, tinged violet; *flowering* May to August; 2n (ranging between) 32–42.

In the British Isles the Common Twayblade *Neottia ovata* is one of the most widespread and frequently encountered of all our native orchids, abundant in many areas. However, because it has rather dull, inconspicuous, yellow-green flowers it is sometimes considered to be an uninteresting plant. Outside the British Isles it is common throughout most of Europe. It is found at latitudes of up to 70° N in Norway, and also ranges eastwards into central Asia.

The specific name *ovata* refers to the shape of the leaves, whilst the common generic name 'Twayblade' is based on the two-leaved character of these plants and was coined by Henry Lyte (1529?–1607), author of *The Niewe Herbal, or Historie of Plantes* (1578). The earliest British records reach back to the sixteenth century, it being accepted that William Turner's reference in 1548 to 'Martagon ... in many places of Englande in watery middowes and woddes' was of this plant. It was also described as 'Twayblade' or 'Herbe Bifoile' by Gerard in his *Herball* of 1597, who recorded it being seen at Southfleet in Kent. He described the flower as resembling a gnat or newly-hatched gosling, and used it in an ointment and balsam for healing wounds. Other colloquial names include 'Sweethearts', from the opposite pairs of leaves; 'Adder's Tongue' and 'Man Orchis', from the shape of the labellum; and, in Ireland, 'Wild Tulip', again from the shape of the leaves.

In France it is known as the *Grande Listère*, and in Germany as *Wiesen-Zweiblatt*.

Neottia ovata is a very adaptable plant, occurring over both acidic and calcareous soils and in a wide range of habitats, although lightly shaded woodland and scrub over base-rich soils, hill pastures and dune slacks are the most favoured. It has also been recorded from amongst heather, and is often a coloniser of man-made sites such as waste-tips and disused railways cuttings. Such a wide tolerance of habitat is reflected in the large number of communities within which it has been identified in the NVC system. It often grows in association with other rarer orchid species, and can be a good indicator for such sites. In calcareous scrub it may be found alongside *Dactylorhiza fuchsii, Ophrys insectifera, Platanthera chlorantha,* and even *Epipactis atrorubens.* It is readily recognised by its distinctive leaves.

Pollination is very efficient, resulting in a high seed-set, and is usually carried out by small flies, ichneumons and beetles. Bees sometimes visit the plant, but they may be too large for pollination to be successful (Summerhayes 1968). Although seedlings may be evident after only a few years, they may require 10 to 15 years to elapse before flowering (Summerhayes 1968). Vegetative propagation through buds on the basal rhizomes can also occur, resulting in the development of small clumps. In deeply shaded woodland, non-flowering plants can persist for a considerable period of time.

Flowering may be over a wide season, from May in open dune habitats in the south, to July or even August at higher altitudes, or in woodlands in the north. Hybrids appear to be unknown, but abnormally shaped labella are sometimes encountered, and trifoliate plants can also occur.

Plate 82. The paired leaves of *Neottia ovata* gave it its common name 'twayblade'. Beech wood, East Kent, 11 May 1996.

3.3. *Neottia nidus-avis* (L.) Rich.

Bird's-nest Orchid

Plate 83. The Bird's-nest Orchid *Neottia nidus-avis*, with young plants of *Cephalanthera longifolia*, in mixed deciduous woodland on limestone, Argyll, 31 May 1990.

Perennial, rootless, mycoheterotrophic herb, ± lacking chlorophyll, with short, creeping rhizomes and a dense mass of short, fleshy, tangled roots; *stem* erect, 20–50 cm, fairly robust; *stem leaves* frequent, primitive, scale-like and sheathing, oblong to lanceolate, brownish, green leaves absent; *bracts* 5–10 mm, lanceolate, tapering to an acute apex, papery; *inflorescence* a spike-like raceme to *c*.20 cm long, cylindrical, dense-flowered above, less so below; *flowers* numerous, relatively large, yellow-brown, scented; *outer perianth segments* 4–6 mm, ± patent, obovate; *inner perianth segments* similar to outer but slightly smaller; *labellum* 8–12 mm long, brown, directed forward, hollowed into a nectar-containing cup, distally divided into two broad, spreading lateral lobes; *spur* absent; *column* cylindrical, pale brownish-white; *anther* oblong, papillose on the outside; *pollinia* two, pale yellow, linear-oblong; *stigma* appearing V-shaped; *rostellum* projecting above the stigma, ligulate, grooved above, downturning at the apex; *ovary* ovate, somewhat pedicellate, with glandular hairs; *flowering* May to July; 2n = 36.

The genus *Neottia* as formerly defined contained nine species – all mycoheterotrophs (saprophytes) – only one of which, the Bird's-nest Orchid *Neottia nidus-avis*, occurs in Europe, the others being Asiatic, seen as far east as Japan. The range of *N. nidus-avis* extends from the British Isles through most of central Europe, to reach an eastern limit in western Russia; it is found as far north as southern Finland, and south to northern Spain, Sicily and the Balkans. It is widely scattered, although patchily so, throughout much of the British Isles, and is decidedly local except to the south-east of its range. It is recorded from more than half of the Scottish vice-counties but appears to be unknown on the Scottish islands, apart from the Isle of Mull. In Ireland, although recorded from 30 counties, it is also very scattered; in Northern Ireland it is a Scheduled Species. For the Channel Islands and the Isle of Man it is unrecorded.

A mycoheterotroph with very little chlorophyll, *Neottia nidus-avis* grows in the leaf litter of shady *Fagus* woodland, often on humus-rich calcareous soils. On the mainland of Britain it also occurs under *Taxus*, and occasionally in other types of deciduous woodland, whilst in Ireland it can be found in mixed *Quercus–Betula* woodland. Both the common name and the scientific epithet refer to the root system, which is in the form of a solid mass with some of the roots projecting randomly, giving the impression of a roughly built bird's nest. This irregular clump of roots is buried in a thick layer of decaying leaves and other vegetable matter and is infected with a mycorrhizal fungus by which the plant derives its nutrients. Perhaps the earliest British record is that of Gerard, given in his *Herball* in 1597, when he referred to finding '*Satyrium abortivum, sive Nidus Avis*' growing in the middle of a wood in Kent, two miles from Gravesend (see p.18).

Within the NVC system its habitat is placed in the W12 community, *Fagus sylvatica – Mercurialis perennis* woodland, as well as in the *Sanicula europaea* subcommunity. It is often found in parts of woodland penetrated only weakly by light, where its associates are consequently few, although another mycoheterotrophic plant *Monotropa hypopitys* may occupy a similar niche. In lighter woodland *Fragaria vesca, Sanicula europaea* and *Viola reichenbachiana*, and other orchids such as *Cephalanthera damasonium* and *Epipactis helleborine*, may be found nearby. In Scotland the plant's main habitat is in beech woodland, but it is also known to occur under yew.

In the British Isles the Bird's-nest Orchid is most frequent in the south of England, where shaded woodland should be searched, especially where there is a deep layer of decaying leaves. It is also helpful to look for the stiff persistent fruiting stems from previous years, which become dark brown and may stand for at least a year.

Pollination is achieved by visiting insects attracted to nectar exuded into the concave lower part of the labellum. The flowers are said to be sweet-scented (Summerhayes 1968), and the fragrance is no doubt an attractant, but it is surprising that this alone is able to entice the pollinators to such inconspicuous flowers in the recesses of woodland. In the absence of cross-pollination, self-pollination can occur, since the pollinia are friable and after a short time break off and fall onto the stigma below. Instances are also known of self-pollination having occurred before the flowers opened, and of plants having flowered whilst completely below ground (Davies *et al.* 1983). Following germination of the seed a period of up to 10 years may elapse, to build up reserves for flowering (Summerhayes 1968). In some cases, individual plants have produced flowering spikes for several consecutive years before dying. Roots can also exist independent of the rhizome, and new plants may be formed vegetatively from these when shoots develop from buds at their tips. No hybrids or varieties have been recorded in Britain, but abnormal flowers are occasionally found.

Plate 84. Often thought of as a plant of deep shade, *Neottia nidus-avis* does sometimes also occur in sparse vegetation at the edge of woodland. South Hampshire, 22 May 1997.

4. *Epipactis* Zinn.

Helleborines

Perennial herbs with stout, usually horizontal rhizomes and thick strong roots; *stems* leafy; *leaves* arranged spirally or two-ranked up the lower part of the stem; *inflorescence* a fairly lax, spiral, or ± secund raceme; *flowers* pedicellate, sometimes pendulous; *labellum* comprising two parts, these jointed, the basal portion (hypochile) cup-shaped or in the form of a shallow depression, the apical portion (epichile) ± cordate or triangular and forward- or downpointing; *spur* absent; *column* short, shallowly hollowed distally (the clinandrium); *anther* free, hinged at the back of the column; *pollinia* two, tapering, sessile, attached to the rostellum; *stigma* ± oblong; *rostellum* large, rounded, positioned above the stigma, or absent at anthesis; *viscidium* a sticky cap or absent; *bursicle* absent; *ovary* untwisted.

A taxonomically difficult genus, especially in respect to the self-pollinated species, *Epipactis* is mainly restricted to the temperate regions of the northern hemisphere. It is widespread throughout Europe, and occurs eastwards through Asia to Thailand and Japan, and south to tropical Africa; it is also found as a native plant in North America, including Mexico. Taxonomic uncertainty and fluidity make it difficult to assess the total number of species in the genus, but conservative estimates are that there are about 15–20 species in Europe, with at least 13 elsewhere. Delforge (2001) recognises no fewer than 54 species in Europe, but these are principally based on very minor morphological distinctions. Eight true species are known in the British Isles, though other infraspecific taxa are also present. The genus shows some morphological affinities to *Cephalanthera* but differs, especially, in having pedicellate flowers with untwisted ovaries, and recent molecular studies (Bateman *et al.* 2005, in press) suggest that it is more closely related to *Neottia*.

The name *Epipactis* derives from the Greek *epipaktoun*, 'close together', and presumably refers to the proximity of the sepals. *Epipactis* was used as a plant name by Theophrastus in about 330 BC.

Cross-pollination occurs in some species but others are self-pollinated, or even cleistogamous, where fertilisation occurs in the unopened flower. Cross-pollination, where it does occur, is effected by visiting insects. In one mechanism the pollinia, having previously fallen onto the rostellum, are removed when the insect touches the rostellum, since the adhesive released from it results in their attachment to the insect. When the insect visits the next flower portions of the fragile pollinia break away and adhere to the sticky stigma, and pollination is achieved. In self-pollinated species either the rostellum is undeveloped or it withers as the flowers open, resulting in 'automatic' deposition of the pollinia onto the stigmatic surface. The result of this is the development of rather uniform populations of plants, in which distinct

Plate 86. The rare hybrid *Epipactis atrorubens* × *E. helleborine* (*Epipactis* ×*schmalhausenii*) on limestone pavement, Westmorland, 20 July 2003. A close-up may be seen overleaf (Plate 87, p. 84).

Plate 85 (opposite). The flowers of the Marsh Helleborine *Epipactis palustris* rival those of many tropical orchids for their beauty. Marshy grassland by chalk stream, North Hampshire, 11 July 2002.

morphological features are perpetuated. These have frequently been recognised as distinct taxa, at either varietal or specific level. Genetic analysis is now beginning to sort out the tangle, but it is probable that a stable taxonomy of European *Epipactis* will elude us for some time to come.

Interspecific hybrids are apparently rare in Britain. Those that have been recorded are mainly between *E. helleborine* and *E. atrorubens*, and *E. helleborine* and *E. purpurata*, and show fertility. Others are recorded in mainland Europe, as also is the intergeneric hybrid with *Cephalanthera* (Davies *et al.* 1983). The North American species *E. gigantea* Douglas ex Hook., which is commonly cultivated and could escape, hybridises with *E. palustris*.

Plate 87 (opposite). *Epipactis atrorubens* × *E. helleborine* (*E.* ×*schmalhausenii*), limestone pavement, Westmorland, 20 July 2003.

Plate 88 (above). *Epipactis helleborine*, limestone pavement, Westmorland, 20 July 2003.

Key to *Epipactis*

1a.   Plants forming large colonies, usually in damp
places; flowers white, cream and pink .... *E. palustris* p.88
1b.   Plants usually solitary or in small clumps,
in drier places; flowers green to deep red 2

2a. Plant to *c*.30 cm; at least the labellum dark red;
in crevices in limestone .... *E. atrorubens* p.90
2b. Plants usually taller; flowers green or marked
with dull purple 3

3a. Flowers normal, with perfect rostellum, viscidium
and pollinia 4
3b. Flowers with reduced or absent rostellum and viscidium,
and crumbling pollinia 5

4a. Lowest leaves as broad as long, mid-green; flowers
usually strongly suffused with dull pinkish
brown; widespread throughout British Isles .... *E. helleborine* p.93
4b. Lowest leaves much longer than wide, dark green;
flowers pale; southern half of England. .... *E. purpurata* p.98

5a. Inflorescence rachis glabrous; flowers pendent,
green, often not opening widely; usually in
woodland .... *E. phyllanthes* p.107
5b. Inflorescence rachis pubescent; flowers held
outwards, opening fully; in woodland or
coastal dune slacks 6

6a. Plants mostly in woodland, often on industrial
spoil-heaps 7
6b. Plants usually on coastal sand dunes, sometimes in
river shingle 8

7a. Rostellum more than half the length of the anthers,
two bosses at its base; ovary usually pubescent;
epichile wider than long; petals sometimes tinged
pink; on industrial spoil-heaps in northern
England, central Scotland .... *E. helleborine* var. *youngiana* p.96
7b. Rostellum less than half the length of the anthers,
without bosses; ovary usually glabrous; epichile
longer than wide; petals usually green;
most frequent in southern England .... *E. leptochila* p.101

Plate 89 (opposite).
Epipactis palustris var.
ochroleuca occurs
occasionally among normal
plants. Marshy grassland
by chalk stream, North
Hampshire, 28 June 2002.

8a. Petals and sepals green, sometimes with some reddish
coloration; dune slacks of north Wales, north-west
English coast, river shingle in Tyne valley .... *E. dunensis* p.104
8b. Petals and sepals yellowish green; Holy Island only,
on dune slacks .... *E. sancta* p.110

4.1. *Epipactis palustris* (L.) Crantz

Marsh Helleborine

Plate 90. The ornate, pale flowers of *Epipactis palustris* easily distinguish it from all other members of the genus. (The whole spike is seen in Plate 85, p. 82.) Dune slack, Holy Island, north Northumberland, 16 July 1996.

Perennial herb with long horizontally-creeping rhizomes, from the ends of which new buds can develop; roots long and slender; *stems* 15–50 cm, erect, green, sometimes streaked red, with white hairs above, slightly sheathed at the base; *leaves* four to eight, ± erect, spirally arranged, 5–15 × 2–4 cm, oblong-lanceolate, decreasing in size up the stem, yellowish green, veined and folded; *inflorescence* a lax, ± secund raceme with 4–20 flowers; *bracts* to 2.5 cm long, lanceolate, acute; *flowers* relatively large for the genus, cream-white, lightly streaked red-violet, at first campanulate, then widening, lacking fragrance; *outer perianth segments* to 12 mm, lanceolate, keeled, reddish within but whitish to pale brown on the outside; *inner perianth segments* slightly shorter than outer, whitish, tinged violet below; *labellum* to 12 mm long, the hypochile cup-shaped, longer than broad, whitish to pale pink and striped pink, yellow-spotted down the centre, nectar-producing, the epichile attached by a flexible hinge, broadly elliptical with a frilled or wavy margin, white, pink-veined, and with a furrowed yellow area at the base; *spur* absent; *column* short; *anther* relatively large, ± elliptical; *pollinia* two, yellowish white; *stigma* ± elliptical; *rostellum* projecting from the centre of the upper edge of the stigma; *viscidium* white, sticky, still present in open flowers; *ovary* shortly pedicellate, becoming pendulous, greenish or brownish; *flowering* late June to August; 2n = 40–48.

Epipactis palustris is widespread but local throughout much of the British Isles, occurring sporadically as far north as Northumberland, with a few additional isolated localities in Scotland. The northernmost of these is in the Central Highlands, where the plant was only discovered in 1983. Elsewhere it occurs throughout most of Europe, ranging from Spain eastwards to Iran, central Asia and Japan, and northwards from the Mediterranean to southern Scandinavia. It has been recorded at altitudes of up to 1600 m in the Alps.

The specific epithet *palustris* reflects its favoured habitat, being derived from the Latin for 'marsh'. The earliest British record traced is that given by William How in 1655 in his publication of some of the work and records of Matthias de L'Obel. This was for plants found in 1601 at St Mary Cray, seven miles from London.

In the British Isles *E. palustris* prefers an unshaded habitat in neutral to calcareous fens, marshes, damp pastures, damp disused quarry floors, and especially dune slacks, all usually in areas of reduced competition. Seasonally inundated areas are often favoured. Other populations are to be found in damp, upland, limestone grassland, as in south Cumbria. Another much less frequent habitat occurs in the south of England, in disused chalk-pits or excavations, although plants at these sites are often of smaller stature. Here they can be found in depressions as well as on the drier mounds, whilst other populations have been known to occur on open chalk downland. Frequent associates include *Anagallis tenella, Carex flacca, C. viridula,*

Dactylorhiza incarnata (and other marsh-orchids), *Hydrocotyle vulgaris, Ononis repens* and, especially in dune slacks, *Salix repens*. The principal communities from which it has been re-corded are rather diverse and are classified by the NVC system as *Schoenus nigricans – Juncus subnodulosus* mire (M13), *Juncus subnodulosus – Cirsium palustre* fen-meadow (M22), *Phragmites australis – Peucedanum palustre* tall-herb fen (S24), and a range of dune-slack communities (SD13–SD17) and other minor asso-ciations. One of the very few remaining Scottish populations is in upland meadow overlying metamorphosed limestone.

Considerable losses of the Marsh Helleborine have occurred in the past in northern England and southern Scotland, as a result of the drainage of fens and marshes. This is also the case in south-ern England and parts of Ireland. It is probable that its dune-slack habitats, rather less likely to be developed or drained, will eventu-ally become its stronghold; here the obvious main threats to its survival are alterations in nutrient content and reduction in the water-table.

The plant ought to be readily identifiable in the field. It initially appears to be rather unlike other members of the genus, and its few-flowered inflorescences of rather large flowers with pinkish-brown sepals and white, yellow-bossed labella, as well as its habit of growing in fairly dense patches owing to its creeping rhizomes, should be sufficient to distinguish it. Perhaps the best place to see it is in its dune-slack habitat, especially on the coasts of northern England and Anglesey.

This is a cross-pollinated species. When an insect (usually a bee) alights on the labellum it depresses the epichile (the distant part of the labellum) because of the flexible hinge between epichile and hypochile. As the insect leaves the flower the

Plate 91. *Epipactis palustris* can form huge colonies in dune slacks, making a spectacular show, as here on the Lancashire coast, 5 July 2000.

epichile springs upwards, forcing the back of the insect's head against the rostel-lum, which is abraded, and released adhesive attaches the pollinia to the insect. The structure of the flower is such that when the insect alights on the next one the pollinia on its head are precisely positioned to make contact with the stigma as it feeds on the nectar. In this way cross-pollination is achieved most efficiently (Summerhayes 1968). Self-pollination can sometimes occur if the pollinia are not removed cleanly, as they are so fragile that they can release pollen against their own stigma. Seed production is usually high, with up to 80 per cent of flowers producing ripe fruit (Summerhayes 1968). This strategy is important in establishing new populations. Additionally, vegetative reproduction can take place, new plants developing from the buds on the extensive rhizome system as they detach from the parent, and this primarily helps to maintain and extend existing populations.

A few varieties have been described: var. *ochroleuca* Barla lacks the reddish brown pigment, and in consequence has yellowish white flowers. It is sometimes found in dune slacks and calcareous marshes, and has also been described under the name var. *albiflora* Lüscher. Var. *ericetorum* Asch. & Graebn. has a short stem and few-flowered raceme, and occurs in moist sand amongst dunes on the south coasts of Wales and England, and also in Wexford. No hybrids appear to have been recorded in the British Isles, although that with the Dark-red Helleborine *E. atro-rubens* (*E.* ×*pupplingensis* Bell) is known from the European mainland.

Plate 92. The Dark-red Helleborine *Epipactis atrorubens* with gorse *Ulex* sp., on the floor of a disused limestone quarry, Co. Durham, 15 July 1997.

4.2. *Epipactis atrorubens*

(Hoffm. ex Bernh.) Besser

Dark-red Helleborine

Perennial, rhizomatous herb with many sinuous roots, whole plant densely hairy when young; *stem* to 70 cm, solitary, erect, reddish below, with basal sheaths and dense, white, pubescent hairs on the stem; *leaves* normally distinctly two-ranked, dark green, sometimes suffused with red at the base of the lowest, 4–10 × 1.5–4.5 cm, the lower ± ovate, the upper ovate-lanceolate, pointed, all keeled and veined; *inflorescence* a spike-like raceme with 5–10(–20) flowers; *bracts* to 3 cm long, lanceolate, veined and reddish towards the base; *flowers* wine-red, at first campanulate, then widening, fragrant; *outer peri-anth segments* to 7 mm, dark wine-red outside, greenish red inside, ovate, blunt and keeled; *inner perianth segments* shorter than outer, but of a similar colour and shape, minutely serrate; *labellum* c.6 mm long, the hypochile cup-shaped, green, con-taining nectar, the epichile darker coloured, transversely ellipt-ical, the tip acute, reflexed; *spur* absent; *column* short; *anther* obtuse, yellow; *pollinia* two, whitish; *stigma* oblong; *rostellum* elliptical; *viscidium* well developed, sticky; *ovary* shortly pedi-cellate, greenish red; *flowering* late June to July; 2n = 40.

The Dark-red Helleborine is a plant which is more or less confined to exposed limestone habitats and is consequently of restricted distribution in the British Isles, occurring on the limestones of northern England, north Wales, east-central, north, and north-west Scotland including Skye, and western Ireland. It is also found throughout much of mainland Europe, from Spain eastwards into western Asia, the Altai mountains and Siberia, and from Greece and Iran to northern Norway. In Scandinavia it occurs on *Dryas* heath near sea-level but in more southern areas of Europe is found in the mountains up to an altitude of 2200 m.

The specific epithet *atrorubens* refers to the dark red colour of the flowers. The earliest published record appears to be that by William How in 1650, given in his *Phytologia Britannica*, for plants seen earlier by a Mr Heaton at 'Lysnegeragh'. A little later John Ray, in his *Catalogus Plantarum Angliae* of 1670, remarked on its occurrence in Yorkshire 'on the sides of the mountains near Malham 4 miles from Settle in great plenty'.

Plate 93. *Epipactis atrorubens* in its classic habitat of a grike in exposed limestone, growing with *Rubus saxatilis*. West Sutherland, 27 July 1991.

Plate 94. The dark-red flowers of *Epipactis atrorubens* give it both its common and its scientific name. Floor of disused limestone quarry, Co. Durham, 15 July 1997.

In Britain it occurs mainly in the fissures of bare limestone or in scree, or in thin soils overlying limestone. Grikes in limestone pavement, ledges of outcrops, the floors of disused quarries, and rocky limestone grassland are especially favoured; some sites may be in light shade. Associates in close proximity often include *Dactylorhiza fuchsii, Epipactis helleborine* (with which *E. atrorubens* has very occasionally been known to hybridise), *Gymnadenia conopsea, Neottia ovata, Ophrys apifera* and *O. insectifera*, as well as many other species typical of an open limestone habitat. In the Burren area of western Ireland – one of the few places in the world where this is possible – it grows in association with *Neotinea maculata*. Typical habitats designated within the NVC system are the *Sesleria caerulea (albicans) – Scabiosa columbaria* (CG8) and *Sesleria caerulea (albicans) – Galium sterneri* (CG9) grasslands, and *Dryas octopetala – Carex flacca* heath (CG13). At one Cumbrian locality it can be found in the bare limestone ballast of a well-used railway track. It has an altitudinal limit of 610 m in Perthshire, but usually occurs much lower than this.

In general, populations of the Dark-red Helleborine appear to be stable, and some new ones have recently been discovered. Owing to its favoured limestone habitat other scarce plants may grow alongside it, and such habitats often have a degree of protection through SSSI status or as nature reserves. The main threat to the plant's survival is from quarrying or removal of limestone pavement at unprotected sites; over-grazing by rabbits or deer can also threaten it.

Recognition in the field is usually easy: the two-ranked leaves and dark red flowers are characteristic. However, plants can also occur that are not so readily assigned, the leaf arrangement being less obvious and the flower colour paler or tinged greenish. It is possible that introgression with *E. helleborine* has taken place in such cases. *Epipactis atrorubens* is often found in relatively small populations, and is nowhere abundant. It is perhaps best looked for on limestone pavements or in disused quarries, and several such sites in north Lancashire and south Cumbria hold good populations.

The fragrant flowers produce nectar and so attract insects such as wasps, bees and hoverflies, which effect cross-pollination by the method already described above for the Marsh Helleborine *E. palustris* (p. 89). In any population there is usually a high proportion of non-flowering plants, but seed dispersal rather than increase by vegetative means appears to be the more important method of propagation. Vegetative reproduction may, however, occur when buds produced on the creeping root system become detached from the parent.

Variation mainly involves flower colour. Plants with cream-coloured flowers have been recorded growing alongside normal specimens at Kishorn in north-west Scotland, and have also been seen in Cumbria. Several varieties have also been recorded from mainland Europe. Possible introgression with *E. helleborine* has been mentioned earlier in respect to plants having a somewhat spiral leaf arrangement and paler flower colour, but good hybrids with the latter (*E.* ×*schmalhausenii* (K. Richt.) Vollm.) have been recorded from north Wales, Yorkshire, Westmorland (Cumbria) and Sutherland. Generally, caution should be exercised when putative hybrids are suspected, because of the potential for variation within both the species and the genus.

4.3. *Epipactis helleborine* (L.) Crantz

Broad-leaved Helleborine

Perennial herb, rhizome short, roots numerous, cylindrical, light brown; *stem* to 90 cm, solit-ary, erect, green, sometimes tinged violet below, with basal sheaths below and short white hairs above; *leaves* arranged spirally, green, 5–17 × 2–5 cm, ovate, ovate-lanceolate, or almost rotund, pointed and veined, the upper becoming bract-like; *inflorescence* a ± secund, lax to fairly dense spike-like raceme of 10–30(–50±) flowers; *bracts* to 5 cm long, lanceolate, often exceeding the flowers, veined; *flowers* fairly large, greenish-pink, campanulate at first, widening later, sometimes slightly fragrant; *outer perianth segments* to 13 mm, greenish or red-violet, ovate to lanceolate, acute, veined, keeled; *inner perianth segments* ovate, shorter than outer and of a somewhat similar colour; *labellum* to 11 mm long, the hypochile cup-shaped, green outside, reddish brown within and containing nectar, the epichile pinkish violet, cordate to triangular, the tip acute and reflexed, and with two bosses at the base of the epichile; *spur* absent; *column* short; *anther* sessile, yellow; *pollinia* two, yellow; *stigma* oblong, facing for-wards; *rostellum* subglobose, white; *viscidium* white, sticky, persistent; *ovary* shortly pedicel-late, green; *flowering* late July to October; 2n = 36–44.

Plate 95. The broad, blunt epichile and fully formed flowers of *Epipactis helle-borine* are useful characters for identification. Deciduous woodland on chalk, Berkshire, 31 July 1996.

Plate 96. An extraordinary and rare sight: the pink shoots of the mycoheterotrophic *Epipactis helleborine* var. *albifolia* M.R. Lowe, entirely lacking in chlorophyll. Deciduous woodland on chalk, Surrey, 31 July 1999.

The Broad-leaved Helleborine is a widespread plant, found throughout most of England and Wales, as well as parts of southern Scotland up to the central industrial belt, and in additional scattered localities further north as far as Sutherland. In Ireland it is found in the north and also on the limestone of the Burren, but is scarce elsewhere. It is widespread throughout much of the rest of Europe, where it is one of the commonest woodland orchids. It ranges from Spain eastwards to the Caucasus and further into central Asia, including the Himalayas, and from North Africa northwards to a latitude of 71° in Scandinavia. It has been introduced to North America, where it can be rather weedy. Recently the British endemic '*E. youngiana*' has been shown to lie within the genetic variation of *E. helleborine*, as discussed below.

The specific epithet *helleborine* is the same as the common English name for the genus, and is a name that seems to have been used in this country since records began, although sometimes applied by the old herbal writers to plants other than those of the genus *Epipactis*. *Epipactis helleborine* was described as a *Satyrion* by Dioscorides. It was first recorded for Britain in 1562 by William Turner, in what is usually considered to be the earliest English herbal. Turner stated that he had seen it 'in England in Soffock'. Gerard, a little later, in his *Herball* of 1597, records it 'In the woods by Digswell pastures halfe a mile from Welwen in Hartfordshire'.

It is a plant mainly of calcareous soils, but can also be found on slightly acidic soil. Habitats are wide-ranging, from deciduous and sometimes even coniferous woodland, as well as scrub, to the grikes of limestone pavement, screes, road- and pathsides, railway embankments, mining debris and dune slacks. It is also known to occur in gardens and other similar secondary habitats. In fact, its greatest abundance in Britain is now thought to be in suburban areas near Glasgow. It is an NVC component of the W8, W10, W12 and W14 woodland communities – a range similar to that of the Violet Helleborine *E. purpurata* (see below, p.99); but, additionally, of calcareous grassland communities (CG2, CG7) and the *Salix repens – Holcus lanatus* (SD16) dune-slack community. Orchid associates include *E. purpurata* in the south of its range and occasionally, and more locally, *E. atrorubens*, *E. leptochila* and *E. helleborine* var. *youngiana*. *Neottia nidus-avis* and the early-flowering *Orchis mascula* may be found nearby.

Populations are lost where deciduous woodland is cleared or replanted with conifers, and this has been a threat in the past. The same applies to quarrying or limestone-pavement removal. However, the recent tendency of *E. helleborine* to invade gardens and spoil-heaps suggests that it is not readily eliminated, and may be spreading.

Identification of *E. helleborine* is not always straightforward. The flower spikes can vary from lax to dense, and from relatively few- to many-flowered. The colour of the flowers can also vary appreciably. However, the epichile is comparatively broad and blunt and at least partly recurved, and so differs from *E. leptochila* and

E. phyllanthes. The spirally arranged leaves help to separate it from *E. atrorubens*, and the absence of violet flushing of its vegetative parts differentiates it from *E. purpurata*, with both of which species it sometimes grows. It can be found without much difficulty in many parts of England in open woodland over chalk or limestone.

Cross-pollination is again the norm and is by insects, in the manner described earlier for the genus – especially, in this case, by wasps. This is an efficient process and seed-set is high. In the absence of insect visitors self-pollination does not occur, and the ovaries soon wither. This is in contrast to other British *Epipactis* species, in which self-pollination can occur. Eight years or more are thought to elapse between germination and flowering (Summerhayes 1968), and in most populations there are considerable numbers of (usually immature) non-flowering plants.

In Britain hybrids with both *E. atrorubens* and *E. purpurata* are known. A white-flowered form has been described as var. *albiflora* Graber. The most significant variant occurring in Britain is the one that was described as *Epipactis youngiana* following the discovery of the original plants by A.F. Porter in 1976. The specific epithet commemorates D.P. Young (1917–1972), who studied *Epipactis*. To take into account recent work demonstrating that this plant is a genetic form of *E. helleborine*, but to continue to recognise its unique morphology and distinct habitat, it is treated here as *Epipactis helleborine* (L.) Crantz var. *youngiana* (A.J. Richards & A.F. Porter) Kreutz.

Plate 97. Despite having no chlorophyll *E. helleborine* var. *albifolia* remains vigorous, supported by its mycorrhiza. Surrey, 31 July 1999.

Epipactis helleborine var. *youngiana*

(A.J. Richards & A.F. Porter) Kreutz

Syn. *Epipactis youngiana* A.J. Richards & A.F. Porter

Young's Helleborine

Plate 98. The flowers of Young's Helleborine *Epipactis helleborine* var. *youngiana* are paler than those of typical *E. helleborine*, and are usually self-pollinating. Lead-mine spoil-heap, South Northumberland, 5 August 1997.

Epipactis helleborine var. *youngiana* resembles var. *helleborine*, but in typical plants can be distinguished by its more yellow colour, its narrower, more two-ranked leaves, and its earlier flowering time. Like var. *helleborine* it is a robust plant, and has rather similar large, pink-green flowers; but its evanescent viscidium and its disintegrating pollinia separate it from the normally cross-pollinating var. *helleborine*. Plants of this classic '*youngiana*' morphology are not found in other populations of *E. helleborine* (Hollingsworth *et al.* 2005, in press). At most sites, however, floral morphology varies, from that characteristic of a self-pollinating flower (slightly smaller, more 'closed' appearance, reduced rostellum) to that more suggestive of normal cross-pollination.

Var. *youngiana* has been thought to be almost entirely self-pollinating, although its hypochile contains nectar and is frequently visited by small insects. Recent studies by Hollingsworth *et al.* (2005, in press), however, show that far from having the low genetic diversity expected from self-pollination ('inbreeding') it is in fact sufficiently diverse to suggest regular cross-pollination, despite its evanescent viscidium. In most populations seed is normally set, and it is possible that new populations have been established in this way.

'*Epipactis youngiana*' was first described by A.J. Richards and A.F. Porter in 1982, from plants discovered at two localities in Northumberland. Further sites were subsequently found in north-east England and Yorkshire, as well as others in the central Scottish industrial belt. All of its known sites are places that have been strongly influenced by man. Usually this is in lightly wooded areas, on soils which are acidic to some extent at least and which are also contaminated with heavy metals. One of the original localities was in oak woodland that had been thinned, roughly drained, and then under-planted with exotics; the other was amongst planted and regenerating vegetation around a disused lead mine. The Scottish sites are also on light deciduous woodland over-growing mining spoil-heaps. In general the associated woodland is deciduous, comprising species of *Alnus*, *Betula*, *Fraxinus*, *Quercus* and *Salix*, and sometimes planted conifers. The ground cover is usually fairly dense *Rubus fruticosus*, with other species of *Epipactis*: *E. helleborine* var. *helleborine*, *E. phyllanthes* and plants resembling *E. dunensis* have been found in close proximity to populations of var. *youngiana*. Woodland clearance and reworking of old mining sites are the main threats; two sites have already been lost through clearance. The plant is perhaps most readily seen at one of the semi-industrialised sites in Scotland.

It was originally thought that '*E. youngiana*' had arisen through hybridisation between *E. helleborine* and the autogamous (self-pollinating) *E. dunensis*, and confusion over the identity of var. *youngiana* has arisen because of the presence of other *Epipactis* taxa growing nearby, some of whose characters (genetic and morphological) are shared by some individuals and populations of var. *youngiana*. Recent

DNA work at the Royal Botanic Garden Edinburgh (Hollingsworth 2001, 2003; Hollingsworth *et al.* 2005, in press) has indicated that var. *youngiana* falls within the genetic variation of *E. helleborine*, with a portion of the genome allowing consistent morphological differentiation to occur under certain ecological conditions, such as where heavy-metal contamination of the soil is present, or in man-made habitats. Hollingsworth *et al.* (2005, in press) also conclude that although the majority of plants of var. *youngiana* have a floral morphology consistent with self-pollination, var. *youngiana* has not achieved true reproductive isolation from *E. helleborine*; they suggest that truly self-pollinating lines may arise in the future.

'*Epipactis youngiana*' has generated a great deal of discussion that its status as a local variant would not seem to warrant. However, if treated at specific rank it is a British endemic species, and is therefore subject to strict conservation measures as laid down in Section 8 of the Wildlife and Countryside Act (1981). As a species it also has a Species Action Plan as part of the UK Biodiversity Action Plan programme (UK Biodiversity Group 1995), and receives an allocation of conservation resources. Its taxonomic rank is therefore a matter of some importance. Hollingsworth *et al.* (2005, in press) suggest that when it comes to such 'taxonomically difficult' (often a synonym for 'rapidly evolving') groups of plants, conservation plans should take into account the importance of this diversification, recognising its significance in the natural process, and protect sites as well as individual 'species'.

Plate 99 (far left). The leaves of *Epipactis helleborine* var. *youngiana* are usually narrower and more two-ranked than those of var. *helleborine*. This plant was growing on a lead-mine spoil-heap in South Northumberland, 5 August 1997.

Plate 100 (near left). The disintegrating pollinia and reduced viscidium of *E. helleborine* var. *youngiana* are clearly visible in this close-up. South Northumberland, 5 August 1997.

4.4. *Epipactis purpurata* Sm.

Violet Helleborine

Plate 101. The name 'Violet Helleborine' for *Epipactis purpurata* comes from the purplish suffusion seen on the leaves: the flowers are usually green with light pink shading. Edge of deciduous woodland on chalk, Chilterns, Oxfordshire, 29 July 1996.

Perennial herb with a deeply buried, sometimes knotted rhizome and sinuous fleshy roots; *stem* to 90 cm, often occurring in clumps, erect, greenish, flushed violet, with white pubescent hairs above and loose sheaths at the base; *leaves* spirally arranged, greyish green, suffused violet, 6–10 × 2–5 cm, ovate-lanceolate to lanceolate, acute, long-sheathed; *inflorescence* a rather dense, many-flowered, secund raceme; *bracts* to 6 cm long, appreciably longer than the flowers, lanceolate, flushed violet, veined; *flowers* relatively large, patent, greenish white, fragrant; *outer perianth segments* to 12 mm, green outside, greenish white within, lanceolate, cucullate, and with a green keel; *inner perianth segments* shorter than outer, white or greenish white and tinged pink, ovate-lanceolate; *labellum* 8–10 mm long, the hypochile cup-shaped, pale green, tinged violet outside, mottled violet within, the epichile wider than long, whitish, with two or three pink or violet-tinged bosses and with a slightly recurved tip; *spur* absent; *column* short; *anther* laterally compressed, obtuse, pale yellow-cream; *pollinia* two, yellowish white, ovoid; *stigma* oblong; *rostellum* globular, whitish; *viscidium* sticky, persisting in the open flower; *ovary* pedicellate, dark green, tinged violet; *flowering* August to September; 2n = 40.

This is a plant restricted to south, south-east and central England, reaching northwards to Shropshire, with outlying records from Yorkshire and Somerset (but these have not recently been confirmed). The largest populations are in Kent, Surrey and the Chiltern area. There have been occasional dubious, unconfirmed records from Scotland but none at all from Ireland. *Epipactis purpurata* also occurs in north-west and central Europe as far north as Denmark, Germany and Poland, and from Portugal to the Balkans and eastwards to Siberia. A similar related plant known as the Eastern Violet Helleborine (*E. condensata* Boiss. ex D.P. Young) occurs in Cyprus and south-west Asia.

The specific epithet *purpurata* refers especially to the violet- or purplish-coloured flushing of the stems and leaves. The earliest definite record so far traced is, surprisingly, only in the early-nineteenth century, but this is probably due to the fact that *E. purpurata* was often confused with other woodland *Epipactis* species. It was described by J.E. Smith in 1828 in his *English Flora*, from a plant found in 1807 by the Revd Dr Abbott which was 'parasitical on the stump of a maple or hazel in a wood near the Noris farm at Leigh, Worcestershire'. This seems to have been a rather atypical colour variant. Another early record is a herbarium specimen collected by Dickson near Tring, Hertfordshire in 1808.

In England *E. purpurata* is generally a lowland plant, and especially one of deep soils. It occurs in various types of woodland, but in particular those of *Fagus* over a flint-clay substrate on chalk. Woods over limestone are also favoured and, less frequently, it can be found in more acidic or sandy deciduous woods, especially those of *Quercus*. It usually grows in deep shade and occasionally in a dense ground covering of scrub. The NVC system describes it as a component of three main communities, but especially *Fagus sylvatica – Rubus fruticosus* woodland (W14). Other subcommunities are those of *Primula vulgaris – Glechoma hederacea* (W8a), *Mercurialis perennis* (W12a), *Sanicula europaea* (W12b) and *Taxus baccata* (W12c). Associates are those typical of the ground flora of such habitats, including *Hedera helix, Monotropa hypopitys, Rubus* spp. and sometimes the orchids *Epipactis helleborine* and *Neottia nidus-avis. Epipactis purpurata* often occurs in clumps of up to 20 flowering spikes, and its robustness and persistence is shown in it once having been recorded as forcing its way though the tarmac of a pathway.

A correct balance in shade level is very important for its survival and, as for *E. helleborine* (see above, p.94), populations have certainly been lost through woodland clearance. Consequently, careful control of the understorey by coppicing will be especially beneficial. It can also be a rather elusive plant, growing as it does in appreciable shade, and so may go unrecorded. This could be the reason for presumed losses in some localities.

Plate 102. *Epipactis purpurata* competing with brambles on a roadside verge at the edge of deciduous woodland on chalk. Chilterns, Oxfordshire, 27 July 2002.

Plate 103 (above left). *Epipactis purpurata*, growing through brambles, ride in deciduous woodland on chalk, Essex, 7 August 1997.

Plate 104 (above right). *Epipactis purpurata*; a plant without chlorophyll which has been given the name of var. *chlorotica*. Deciduous woodland on chalk, West Sussex, 31 July 1999.

Epipactis purpurata is perhaps most readily recognised by the violet flushing of its vegetative parts, by its tendency to grow in clumps, and by the habitat in which it grows. In doubtful cases a close examination of the flowers should be sufficient to distinguish it. Perhaps the best place to see it is in chalk-based *Fagus* woodland in the Chilterns or elsewhere in the south-east, where it is a fairly frequent plant.

Pollination is usually carried out by wasps attracted to the flowers by the fragrance of the nectar. The method is that typical of the other cross-pollinated species within the genus. Seed-set is efficient, and dispersal is the main method of propagation. Because of the plant's vertical root structure, vegetative propagation by horizontally-spreading rhizomes, as in *E. palustris*, is unlikely. Growing as it does in conditions of low light the leaves are often pale pink-violet rather than green. In such cases photosynthesis is only partially efficient and the plant places appreciable reliance on its fungal associate for nutrients. However, plants occurring in more or less open locations in parts of mainland Europe have greener leaves and so are less dependent on their mycorrhizal associate.

Hybrids with *E. helleborine* (*E. ×schulzei* P. Fourn.) have been recorded from Britain, but owing to the fact that these are fertile, and because of the inherent variation within the parents, such hybrids are not readily identified. Varieties are infrequent, although one with pink stems and leaves lacking chlorophyll has been described as var. *chlorotica* Erdner.

4.5. *Epipactis leptochila* (Godfery) Godfery

Syn. *Epipactis muelleri* Godfery var. *leptochila* (Godfery) P.D. Sell;
   Epipactis viridiflora (Hoffm.) Krock. var. *leptochila* Godfery

Narrow-lipped Helleborine

Perennial herb with a deep rhizome and long, fleshy, sinuous roots; *stem* to 60 cm, erect, rigid, single or sometimes a few in small groups in mature plants, greenish white, tinged violet, hairy, with basal sheaths; *leaves* normally distinctly two-ranked, yellow-green to dark green, 4–10 × 1.5–5 cm, lanceolate or ovate, pointed, veined; *inflorescence* a ± lax, secund, spike-like raceme of 10–25 flowers; *bracts* to 2 cm long, linear-lanceolate, veined, yellowish green to green, appreciably longer than the flowers; *flowers* yellow-green, relatively small, lacking scent, patent to ± closed; *outer perianth segments* to 15 mm, pale green, lanceolate, keeled, patent; *inner perianth segments* shorter and broader than outer but of a similar colour, sometimes tinged pink; *labellum* to 10 mm long, the hypochile cup-shaped, pale green outside, mottled red within, the epichile yellow-green or pinkish, cordate and acuminate, the apex not recurved; *spur* absent; *column* short; *anther* ovate with an acute apex, stalked, cream to yellow-green; *pollinia* two, cream-white, joined at the apex; *stigma* oblong; *rostellum* globose; *viscidium* very small or absent; *ovary* to 10 mm, green, somewhat hairy or ± glabrous; *flowering* June to August; 2n = 36.

Epipactis leptochila is locally frequent but found usually in geographically well separated areas of England. It also occurs in Scotland in the central industrial belt, but is absent from Ireland. It is also widespread in central Europe as far north as Denmark, and eastwards to the Balkans.

   The specific epithet *leptochila* derives from the Greek *leptos*, 'thin' or 'narrow', and *kheilos*, 'lip', and refers to the narrowness of the labellum. The plant has also been known under the synonym *E. viridiflora*, undoubtedly a reference to its green

Plate 105. A sharply-pointed, narrow epichile is characteristic of *Epipactis leptochila*, the Narrow-lipped Helleborine. Deciduous woodland on chalk, Chilterns, Oxfordshire, 29 July 1996.

flowers. The earliest record for *E. leptochila* is from Shropshire where it was described in 1841, in Leighton's *Flora of Shropshire* (under the name *E. viridiflora*), as occurring in 'Woods at Bomere pool'.

The taxonomic history of the species, with its numerous variants, is rather complicated. The uniform nature of self-pollinating *Epipactis* has tended to lead to the description of an excessive number of taxa whose relationships are not clearly apparent. Fortunately, the advent of genetic analysis means that these problems can now be addressed. The *E. leptochila* group has been studied in detail at the Royal Botanic Garden Edinburgh and much clarification has resulted (Squirrell *et al.* 2002). It is now considered that members of this group (*E. leptochila*, *E. muelleri*, *E. dunensis* and *E. sancta*) have each arisen from self-pollination events (autogamy) in *E. helleborine* (or an ancestral form), and that their individual characteristics are due to the rapid loss of genetic diversity that results from such inbreeding. The recent work shows that *E. leptochila* and *E. muelleri* have distinct genetic origins, and should not be conflated as has been done by Sell & Murrell (1996). *Epipactis muelleri* Godfery appears to be restricted to mainland Europe, although plants from Sussex have been recorded under this name.

In addition to typical plants that are fertilised after the flowers open (var. *leptochila*), a cleistogamous population occurs in beech woods on the steep western slope of the Cotswolds near Wotton-under-Edge, Gloucestershire, in the NVC community *Fagus sylvatica – Rubus fruticosus* woodland (W14). This has been named *E. leptochila* var. *cleistogama* (C.A. Thomas) D.P. Young (*E. cleistogama* C.A. Thomas). Although a minor variant, it is thought to be endemic and, as the name implies, has cleistogamous flowers that do not open and are self-pollinated.

There are also records for the recently published *E. leptochila* var. *neglecta* (Kümpel) A. Gévaudan, from southern England, mainly in the Chilterns, in shaded deciduous woodland. This differs from var. *leptochila* in its broader, more cordate epichile, which is also folded under.

Shaded *Fagus* woodland over calcareous soils, light *Betula* woodland over well-drained, heavy-metal contaminated soils, spoil-heaps and river gravels are the principal habitats of *E. leptochila*. In the deep shade of *Fagus* woodland the ground cover is sparse and comprises plants such as *Epipactis helleborine*, *E. purpurata*, *Neottia nidus-avis*, *Hedera helix*, *Viola* spp., and a range of mosses. The NVC associations in which var. *leptochila* occurs are largely similar to those for *E. helleborine*, and both plants can also be occupants of heavy-metal soils. *Epipactis leptochila* was probably under-recorded in the past but a better understanding of the species has rectified this. In its woodland habitat it is susceptible, like other orchids, to clearance, and to the adverse effect of heavy machinery used for that purpose.

Epipactis leptochila is perhaps most similar to *E. helleborine* but is less robust than the latter, has leaves arranged in two rows, flowers which usually lack any reddish coloration, and a relatively longer and more pointed, unrecurved epichile. The varieties of *E. leptochila* are readily differentiated from the type. To see var. *leptochila* it is best to visit the chalk beech woods of the Chilterns.

Fertilisation is by self-pollination. The rostellum is present in the flower bud but usually dries up and withers as the flowers open, or before. On the rare occasions that the rostellum persists, the pollinia may attach to it and then be removed by a visiting insect, but almost invariably the anther projects so far forward that the pollinia fall directly onto the stigmatic surface, with resulting self-pollination.

Plate 106 (opposite). A small plant of the Narrow-lipped Helleborine *Epipactis leptochila*, in dry beech woodland on chalk, Chilterns, Oxfordshire, 27 July 2002.

4.6. *Epipactis dunensis* (T. & T. A. Stephenson) Godfery

Syn. *E. leptochila* var. *dunensis* (T. & T.A. Stephenson) T. & T.A. Stephenson

Dune Helleborine

Plate 107. The whole plant
of the Dune Helleborine
Epipactis dunensis
is yellowish-green.
Dune slack, Sefton coast,
Lancashire, 11 July 2003.

Perennial herb with a deep rhizome and long, fleshy, sinuous roots; *stem* to 50 cm, erect, rigid, single or sometimes a few in small groups in mature plants, greenish white, tinged violet, hairy, with basal sheaths; *leaves* normally distinctly two-ranked, yellow-green, 4–10 × 1.5–5 cm, lanceolate or ovate, pointed, veined; *inflorescence* a ± lax, secund, spike-like raceme of up to 20 flowers; *bracts* to 2 cm long, linear-lanceolate, veined, yellowish green to green, shorter than the flowers; *flowers* yellow-green, relatively small, lacking scent, patent to ± closed; *outer perianth segments* to 15 mm, green-yellow, lanceolate, obtuse at the apex; *inner perianth segments* shorter and broader than the outer but of a similar colour, sometimes tinged pink; *labellum* to 10 mm long, the hypochile cup-shaped, deep pink, the epichile as wide as, or wider than long, green, often tinted pinkish, the apex recurved, with a green tip; *spur* absent; *column* short; *anther* stipitate, cream to yellow-green; *pollinia* two; *stigma* oblong; *rostellum* often absent or withering early; *viscidium* very small or absent; *ovary* to 10 mm, green, hairy or ± glabrous; *flowering* June to August; 2n unknown.

The Dune Helleborine was first formally recognised and described by the Stephensons in the early-twentieth century, as *E. viridiflora* forma *dunensis* T. & T.A. Stephenson (*E. viridiflora* is a synonym of *E. leptochila*). It has since been treated as either a full species, *E. dunensis* (T. & T.A. Stephenson) Godfery (e.g. Delforge 1995) or as *E. leptochila* var. *dunensis* (T. & T.A. Stephenson) T. & T.A. Stephenson (by both modern British floras: Sell & Murrell 1996, Stace 1997). As one of the 'taxonomically difficult' group of autogamous (self-pollinating) *Epipactis* it has been the subject of much interest, and recent studies by Jane Squirrell, Peter Hollingsworth and their colleagues at the Royal Botanic Garden Edinburgh, using molecular and morphometric methods, have resulted in its specific status being confirmed (Squirrell *et al.* 2002).

Epipactis dunensis is regarded as a British endemic occurring in two main areas, one coastal, the other inland. Dune slacks on the coast of north-west England and Anglesey are the classic locality, giving rise to its specific epithet, where it occurs scattered amongst low-growing shrubs of *Salix repens*. At some localities on the

Lancashire coast it also colonises the adjacent coniferous plantations. Populations originally referred to as *E. leptochila* are also
present in riverside habitats in the Tyne valley. Recent genetic analysis has shown that the plants in these populations are indeed
referable to *E. dunensis*, and suggests that *E. dunensis* originated
by selfing from *E. helleborine* or a similar ancestor (Squirrell *et al.*
2002). The Tyne valley plants are genetically slightly dissimilar to
those of the west coast, the small differences probably resulting
from occasional mutations rather than from separate origins. The
same research project also demonstrated that a population of
Epipactis growing in dune slacks on Holy Island, Northumberland, also formerly considered to be *E. dunensis*, was in fact of
separate genetic origin and best treated as a distinct species, *Epipactis sancta* (see below, p.110).

In the central industrial belt of Scotland, plants of *Epipactis*
growing on coal spoil-heaps (bings) have also been thought to be
E. dunensis (Dickson *et al.* 2000). Again, however, recent genetic work (Hollingsworth *et al.* 2005, in press) suggests otherwise, indicating that they are part of the
complex gene pool comprising *E. helleborine* and *E. helleborine* var. *youngiana*
and do not have the distinct genetic lineage of *E. dunensis* on the west coast. A
further population discovered in 2002 growing near disused railway lines at Car-
lisle, Cumbria has also been referred to *E. dunensis* (Clarke *et al.* 2003), as have
plants of an *Epipactis* in Lincolnshire, but neither population has been genetically
investigated.

In its dune habitat *E. dunensis* is a component of the *Ammophila arenaria –
Festuca rubra* semi-fixed dune (SD7), *Festuca rubra – Galium verum* fixed-dune
(SD8), *Carex arenaria – Festuca ovina – Agrostis
capillaris* dune-grassland (SD12) and *Salix repens
– Holcus lanatus* dune-slack (SD16) communities.
At these dune sites increased public pressure and
an imbalance of rabbit grazing will adversely affect the plant. Localities in the Tyne valley are
amongst birch scrub and are mainly on riverside
gravels contaminated with heavy metals, with at
least one site by a disused lead mine. Associated
species include *Dactylorhiza fuchsii, Epipactis
helleborine, Galium saxatile, G. verum, Minuar-
tia verna, Thlaspi alpestre, Ulex europaeus* and
Viola lutea.

Plate 108. The British
endemic *Epipactis dunensis*,
growing with *Salix repens*
in a dune slack, its typical
habitat. Sefton coast,
Lancashire, 5 July 2000.

The dune slacks of south-west Lancashire and
Anglesey are probably the most convenient places
to see *E. dunensis*. It is morphologically distinguished from *E. leptochila* in that its sepals are more
obtuse and its epichile is as wide as, or wider than
long, and recurved at the apex (usually longer than
wide and not recurved in *E. leptochila*).

Fertilisation is by self-pollination, and occurs by
the same means as in *E. leptochila.*

4.7. *Epipactis phyllanthes*   G.E. Sm.

Syn. *Epipactis vectensis* (T. & T.A. Stephenson) Brooke & F. Rose;
  Epipactis pendula C.A. Thomas; *Epipactis cambrensis* C.A. Thomas

Green-flowered Helleborine

Perennial, rhizomatous herb with many thick, fleshy roots; *stem* to 50 cm, solitary or in small groups, erect, glabrous to sparsely hairy, with basal sheaths; *leaves* two-ranked, medium- to dark green, 3.5–7 × 3–5 cm, ovate to lanceolate, indistinctly veined, ± acuminate at the tip, margins often undulate; *inflorescence* a spike-like raceme with up to 30 flowers; *bracts* to 5 cm long, shorter above, but longer than the lower flowers, linear-lanceolate, veined; *flowers* variable in size but usually rather small, pendulous, ± downward-facing, wide-opening to closed; *outer perianth segments* to 8 mm long, greenish yellow, ovate-lanceolate, acuminate; *inner perianth segments* green, sometimes tinged violet, ovate-lanceolate; *labellum* greenish, the hypochile shallowly cup-shaped, green or whitish, the epichile rather indistinct, ± ovate-lanceolate or more variable in shape, usually longer than wide, the tip acute, greenish white or pinkish; *spur* absent; *column* decaying when in full flower; *anther* sessile; *pollinia* two, disintegrating in bud; *stigma* base with two bosses; *rostellum* and *viscidium* very small, shrivelling early; *ovary* ± glabrous; *flowering* late July to August (to September); 2n = 36.

The Green-flowered Helleborine *Epipactis phyllanthes* has been recorded in the British Isles as far north as Northumberland but the majority of its localities are in the south of England. Elsewhere it is very scattered, in parts of central England, south and north Wales and also rarely in Ireland. It is essentially western European, known from southern Scandinavia through Denmark to Germany and western France.

The specific name *phyllanthes* is derived from the Greek *fyllon*, 'leaf' or 'blade', and *anthos*, 'flower', and appears to refer to the green, leaf-like perianth segments of the flowers. The plant was first described by G.E. Smith in 1852. Most of the subsequently described varieties were originally considered to be separate species, but following work by D.P. Young in the mid-twentieth century the situation was clarified and their intrinsic relationship to *E. phyllanthes* was recognised at the status of variety. This treatment is retained here, although there is little if any molecular differentiation between the infraspecific taxa (P. Hollingsworth, pers. comm.

Plate 110 (above). *Epipactis phyllanthes* var. *phyllanthes*, with characteristic weakly differentiated labellum. Road verge under deciduous trees, Surrey, 1 August 1996.

Plate 109 (opposite). *E. phyllanthes* var. *pendula*, road verge, deciduous woodland, Berkshire, 22 July 1993.

2004). As with many self-pollinating plants, small variations rapidly become fixed in populations, leading to deceptive morphological variability.

In the British Isles *E. phyllanthes* is a lowland plant of dry, shaded, lightly vegetated places, often over acidic substrates, although it also occupies calcareous habitats and those with heavy-metal polluted soils. *Fagus* woodland over clay or sandstone, *Pinus*, *Betula* and *Corylus* scrub, coppiced woodland over chalk, coastal dune-slack margins and the dunes themselves, both open and planted with *Pinus*, are all typical. Mining spoil-heaps and occasionally inundated riverside *Salix* scrub are other habitats where it is found.

It has been recognised in at least five different varieties, mainly based on flower size and labellum shape, some of which occupy specific habitats. Intermediates between the accepted varieties can also exist and may be confusing.

The type, *E. phyllanthes* var. *phyllanthes*, found mainly in southern England, has flowers which rarely open widely and are sometimes cleistogamous. The labellum is not clearly separated into two parts, and is similar in shape and colour to the two lateral inner perianth segments. The variety *vectensis* (T. & T.A. Stephenson) D.P. Young (*E. viridiflora* var. *vectensis* (T. & T.A. Stephenson) Wilmott), colloquially known as the 'Isle of Wight Helleborine' (having been described from plants found on the Isle of Wight in 1917), has flowers that are at least partially cleistogamous. The labellum usually closely embraces the stigma, the hypochile is green, to 3.5 mm long, and hemispherical, whilst the epichile is longer, cordate, elongate and pink-white. The plant is infrequent in *Fagus* woodland in southern England, occurring northwards to the Midlands and South-East Yorkshire. Recently rediscovered populations from sand dunes in South Wales have been described as var. *cambrensis* (C.A. Thomas) P.D. Sell (*E. cambrensis* C.A. Thomas). The plants have few, partly to

Plate 111 (top left). *Epipactis phyllanthes* var. *phyllanthes*, roadside verge under deciduous trees, Surrey, 1 August 1996.

Plate 112 (top right). *Epipactis phyllanthes* var. *phyllanthes*, beech hanger on chalk, North Hampshire, 3 August 1996.

Plate 113 (bottom left). *Epipactis phyllanthes* var. *pendula*, roadside verge under oak, North Hampshire, 5 August 1996.

Plate 114 (bottom right). *Epipactis phyllanthes* var. *vectensis*, roadside verge in deciduous woodland, N. Hampshire, 28 July 2002.

fully opened flowers and a relatively long, narrow ovary. An important characteristic is the comparatively long, narrow folded leaf (Lewis & Spencer 2005; A.J. Richards, pers. comm. 2005). Other plants with partially closed or fully cleistogamous flowers, a labellum that is poorly differentiated, the hypochile represented by a shallow depression and the epichile often with lateral bosses at the base, have been described as var. *degenera* D.P. Young. These are mainly found in southern England. Lastly, there are plants usually found in sand dunes in north-west England and north Wales which only rarely have cleistogamous flowers but have a clearly differentiated hypochile and epichile, each to *c.* 4 mm long, the epichile with a strongly recurved apex. These plants are referred to var. *pendula* (C.A. Thomas) D.P. Young (*E. pendula* C.A. Thomas non A.A. Eaton). In south-central England intermediates between this and var. *vectensis* also occur.

Associated species are wide-ranging and typical of the habitats mentioned above. Most are listed above for other *Epipactis* species that grow with *E. phyllanthes*. The NVC system recognises the dune communities where *E. phyllanthes* grows as the semi-fixed dune *Ammophila arenaria – Festuca rubra* (SD7) and the fixed-dune *Festuca rubra – Galium verum* (SD8) communities.

Plate 115. *Epipactis phyllanthes* var. *degenera*, with distinctive cleistogamous flowers. Roadside verge under oak, North Hampshire, 5 August 1996.

Threats to these plants are broadly the same as those that affect other *Epipactis* species of similar woodland habitat, the most destructive being woodland clearance or reduction in shade by severe coppicing. Populations appear to be somewhat transitory and may not persist for longer than 30 years or so, but new ones are also sometimes found and others are increasing in size.

In the field the species is most readily identified by its almost glabrous stem and green, pendent, sometimes unopened flowers with a minute, disappearing viscidium and, in some varieties, a labellum poorly differentiated into two components. Woodland, its typical habitat in the south of England, or coastal dunes in the northwest, sometimes planted with *Pinus*, are places where it can most readily be found.

The Green-flowered Helleborine is almost always a self-pollinating species. The pendent, more or less downward-facing flowers, which often do not open fully or are cleistogamous, deter insect visitors. This, together with the rapidly withering rostellum and column, virtually precludes cross-pollination. Some varieties are cleistogamous; in others self-pollination takes place as the flowers open, with the swelling pollinia coming into contact with the stigma. Fertilisation by this method is evidently very effective as most flowers readily produce large, well-developed seed pods. Hybrids with other *Epipactis* species appear to be unknown.

4.8. *Epipactis sancta* (P. Delforge) P. Delforge & A. Gévaudan

Syn. *E. peitzii* H. Neumann & Wucherpfennig var. *sancta* P. Delforge

Lindisfarne Helleborine

Perennial, rhizomatous herb; *stem* to 60 cm, although often less; *leaves* distinctly two-ranked, yellowish green, with strongly impressed veins, fairly rigid; *inflorescence* a ± lax, secund, spike-like raceme bearing up to 30 flowers; *flowers* yellow-green; *labellum* pale green, the hypochile joined narrowly to the epichile, brown on inner surface, the epichile broader than long, the apex recurved, whitish green; *pollinia* erect with the bases touching the stigma; *stigma* having its surface perpendicular to the ovary; *rostellum* elongate; *viscidium* very small or absent; *flowering* early July to August; 2n = 32.

This British endemic is known only from Holy Island (Lindisfarne), Northumberland, where there is a population of about 200–300 plants. The population has been known for many years but was considered to be an outlier of *Epipactis dunensis*. Recent studies, however, by Delforge and others, suggested that it was a distinct taxon, differing in several small morphological details (the yellowish green pedicel as opposed to the purplish one of *E. dunensis*; slight toothing of the leaf margins; and the pubescence of the stem), and in 2000 it was named *E. peitzii* H. Neumann & Wucherpfennig

Plate 116 (above) and Plate 117 (opposite). The 'newest' British orchid, the Lindisfarne Helleborine *Epipactis sancta*. Dune slack, Holy Island, Northumberland, 5 July 2003.

var. *sancta* P. Delforge. However, the Northumberland plant differs from *E. peitzii*, a plant of the Taunus mountains, Germany, in its more delicate stature, yellow-green coloration, more rigid canaliculate leaves, reduced hypochile and more elongated rostellum. Following genetic work by Squirrell *et al.* (2002), it has been raised (Delforge & Gévaudan 2002) to specific rank as *E. sancta*. Such taxa, with a distinct genotype and recognisable, if slight, morphological differences, have been graphically described by Bateman (2004) as 'Robinson Crusoe' species, for having evolved in remote, often island locations, where they are genetically isolated. *Epipactis sancta* remains a poorly known taxon, for which even morphological measurements are unavailable.

On Holy Island *E. sancta* occurs in dune slacks, in loose association with *Echium vulgare*, *Salix repens* and *Senecio jacobaea*. The plants are scattered in several small colonies over just a few hectares and occur in the slightly drier areas at the margins of the slacks, either in loose sand or amongst sparse vegetation. Other orchids such as *Dactylorhiza purpurella*, *D. incarnata* and *Epipactis palustris*, as well as *Anagallis tenella*, occur nearby, but in the rather more damp, lower parts of the slacks. *Epipactis sancta* is thought to be self-pollinated.

Although the population of *E. sancta* lies wholly within the Lindisfarne National Nature Reserve, the plants have no additional protection. The Latin epithet *sancta*, 'holy', is a clear reference to Holy Island.

5.1. *Epipogium aphyllum* Sw.

Ghost Orchid

Perennial, rootless, mycoheterotrophic herb, lacking chlorophyll, with whitish, highly branched, coral-like rhizomes which can also generate subsidiary stolons; *stem* erect, 5–25 cm, whitish and tinged dull pink; *leaves* few, scale-like, mainly basal and sheathing, occasionally also occurring up the stem; *bracts* c.7 mm, ± oblong, semi-transparent; *inflorescence* a few-flowered spike; *flowers* usually one to four, well spaced, pedicellate, patent to pendent, not inverted, the labellum and spur pointing upwards; *outer perianth segments* c.10 mm long, linear, yellowish, tinged pink; *inner perianth segments* similar in length, lanceolate, downcurving, semi-transparent, yellowish with some violet lines; *labellum* bent backwards in the middle, the basal half with two short, forward-directed, rounded lobes, the distal half cordate, acute, concave, white with violet spots; *spur* erect, saccate, white, tinged yellow or violet; *column* broad-based with a cupped apex; *anther* rounded, sessile; *pollinia* two, pyriform, pale yellow; *stigma* on the base and face of the column; *rostellum* large, white, cordate; *ovary* ovoid, glabrous, short-stalked and curved, yellowish, streaked violet; *flowering* (April to) June to July (to October); 2n unknown.

Perhaps the most enigmatic of British orchids, certainly one of the rarest, and that whose appearance is the least predictable, well-earning its name Ghost Orchid, *Epipogium aphyllum* has been recorded in the British Isles on relatively few occasions. All known localities are, or have been, either in the Welsh border area or in the Thames valley. It is a mycoheterotrophic (saprophytic) plant, lacking chlorophyll and reliant on the mycorrhizal fungal associate that infects its rhizome system to convey nutrients from the rich humus and decaying leaf litter of its favoured habitat. At present there are thought to be just two localities where it might reasonably be expected to be found and both are in the Thames valley. These are over chalk in old-established *Fagus* woodland, in deep shade amongst rotting leaves. Outside the British Isles the main area of distribution is in central Europe, especially Germany (where it can occur in *Picea abies* forest), the Balkans, and around the Baltic, including Sweden and Finland. There are also scattered occurrences eastwards throughout much of Asia. Over most of its range it is an infrequent and often very rare plant and occupies a similar habitat to that in which it is found in Britain, but it can also occur in *Pinus* and *Quercus* woodland. It is legally protected in several European countries. Within the genus *Epipogium* there are two other species, one of which, *E. roseum* (D. Don) Lindl., is widely distributed throughout the tropics of the Old World.

The Ghost Orchid was first recorded in the British Isles in July, 1854 by Mrs Anderton Smith, who found a single plant in a woody dingle in Herefordshire on the banks of the Sapey Brook at Tedstone, close to the county border with Worcester-

Plate 118 (opposite). A British Ghost Orchid *Epipogium aphyllum* flowering in a beech wood near Marlow, Buckinghamshire, 14 July 1987.

shire. This was dug up and replanted in a garden but did not survive, and no other plants have been seen there since. It was next recorded by Mary Lewis in Shropshire at Upper Evens on Bringewood Chase, near Ludlow, several times between 1876 and 1892, and then later, in 1910, at another locality in Herefordshire near Ross-on-Wye. It did not subsequently reappear at any of these sites or elsewhere in this part of the country until two flowering plants were found in Herefordshire in September 1982. It is not clear whether this was at one of the old localities, but even if so it has not been found there since.

After 1910 the local centre of distribution appears to have moved to the Thames valley, where in 1924 it was found in an Oxfordshire wood to the west of Henley by a schoolgirl, Vera Paul, and was also seen there by G.C. Druce and a Miss Holly. It was next found in 1931 in a nearby wood at Satwell, growing out of the decaying stump of a tree; this plant is illustrated in the photograph given in Summerhayes (1968). It was also seen there in 1933, but then not again until 1953 when recorded by J.E. Lousley. It has since appeared there intermittently, certainly in 1961, 1963, 1979, 1994, and reputedly as recently as 1994 and 1999.

For the twenty years after 1933 there was not a single British record, until a population comprising 24 flowering plants was found by R. Graham at a new locality to the west of Marlow and not very far from the other known sites. This was by far the largest population of flowering plants of *E. aphyllum* ever known in Britain, its numbers apparently exceeding the combined total previously recorded. The plant has subsequently appeared spasmodically, from 1961 to 1987, since when it has not been refound; in 1986 about five plants flowered, one of which seeded. A new Oxfordshire locality near Henley was discovered in 1994, and the plant was reportedly seen there again in 1998. Although these reports have not been confirmed by photographs, suggestions that the Ghost Orchid is now extinct in Britain seem premature, especially given the lengthy periods between its appearances in the past.

Epipogium aphyllum is a plant of beech woodland, where it grows in deep shade amongst dead leaf litter and humus, in the habitat described in the NVC system as the *Fagus sylvatica – Mercurialis perennis* community (W12). Although extremely rarely recorded it could, however, be more frequent than is supposed, since it is difficult to detect amongst the ground cover, and is easily overlooked. It remains above ground for a very short period, maturing its seeds two to three weeks after flowering, by which time the plants are prostrate (J.M. Grimshaw, pers. comm. 2003). The plants are also often attacked and disfigured by slugs and so may not remain readily recognisable for long. An example of how it can easily be missed is given in a letter to Prof. Charles Babington (copy in the Natural History Museum, London) relating to the Ludlow plant, where one recorder in the 1880s thought it to be 'an abortive bee orchis' and did not examine it further 'as the colour etc. was so poor'.

Plate 119. The usual experience of ghost-hunters is that there is nothing there. A Chilterns site for *Epipogium aphyllum*, Buckinghamshire, 27 July 2002.

Plate 120. In England *Epipogium aphyllum* is associated with the deep shade of beech woods but in Continental Europe it often grows in more open conditions below coniferous trees, in this case *Picea abies* forest on limestone, southern Black Forest, Baden-Württemberg, Germany, 27 July 1998.

Threats to the survival of the plant will be mainly from woodland clearance, including increase in light intensity through opening up of the tree canopy; from accidental trampling by botanists and walkers; and also, no doubt, from unscrupulous collectors.

The generic name *Epipogium* derives from the Greek *epi,* 'on', and *pogon,* 'beard' or 'lip', the old name being *Epipogon* rather than *Epipogium*. The specific epithet *aphyllum* means 'without leaves'. As well as being known by its common name Ghost Orchid it has also been called the Spurred Coral-root, although it is quite a different plant from the much more widely known Coralroot Orchid (*Corallorhiza trifida*). As stated earlier, the first British record was not until 1854, this presumably owing to the plant's general rarity, the difficulty of its detection in shaded woodland, and its highly unpredictable and spasmodic appearance above ground. Its scarcity also appears to account for the surprising lack of folklore attached to it.

The Ghost Orchid

Michael Longley

Added to its few remaining sites will be the stanza
I compose about leaves like flakes of skin, a colour
Dithering between pink and yellow, and then the root
That grows like coral among shadows and leaf-litter.
Just touching the petals bruises them into darkness.   (1995)

In the wild it is probably best recognised by its few-flowered spike, the flowers with upward-pointing labella, and by its generally creamy-pink and mauve-tinged coloration and fleshy appearance. For obvious reasons no suggestions can be made as to where it might occasionally be seen. Coloured drawings of plants from Ludlow in the 1880s and from near Henley in 1926 are in the herbarium of the Natural History Museum, London.

Although the flowers are faintly scented the opportunities for cross-pollination in Britain appear to be rather limited: populations are usually extremely small, often with just the odd flowering plant, and the plants grow in dense shade where they might be unlikely to be encountered by visiting insects. There are, however, a few recorded instances of mature capsules being formed, and in these cases bees or small crawling insects were probably the pollinators. The plants can also form extensive underground rhizome systems with stolons, covering a large area, and the buds at their tips are able to form into separate new plants when the parent dies. This is probably the most frequent method of their propagation in Britain. In this way, incipient plants are able to survive for a long time below ground, reappearing as above-ground plants after many years of apparent absence. Occasionally, as with other mycoheterotrophic orchids, flowers may open beneath the humus in which they grow (Davies *et al.* 1983). This character approaches that of the more extreme Australian species of the genus *Rhizanthella*, which possesses an entirely underground life-cycle. It is thought that flowering of *E. aphyllum* is much more likely after a wet spring when the rhizomes are able to store water, which leads in turn to the production of a flowering structure.

In Britain variation is difficult to detect, owing to the small number of plants recorded, but it appears to manifest itself only in subtle changes in flower colour. At one site in the Black Forest, Germany, anthocyanin-free plants occur.

Plate 121 (opposite). *Epipogium aphyllum*, southern Black Forest, Baden-Württemberg, Germany, 27 July 1998. Another view can be found on p. 363. The fragile beauty of the Ghost Orchid is captured by Michael Longley's poem (above).

6.1. *Liparis loeselii* (L.) Rich.

Fen Orchid

Perennial herb with two adjacent, basal pseudobulbs; *stem* 5–20 cm, erect, trigonous above, glabrous; *leaves* two, subopposite, oblong-elliptical to ovate, keeled, acute or obtuse at the apex, yellow-green to green, having a greasy appearance, scale-like at the base and ± sheathing the developing pseudobulb; *inflorescence* a lax spike with 4–8(–18) flowers; *bracts* small, lanceolate; *flowers* small, green-yellow; *outer perianth segments* 4–5 mm, linear, green-yellow, patent; *inner perianth segments* similar, but smaller and narrower; *labellum* usually upward-pointing but occasionally not so, as long as the perianth segments but broader, crenate, trough-like, yellow; *spur* absent; *column* erect, cupped at the apex where it contains the pollinia; *anther* sessile; *pollinia* two; *stigma* four-sided, oblong; *rostellum* toothed; *ovary* fusiform; *flowering* June to July; 2n = 32.

The genus *Liparis* contains about 350 species widely distributed in temperate latitudes from China to North America, as well as in tropical regions, where some members occur as forest epiphytes. *Liparis loeselii* is the sole European member of the genus, occurring in fens and neutral bogs. Other than in Britain, where it is very scarce, *L. loeselii* is found in central Europe eastwards into Russia and north to southern Scandinavia. It is absent from the Mediterranean, but also occurs in North America; it is declining throughout its European range, principally through habitat loss. The generic name is derived from the Greek *liparos*, 'greasy' or 'fatty', and refers to the appearance of the leaves. The specific name honours Johann Loesel, a seventeenth-century Prussian botanist.

Like its close relative the Bog Orchid *Hammarbya paludosa*, the Fen Orchid is one of the few European orchids able to form pseudobulbs. These serve the same purpose as root tubers and represent the present and previous year's growth; they are a character more frequently found in tropical epiphytic orchids.

The plant was first noted in the British Isles in 1660 by John Ray, as '*Orchis lilifolius minor sabuletorum …*', growing 'In the watery places of Hinton and Teversham Moors [Cambridgeshire]'. It was still recorded there, as well as from Fulbourn and Sawston 'Moors', into the eighteenth century, and was locally abundant at Burwell Fen in the early-nineteenth century. It persisted at Chippenham and Wicken Fens into the last century, the last Wicken record being in 1945. In Suffolk, where it is now presumed extinct, it was formerly found in good numbers in a few places. Its most recent appearance seems to have been at Theltnetham Fen in 1974, but it had also been recorded in fens at Tuddenham St Mary, Lakenheath, Redgrave and Hinderclay. Although at one time there were more than ten localities in Norfolk, only three now appear to be extant, with a combined population of under 250 plants; these are in Broadland. It was first recorded in this general area by John Pitchford in 1767, at Newton St Faiths.

Plate 122 (opposite). The endangered Fen Orchid *Liparis loeselii* receives special protection under the EU Habitats and Species Directive; loss of habitat through drainage and changes in management regime have confined it to very few sites. Var. *ovata* in dune slack, South Glamorgan, 26 June 2002.

In the British Isles *L. loeselii* is now restricted to just a few localities in East Anglia, south Wales and possibly Devon. In East Anglia it occurs in alkaline to neutral fens, as var. *loeselii*, where the leaf shape is oblong-elliptical with an acute apex, whilst in the other two areas it is a dune-slack plant known as var. *ovata* Ridd. ex Godfery. This is of shorter stature and has ovate leaves with obtuse apices. As well as in these localities, *L. loeselii* formerly occurred in Lincolnshire, Huntingdonshire, Cambridgeshire, Kent, and possibly Surrey. The varieties mentioned above,

Plate 123. *Liparis loeselii* var. *loeselii* is dependent on appropriate management for survival at its few remaining fen sites. Reed bed, Norfolk Broads, East Norfolk, 10 June 2002.

loeselii and *ovata*, are sometimes considered as subspecies. Other than these, significant variation appears to be unrecorded.

The dune systems of southern Wales hold by far the largest British populations, the chief ones being in Glamorgan. The plants here all belong to var. *ovata*. In the last century it was recorded from eight Welsh dune localities but it is now confined to just four sites, with a combined population exceeding 10,000 plants. It was first found in south Wales at Pembrey Burrows, Carmarthenshire, at the end of the

Plate 124. Growing in dune slacks in south Wales, *Liparis loeselii* var. *ovata* is also distinguished from the East Anglian, narrow-leaved var. *loeselii* by its broader, blunt leaves. South Glamorgan, 26 June 2002.

nineteenth century, but was not discovered in Glamorgan until 1905, when it was found by H.J. Riddelsdell at what is presumed to have been Kenfig Burrows. This remained the only site in the county until 1927, when it was found at Margam Burrows (now a steelworks) by Vachell and Insole. Shortly afterwards, in about 1931, it was also found at Crymlyn Burrows. Later discoveries were at Oxwich, where it is now rare, and Whiteford. The plant has also been recorded from localities in Carmarthenshire, at Towyn and Laugharne.

The Devon locality was discovered by A.J. Willis in June 1966, when he found a single clump amongst *Salix repens* in an interdunal slack at Braunton Burrows, during a general ecological study of the habitat. The clump is presumed to have originated from seed dispersed across the Bristol Channel from one of the south Wales populations, since the precise site where it was found is known to have been almost devoid of vegetation in the early 1950s, being recolonised shortly thereafter. Unfortunately there have been no further records since 1987, and it is possible that the plant may now be extinct at this site.

The Broadland habitats of var. *loeselii* are species-rich, tall fen communities over infertile soils with a high water content, especially sites which have a history of having been cut for peat. *Cladium mariscus, Juncus subnodulosus, Phragmites australis* and *Schoenus nigricans* are associates, along with *Dactylorhiza* species, especially *D. incarnata* and, very rarely, its subsp. *ochroleuca*. The Welsh populations (var. *ovata*) are mainly restricted to dune slacks in which *Salix repens* is dominant. Other associates include *Anagallis tenella, Carex flacca, C. viridula* subsp. *viridula, Dactylorhiza incarnata, Epipactis palustris, Hydrocotyle vulgaris, Mentha aquatica, Ranunculus flammula* and *Sphagnum* spp. The Devon locality is similar, with *Blackstonia perfoliata, Juncus articulatus, Leontodon taraxacoides, Sagina nodosa* and *Salix repens* amongst the associates. The NVC classification of the British localities encompasses the mire and sand-dune communities M9, M16, S24, SD14 and SD15.

The Fen Orchid is described as 'Endangered' in the British Red Data Book, having undergone a severe decline. In East Anglia drainage of some of the old localities has had an adverse effect, although water levels at the remaining sites are now usually controlled. Also, cessation of peat-cutting and of mowing have allowed habitats to be encroached upon by scrub. Flowering may be induced by reed-cutting, but will again decrease if this cutting is subsequently neglected. In south Wales losses have occurred through habitat disappearance due to industrialisation. Stabilisation of dune systems with resultant loss of slack habitat is also a threat, as is under-grazing leading to scrub encroachment.

The plant is readily recognised in the field by its broad, often ovate, waxy leaves, its triangular stem, and its lax, few-flowered spike of yellow, rather spiky flowers. It is most likely to be found in its dune-slack habitats along the south Wales coast.

Cross-pollination is by insects, but self-fertilisation is also achieved when the anther at the top of the column drops away, allowing the pollinia to slide out of their shallow cup and become attached to the stigma. The latter appears to be an efficient method, with good resultant seed-set, but it has been suggested that different populations may behave differently in their method of fertilisation (Summerhayes 1968). The plant can also propagate vegetatively, by the production of more than one pseudobulb at the base of the stem. Each of these forms a separate shoot, which develops its first leaf after a further two years (Summerhayes 1968); the shoots then part company and develop into independent, though clonal, plants.

Plate 125 (opposite). The flowers of the Fen Orchid are resupinate, but are angled backwards or upwards, making the labellum appear uppermost. *Liparis loeselii* var. *ovata*, dune slack, South Glamorgan, 26 June 2002.

7.1. *Hammarbya paludosa* (L.) Kuntze

Bog Orchid

Perennial herb with two pseudobulbs connected by a rhizome; *stem* 3–8(–12) cm, erect, angled above, sheathed below; *leaves* two to three, to 10 × 5 mm, ovate to oblong, ± acute, pale yellow, often with the margin fringed with small bulbils; *inflorescence* a spike-like raceme, dense at first, later elongating, with up to 20 flowers; *bracts* small, 2–3 mm, lanceolate; *flowers* small, *c*.7 mm long, yellow-green; *outer perianth segments* to *c*.3 mm, ± ovate; *inner perianth segments* linear-lanceolate, with the tips recurved; *labellum* upward-pointing, lanceolate, acute, yellow-green, with its base clasping the column; *spur* absent; *column* very short; *anther* united to the column; *pollinia* two, waxy; *stigma* borne on the front of the column; *rostellum* minute, ligulate, viscid; *ovary* small, stalked; *flowering* June to September; 2n = 28.

Hammarbya is a monospecific genus, with its single species closely related to, but very much smaller than, *Microstylis monophyllos* Lindl. The latter is unknown in Britain but is recorded from fens and swamps in central Europe, Scandinavia and Russia, and is otherwise circumpolar. Both species have in the past been considered to belong to the single genus *Malaxis*, comprising about 300 species. Despite some similarities between *Hammarbya* and *Liparis*, genetic analysis indicates that these two genera are not closely related (P. Cribb, pers. comm. 2004). The generic name *Hammarbya* commemorates the small estate of Hammarby purchased in 1758 by the Swedish botanist Carl Linnaeus, the father of plant taxonomy, when he wished to escape oppressive living conditions in Uppsala. The Latin epithet *paludosa*, 'of marshes', refers to the habitat in which *H. paludosa* grows.

The Bog Orchid *H. paludosa* has a circumboreal distribution, occurring in North America, Scandinavia, most other countries of northern Europe, and in Asia. In the British Isles it is the smallest native orchid, and is scarce. It is generally northern and western in distribution, found mostly in Scotland, northern England and Wales, growing in both lowland and upland bogs, usually where the conditions are acidic. However, it is not a truly montane plant and is recorded only to an altitude of about 500 m. It also occurs in Hampshire, especially in the New Forest, and in the West Country, but is unknown in the Channel Islands. It was formerly known from other southern lowland counties of England, such as Cambridgeshire, where it was last seen in 1855. It has disappeared from Norfolk in the past few years, principally because of the drying-out of its sites, although the last few plants were illicitly

Plate 127 (above). The Bog Orchid grows from pseudo-bulbs perched amongst cushions of *Sphagnum* or other mosses, just above the waterline. Glen Isla, Angus, 24 July 2002.

Plate 126 (opposite). The smallest orchid in the British Isles, *Hammarbya paludosa* is nevertheless beautiful when viewed close-up. Wet acidic moorland flush, West Ross, 9 July 2002.

Plate 128. The Bog
Orchid *Hammarbya
paludosa* is inconspicuous
and easily damaged by
careless trampling in its
sensitive bog habitat.
West Ross, 9 July 2002.

Plate 129. The flowers
of *Hammarbya paludosa*
are described as being
'hyper-resupinate', being
twisted through 360° so that
the labellum is uppermost.
Wet acidic moorland flush,
West Ross, 10 July 1990.

removed (J. Oxenford, pers. comm. 2005). The first British record, made by John
Parkinson in his *Theatrum Botanicum* (1640), comes from just such now-disappeared
localities in southern England: '*Bifolium palustre* … In the low wet grounds be-
tweene Hatfield and S. Albones; in divers places of Romney Marsh'. In Ireland the
plant was previously widely though thinly scattered throughout much of the island,
but recently it has been noted at only six sites. Although it is small and inconspicuous, and therefore easily overlooked, its decline there is thought to be real,
resulting from the destruction of its peatland habitat. It is now a protected plant,
'Scheduled' in the Irish Red Data Book.

Hammarbya paludosa is usually found in wet acidic *Sphagnum* bogs, often growing where there is slight movement of the
surface water; it can also occur in rather more open habitats in
damp, peaty mud, as well as in flushes where the water is more
base-rich. It has a wide range of associates, all of them typical of
such habitats, including several species of *Carex* and *Sphagnum*,
especially *S. auriculatum*, as well as *Drosera rotundifolia*, *Eriophorum angustifolium*, *Juncus squarrosus*, *Menyanthes trifoliata*,
Molinia caerulea, *Narthecium ossifragum*, *Pinguicula vulgaris*,
Potamogeton polygonifolius and *Rhynchospora alba*. It is a member of the M1 and M21 mire communities of the NVC classification. In remote areas of the British Isles it is no doubt frequently
overlooked and therefore under-recorded, and many populations
may remain undetected. Also, it flowers erratically, and since vegetative plants are difficult to locate, this may have led to an exag-
gerated impression of its scarcity. All this notwithstanding, it is
very much under threat, and in consequent decline, wherever
its habitat is subject to improved drainage. This is especially the
case in the lowlands.

The plants usually grow loosely rooted in mosses, with their
two pseudobulbs, storing nutrient, placed one above the other
and only partially buried. This means that they can easily be

damaged or dislodged by trampling in such a sensitive habitat. The roots are sparse and hair-like, and infected by a mycorrhizal fungus upon which the plant is largely dependent for its nutrients throughout its life cycle. Since they can be so easily damaged, observation and monitoring of populations should be carried out with the greatest of care.

It is not easy to recommend a locality where the Bog Orchid may be found with any degree of certainty. There are several easily accessible small populations in Cumbria that may be successfully located, given patience and a practised eye; the same can also be said for the New Forest area. As observers become used to re-cognising such small, insignificant yellow-green plants, so their detection rates should improve.

Little is known about the means of sexual reproduction in *Hammarbya*. Evidence for cross-pollination lies in the fact that when the flowers are closely examined the pollinia are usually found to have been removed. This is presumably achieved by the small insects that occur in the plant's general habitat. Ultimately seed will be dispersed onto the water which, if it is flowing, may lead to the development of a new population elsewhere. Vegetative multiplication is, however, the more likely means of reproduction. The tiny bud-like bulbils on the leaf margins eventually become detached; they then become infected with the mycorrhizal fungus, and eventually develop into independent plants. This would seem to be a more reliable means of reproduction than by seed. No varieties or hybrids are recorded from the British Isles.

Plate 130. More information is needed on the pollination system of *Hammarbya paludosa*. West Ross, 9 July 2002.

8.1. *Corallorhiza trifida* Châtel.

Coralroot Orchid

Perennial herb, the rhizome much branched and forming a coral-like structure; *stem* erect, 7–15(–30) cm, glabrous, yellow-green to red-purple (in the dune-slack form); green *leaves* absent but with two to four membranous, scale-like, pale brown leafless sheaths around the lower stem; *inflorescence* a lax two- to twelve-flowered spike; *bracts* small, membranous; *flowers* small, insignificant, yellow-green; *outer perianth segments* c.5 mm, linear-lanceolate, yellowish; *inner perianth segments* similar in size, elliptic-oblong, obtuse, yellowish, spotted or sometimes streaked reddish or violet; *labellum* c.5 mm, oblong, entire or slightly lobed at the base, ligulate, white with red markings; *column* long, streaked violet; *anther* nearly flat, yellowish; *pollinia* four, ± ovoid; *stigma* placed just below the anther; *rostellum* globose; *ovary* fusiform; *flowering* May to August; 2n = 42.

The genus *Corallorhiza* comprises about 15 species found in the temperate regions of the northern hemisphere, from Asia westwards to Europe, where there is only one species, to the North American continent, and south to Mexico. North America is the centre of diversity for the genus, having the majority of the species. Both the generic name and the common name 'Coralroot' are derived from the branched coral-like structure of the rhizome. The specific epithet *trifida* refers to the tripartite, lobed labellum. The first British record appears to have been given in 1777, by Lightfoot, who found what he described as '*Ophrys Corallorhiza*' in 'a moist hanging wood near the head of Little Loch Broom on the western coast of Ross-shire'. Rather surprisingly, this must have been at a similar place and perhaps on the same occasion as when he made the first British record for Creeping Lady's-tresses *Goodyera repens* (see p.133).

The Coralroot Orchid *Corallorhiza trifida* is in many ways similar to the Ghost Orchid *Epipogium aphyllum* and the Bird's-nest Orchid *Neottia nidus-avis*, in being mycoheterotrophic (saprophytic) and so gaining the majority of its nutrients by mycorrhizal activity, but it also possesses a limited amount of chlorophyll, especially in its stem and ovaries, and so has the ability to manufacture some of its food by photosynthesis (Lang 1980). The plant is restricted to northern Britain, occurring as far south as Yorkshire but with its main area of distribution in moist woods and other damp areas of eastern Scotland. It is not known from Ireland. In mainland Europe it has a distinctly eastern distribution, occurring locally as far west as southern France, including the Pyrenees, and northwards to Scandinavia. Its western European limit is in Scotland, whilst its world distribution is similar to that of the genus itself, extending to eastern Asia and North America. In northern Europe it is a plant of tundra and damp, lowland woodland, but further south it occurs at considerably higher altitudes.

Plate 131 (opposite). Although the Coralroot Orchid *Corallorhiza trifida* is a mycoheterotroph, its leafless stems contain sufficient chlorophyll to colour them green, and must contribute some photosynthate to its energy budget. Roxburghshire, 1 June 1991.

Plate 132. The inflorescence is the only part of the *Corallorhiza trifida* plant to appear above ground. The pallid colour is distinctive and often conspicuous. Upland *Salix/Alnus/Betula* bog, Roxburghshire, 1 June 2002.

In Britain it is most frequently found in the damp, mossy carpet and leaf litter of pine, birch and alder woodland, where it may grow with *Goodyera repens, Moneses uniflora* and *Neottia cordata*, and also in dense willow or alder carr over mires, or at the margins of lochs. A third habitat is in coastal dune slacks, growing amongst *Salix repens*, and variously with *Anagallis tenella, Hydrocotyle vulgare, Juncus balticus* and *Schoenus nigricans*. In this habitat it appears that moisture levels are critical, the plant being found in a strict zone within the slack. One dune-slack population on the coast of north-west England supports a population estimated at several thousand flowering plants, and is thought to be the strongest in England. An unusual habitat occurs in North Yorkshire, where one small population exists under shade on the damp, stony ledges of a disused limestone quarry. Another rather atypical habitat is on heather moorland. In at least one of its English localities it is thought to have been introduced on the roots of planted Scottish pine, in a similar manner to that of Creeping Lady's-tresses *Goodyera repens* in Norfolk (see p.134). In Britain it is a lowland plant, but occurs to an altitude of up to 350 m in eastern Scotland. Its recorded NVC classification includes *Salix pentandra – Carex rostrata* woodland (W3), the *Empetrum nigrum* heath subcommunity (H7d), and the *Carex rostrata – Equisetum fluviatile* swamp and fen subcommunity (S27a).

Except when flowering it is entirely subterranean. The aerial flowering spikes frequently occur in small groups, presumably from a mature, much-branched rhizome. As the plants are yellowish and small, with stems often less than 15 cm high, they can be difficult to detect against the background vegetation. This, and their somewhat unpredictable flowering appearance, may have led to populations being under-recorded or even completely overlooked. A recent survey in Scotland of suitable habitat resulted in the discovery of many new populations, some quite large with up to 500 flowering plants. The species does not appear to be under particular threat in Britain, but potential for this lies in improved drainage of its habitat, destruction of woodland, and commercialisation or human pressure on coastal habitats.

The Coralroot Orchid can only be found with certainty when in flower or fruit, and even then its dingy appearance renders it not easily detectable. Once it is located, however, its pale yellow, scaly and apparently leafless stem, and small, white labellum, reddish-spotted at the base, should confirm its identity. Finding it will probably require a visit to the pine woodland of the eastern Scottish Highlands, or to one of its northern-England dune-slack localities. Even then a patient search will be needed, and the chance of success is not improved by the plant's erratic flowering habit.

It is unclear to what extent the flowers secrete nectar but small insects, including hoverflies and dungflies, are attracted to the flowers. The insects alight on the labellum and ascend its frontal groove until they come into contact with the column, from which the pollinia may become detached. This is not always the case, however, since the rostellum is small and degenerate and the pollinia can detach unaided, to fall onto the stigma below; it seems probable, therefore, that self-pollination is the most common method of fertilisation (Summerhayes 1968). Whatever the means, there is a high rate of seed-set, and the green, chlorophyll-containing ovaries assist in producing nourishment for the maturing seed. Such efficient seed production is in marked contrast to that of the Ghost Orchid *Epipogium aphyllum* (also mycoheterotrophic). However, the latter can reproduce vegetatively through its extensive system of subterranean stolons, whereas in *Corallorhiza* this facility is absent and vegetative reproduction is only occasional, when small branches of the rhizome become detached. The highly efficient seed production of *C. trifida* provides the plant with the opportunity of pioneering new habitats.

In the British Isles variation is slight. Plants growing in dune slacks are much redder than specimens found in shaded habitats, the difference being due to increased anthocyanin pigments stimulated by higher light intensities. A peloric variant has been recorded from Scotland, but varieties are otherwise unrecorded, and hybrids are unknown.

In shaded habitats the Coralroot Orchid is pale green in overall coloration, but where sunlight is more intense, as in dune slacks, the plant develops more anthocyanin pigments and the stems and ovaries become deep brown-red. Plate 133 (below left): *Corallorhiza trifida*, upland *Salix/Alnus/Betula* bog, Roxburghshire, 1 June 1991; Plate 134 (below right): *C. trifida*, dune-slack, Holy Island, north Northumberland, 1 June 2002.

9.1. *Goodyera repens* (L.) R. Br.

Creeping Lady's-tresses

Perennial herb with creeping rhizomes; *stem* 10–35 cm, glandular-hairy, erect, scaly; *leaves* in a basal rosette, ovate-lanceolate, entire, net-veined, dark green, sometimes mottled lighter green, glabrous, evergreen; *inflorescence* a short, lax, one-sided, slightly twisted spike; *bracts* linear-lanceolate, pale green; *flowers* small, white, ± tubular, sweet-scented; *outer perianth segments* 3–4 mm, the upper longer than the lateral, ovate, concave, white; *inner perianth segments* lanceolate, white; *labellum* shorter than the outer segments, undivided, the basal portion pouched, the distal portion lingulate, narrow, furrowed; *column* short, forward-projecting; *anther* stalked, resting on the upper surface of the rostellum; *pollinia* two, ovoid, yellow; *stigma* ± circular; *rostellum* projecting beyond the stigma; *ovary* sessile or subsessile, glandular-hairy, pale green; *flowering* July to August; 2n = 30.

The genus *Goodyera* comprises about 40 species, distributed throughout northern temperate latitudes as well as parts of the tropics, including Asia and Madagascar. In Europe two species occur: *G. macrophylla* Lowe, endemic to Madeira, and the much more widespread *G. repens*. This latter is the plant present in the British Isles. It is also widely distributed through northern, central and western Europe, from 70° N in Scandinavia, southwards to the Pyrenees, the Alps and the Balkans, and through eastern Europe to Turkey, the Caucasus and Russia. Still further east it is found in Afghanistan, the Himalayas, Siberia, China and Japan, and it also occurs in North America. It is recorded to an altitude of up to 2000 m in the Alps, but in the northern part of its range it may be found at sea level. In Europe it is largely restricted to coniferous or mixed woodland, growing amongst a ground cover of mosses, often in places where the light level is low.

The genus is named after the English botanist John Goodyer (1592–1664), who was active in the seventeenth century; he never saw his namesake plant, which was given its name after a confusion arose later over his notes on the Marsh Helleborine *Epipactis palustris*, another stoloniferous species (Gunther 1922). The Latin specific name *repens* refers to the plant's creeping habit. Alternative common names in English appear to be scarce, but in North America this and several related species are referred to as 'rattlesnake plantain'. Very surprisingly the first British record, made by Lightfoot in 1777 (Clarke 1900), was from Ross-shire where it is now rare: '*Satyrium repens* [the Linnean name] … in an old shady hanging birch wood … about two miles from the head of Little Loch Broom'.

Plate 136. *Goodyera repens* with Heather *Calluna vulgaris* in Scots Pine *Pinus sylvestris* plantation, Roxburghshire, 17 July 2000.

Plate 135 (opposite). Creeping Lady's-tresses *Goodyera repens* can be abundant in the sparse vegetation below mature Scots Pine *Pinus sylvestris,* both in plantations and in native forest. Roxburghshire, 22 July 1989.

In the British Isles Creeping Lady's-tresses is mainly a Scottish plant, though it does also occur in northern England as far south as Northumberland and Cumbria. It was also recorded in Yorkshire to the north-west of Hull, as early as 1841, and was still there in 1888, but is now extinct at this site (Crackles 1990). This may have been its most southerly native British locality. In its pine-woodland sites in East Anglia it seems to have been introduced, presumably brought in on the roots of seedlings of non-local origin when the woods were first planted. Its British centre of distribution is in the eastern highlands of Scotland, in the remnants of the ancient Caledonian pine forest. Additionally it is found as far north as Sutherland, and in East Lothian and Roxburghshire in the south. It is absent from most of the west of Scotland and the Isles but, though extinct there now, it was recorded in Orkney during the 1950s. It is not known in Wales or Ireland.

The typical habitat of *G. repens* is shady, mature pine woodland, occasionally with birch. It grows in the loose humus and moss of the soil surface, where the ground cover is open and competition is slight, the plants' many stolons penetrating just under and through the loose carpet. It also grows in more open areas such as woodland margins and clearings. There are rare occurrences in coastal areas amongst heathy shrubs, such as Heather *Calluna vulgaris*, in the apparent absence of pines, although the latter are invariably close by; it has also been recorded from damp fixed-dune systems. *Neottia cordata* and *Vaccinium myrtillus* are frequent associates. In Scotland other interesting plants, such as *Linnaea borealis, Moneses uniflora, Orthilia secunda* and

Plate 137. *Goodyera repens* is the only evergreen orchid in the British Isles. Overwintering leaf rosettes, East Lothian, 8 March 2004.

Pyrola species, may be found nearby. The NVC classification is within the W17 and W18 associations, which include the eponymous *Erica cinerea – Goodyera repens* subcommunity (W18a). In many localities, especially in north-east Scotland, the plant may be found in great profusion, often with tens of thousands of inflorescences emerging at the peak of the flowering season in late summer. Its persisting dead spikes and evergreen leaves enable it to be recorded long after flowering is over. The Scottish habitats are usually rather dry but some of the sites in northern England, especially in Cumbria, are in wooded mossland, and are in consequence much damper; there is some uncertainty, however, as to whether the latter populations are truly native.

Creeping Lady's-tresses is easily separated from other lady's-tresses (*Spiranthes*) by its habitat, but its ovate-lanceolate, net-veined leaves and stoloniferous habit will also help to identify it. The plant is most easily found in the pine forests of the Spey valley, where it can be abundant; another good spot is in the woods of the Culbin Forest near Nairn.

The flowers are sweetly scented, and nectar is secreted into the lower part of the labellum. Initially the flower's tube is constricted, allowing an insect access to the pollinia only by way of its proboscis. On removal of the pollinia the labellum moves downwards to expose the stigma, and cross-pollination is achieved when contact is made with pollinia attached to the next insect visitor. Seed-set is good; existing populations, however, are more likely to multiply vegetatively, while seed can lead to the development of new ones. After flowering, the main stem dies back but the several side-shoots or stolons gradually separate and develop into new plants. No varieties and hybrids are recorded in the British Isles.

Plate 138 (above left). Clonal patches of *Goodyera repens* develop as the rhizome grows and divides, with the inflorescences appearing from mature rosettes after about eight years of growth. Scots Pine *Pinus sylvestris* plantation, Roxburghshire, 22 July 1989.

Plate 139 (above right). The upper part of the inflorescence and the outer perianth segments of *Goodyera repens* are glandular-pubescent. Roxburghshire, 17 July 2000.

10. *Spiranthes* Rich.

Lady's-tresses

Perennial herbs with ± tuberous roots; *leaves* both basal and on the stem; *flowers* small, sessile, white, borne spirally in a tight spike; *perianth segments* ± equal; *labellum* unlobed with a frilled margin, furrowed below, the borders overlapped by the inner perianth segments; *spur* absent; *column* horizontal, with the stigma below; *pollinia* unstalked; *rostellum* well developed.

The taxonomic delimitation of this genus is difficult but there are thought to be about 30 species world-wide. The centre of its distribution is in northern and central America and its range includes the temperate parts of Europe and Asia, South America and Australasia. Throughout this range the different species exhibit a wide variation in habitat preference. Three species occur in mainland Europe and all three were also once found in the British Isles, but one of them, *S. aestivalis*, is now extinct here. The generic name derives from the Greek for 'coiled', *spira*, and 'flower', *anthos*, reflecting the twisted arrangement of the flower spike. The common name 'lady's-tresses' is clearly an allusion to this 'ringleted' look.

Pollination is carried out by insects attracted to the nectar secreted near the base of the labellum. Although bees have been recorded as visiting the flower (Summerhayes 1968), Delforge (1995) indicates that aphids are the most regular pollinators. In freshly opened flowers the perianth segments form a narrow tube around the column and the rostellum lies close to the lip, leaving only a small aperture through which the insect can insert its proboscis. In doing so it touches the viscidium, and the pollinia then adhere to the proboscis as it is withdrawn. As the flower matures the column and lip move apart, exposing the stigma at the base of the column. Insect visitors bearing pollinia can therefore make contact with the stigmatic surface and effect pollination. This temporal-exclusion mechanism maximises the chances of cross-fertilisation between plants in the population.

In addition to the native species, the North American *S. cernua* (L.) Rich. is commonly cultivated in British gardens and could be confused with *S. romanzoffiana*. The pink-flowered *S. sinensis* (Pers.) Ames, from Asia and Australasia, will self-sow in greenhouses, though is apparently not hardy enough to survive a British winter (Cribb & Bailes 1989).

Plate 141 (above). The name Irish Lady's-tresses belies the occurrence of *Spiranthes romanzoffiana* on both sides of the Atlantic. Here it is growing in wet peaty moorland, Island of Barra, Outer Hebrides, 15 August 2000.

Plate 140 (opp.). A clonal group of *Spiranthes spiralis*, in short turf over ancient chalk-workings. N. Hampshire, 6 September 1994.

10.1. *Spiranthes romanzoffiana* Cham.

Irish Lady's-tresses

Perennial herb with slightly thickened tuberous roots; *stem* 10–35 cm, erect, pale green; *leaves* both basal and cauline on the current flowering stem, erect, linear-lanceolate, acute; *inflorescence* a spike, 2–5 cm, with flowers in a dense, somewhat twisted, three-ranked arrangement; *bracts* lanceolate to ovate, acute; *flowers* white, scented, 10–14 mm; *outer perianth segments* to 12 mm, lanceolate, acuminate, white; *inner perianth segments* linear, white; *labellum* lingulate to pandurate, white, green-veined, frilled and denticulate distally; *column* horizontal, beaked; *anther* cordate; *pollinia* two; *stigma* crescent-shaped; *rostellum* green; *ovary* cylindrical, subsessile; *flowering* July to August (to September); 2n = 60.

In Europe *S. romanzoffiana* is known only from Ireland and western Scotland where, in both areas, it is very local; and from a single locality in Devon, where it may now be extinct. It is a plant of very asymmetric amphi-Atlantic distribution, otherwise occurring only in North America and the Aleutian Islands. It is therefore one of the small group of plants possessing a so-called Hiberno-American distribution pattern, that also includes *Eriocaulon aquaticum*, *Hypericum canadense*, *Sisyrinchium bermudiana*, and perhaps *Najas flexilis*. *Spiranthes romanzoffiana* is presumed to be a plant of pre-glacial survival, but another theory is that it might have been introduced from America by migrating geese.

The first record in the British Isles was made in 1810, though not published until 1828 by J.E. Smith, when he stated '*Neottia gemmifera* [an early synonym] … Near Castletown opposite to Bearhaven on the northern side of Bantry Bay, County of Cork, Mr Drummond … communicated to me in 1810'. The specific name, given to the plant by Chamisso, commemorates Nicholas Romanzoff, a Russian minister of state who gave financial support to scientific exploration. Common names are few, with alternatives being Hooded, or American Lady's-tresses.

In the south-west of Ireland the plant has been known since at least 1810, and has been recorded in 15 separate localities in that area. In 1892 it was found in what is now Northern Ireland, around the shores of Lough Neagh, and later still in other areas more distant from the lake basin, including parts of Fermanagh, Antrim and the Mourne mountains. It was also found in the Connemara district of the Republic of Ireland in 1958, around the shores of Lough Corrib. It appears to have been first noticed in Scotland on the island of Coll in the early 1920s, although initially there was some confusion about its identity. In 1930 it was discovered on Colonsay, and since then there have been records from several other Hebridean islands such as Barra, Benbecula, South Uist, Islay, Mull and Vatersay. At some time in the 1950s it was first found on the Scottish mainland, in Ardnamurchan, and a few years later in Morven. Subsequently it was recorded for Moidart and Kintyre. The first discovery in England was made during botanical survey work in Devon in 1957, but it is not clear whether this population still survives.

The typical habitat for *S. romanzoffiana* is valley bogs and damp, peaty meadows, pastures and heaths, especially those which are susceptible to inundation in winter.

Plate 142 (opposite).
The flowers of *Spiranthes romanzoffiana* are comparatively large, held in a dense inflorescence. Wet peaty grassland by loch, Island of Barra, Outer Hebrides, 16 August 2000.

Plate 143. A typical habitat for *Spiranthes romanzoffiana*, in wet lochside grassland. Island of Barra, Outer Hebrides, 16 August 2000.

Another habitat is in damp *Molinia* grassland through which water percolates, and yet another is in 'lazy beds' (potato-growing areas). In western Ireland it grows in places on the stony shore around Lough Corrib, at a clearly defined level where it is subject to occasional flooding (Webb & Scannell 1983). It has also been recorded in areas where cattle have overwintered, and it is quite possible that the ground disturbance that this causes may stimulate the plant into growth, or allow a more open habitat to prevail (Lang 1980). Everywhere it is a local and scarce plant, and may even be decreasing, but this is very difficult to establish because of its well-known propensity to erratic flowering. It is also extremely difficult to detect when not in flower or bud. In addition it is a late flowerer, often growing in remote areas, and so may still be under-recorded, so future discoveries in new areas will not necessarily mean that its range is being extended. The number of flowering plants in any population is never very high, although some populations are known where up to one hundred or more are frequently found in flower. Typical associates are varied but *Molinia caerulea* is most frequently present; others can include *Anagallis tenella, Carex panicea, Drosera* spp., *Filipendula ulmaria, Juncus acutiflorus, Leontodon autumnalis, Myrica gale, Ranunculus flammula, Salix repens* and *Succisa pratensis*. Much rarer associates are *Lycopodium inundatum* and *Rhynchospora fusca*. Recent work on the island of Colonsay has assigned populations of the plant to various NVC mire communities, including M6, M10, M23 and M25. Although the most typical has been difficult to identify in such terms, all refer to wetland associations.

Recognition of Irish Lady's-tresses in the field ought not to present a problem, the short, dense, three-ranked arrangement of the flower spike being diagnostic. To observe living plants it will probably be most convenient, after contacting the local conservation group, to visit suitable habitat in the west of Scotland or in Ireland.

Little appears to be known about the reproduction and life cycle of the plant. The flowers are strongly scented, and it is claimed that they can be detected from some distance away. Pollination by insects, including moths, is therefore the most likely means of reproduction; visits by bees have been recorded in Canada (Summerhayes 1968). No fertile fruiting spikes have ever been recorded in Scotland, however, and only one has been found in Ireland (Gulliver *et al.* 2005, in press). Genetic analysis has shown that despite the low rate of seed-set, the more northerly

Scottish populations on Barra, Coll and Vatersay show high genetic diversity (and share a distinct genotype), while those on Colonsay and in Ireland are also genetically distinct but are highly uniform with low genetic diversity. The reasons for this are not fully clear (Forrest 2001, Forrest *et al.* 2004). Reproduction can also occur through the development of basal lateral buds, and the possibility of new plants developing from the roots has been suggested (Gulliver *et al.* 2005, in press). Such vegetative reproduction may maintain populations in the absence of seedlings.

Several infraspecific taxa have been recognised as either subspecies or varieties. *Spiranthes romanzoffiana* was originally described from Unalaska in the Aleutian Islands, and it is possible that the plant of North America may differ from that of the British Isles. In Ireland, subsp. *stricta* (Rydb.) A. Nelson is reported to be confined to the north; this has almost cream-coloured flowers, a narrower labellum, and narrower, more keeled leaves than the more densely-spiked, white-flowered subsp. *gemmipara* (Sm.) A.R. Clapham. The latter is known from south-west Ireland, and also possibly from Devon, and is so named because at one time it was thought to produce small buds which then became detached to form new plants. The Scottish plants are referred to subsp. *stricta*. Plants intermediate in character between the two subspecies occur frequently, however, and it is doubtful whether their continued separation is justified. No hybrids have been recorded in Britain, although that with *S. cernua* (*S.* ×*steigeri* Correll) has been claimed to occur in America.

Plate 144. Often continuing to flower well into September, *Spiranthes spiralis* is aptly named Autumn Lady's-tresses. North Hampshire, 3 September 1995.

10.2. *Spiranthes spiralis* (L.) Chevall.

Autumn Lady's-tresses

Perennial herb with elongated tubers; *stem* 5–20 cm, terete, pale green; *leaves* developing laterally in late summer, simultaneously with or shortly after the development of the flower-spike from the previous year's growing point, forming an overwintering basal rosette from which the following year's flower-spike will emerge, ovate-elliptic, acute, entire, patent, glossy green, withering in early summer; *inflorescence* a spike of 5–15(–20) flowers; *bracts* small, lanceolate; *flowers* very small, white, sweet-scented during the daytime, usually arranged in a single spiral rank; *outer perianth segments* 6–7 mm, oblong, white, green-nerved, faintly toothed; *inner perianth segments* slightly smaller than outer, lingulate, white; *labellum* 6–7 mm, oblong, concave, pale greenish white, with an indented margin; *spur* absent; *column* obconical, greenish; *anther* sessile; *stigma* on under surface of column; *rostellum* divided into narrow lobes; *ovary* narrow, green; *flowering* July to September; 2n = 30.

In the British Isles Autumn Lady's-tresses *Spiranthes spiralis* is widespread in suitable habitats, with a northern limit running from north-east Yorkshire through south Cumbria, the Isle of Man and Co. Sligo. It also occurs

Plate 145. The spiralled
inflorescence of this
demurely charming plant
suggested both its scientific
and its common name.
Spiranthes spiralis, short
grassland, New Forest, South
Hampshire, 29 August 1997.

throughout much of mainland Europe northwards to Denmark, and in the Mediterranean region, North Africa, western Asia and
Russia. Although mainly a lowland plant it
has been recorded in the Alps to altitudes of
up to 1000 m.

The origin of the specific name *spiralis* is
self-evident, based on the shape of the inflorescence, and much the same can be said for
the common English name. An early British
record is that published by William Turner in
1548, who stated that 'Satyrion ... groweth
besyde Syon [Sion House, opposite Kew
Gardens] ... it bryngeth forth whyte floures
in the ende of harveste, and it is called Lady
traces'. By inference, therefore, it had been
known and named prior to Turner's record.
John Gerard, in his *Herball* (1597), included
Lady Traces under 'Sweet Cullions' [testicles].
He found they had little medicinal use other
than that 'the full and sappy rootes of Ladie
Traces eaten or boiled in milke and drunke,
provoke venery, nourish and strengthen the
bodie, and be good for such as are fallen into
a consumption or fever Hectique'.

In the British Isles *Spiranthes spiralis* is
especially a plant of old, short-grazed turf
over chalk and limestone. Ancient, undisturbed pastures and downs, rabbit-grazed
cliff tops, coastal grassland and stabilised
calcareous dunes are its most typical habitats, but it has also been frequently found
on old garden lawns. At many localities it
is an inconsistent flowerer, being present
some years in large numbers but in other
years very scarce. In such cases, however, it
has been shown that the plants still survive
in an underground or a vegetative state, and
the size of the population remains largely
unchanged (Lang 1980). This inconsistency
in flowering, together with the plant's usu-
ally late flowering time, towards the end of August or early in September, may have
led to it having been somewhat under-recorded.

It is well adapted to its habitat since the basal rosette leaves, lying flush with the
ground, are almost unaffected by grazing, although the flowering spike may be
destroyed by this means. Populations appear to have been lost from many inland
sites as a result of adverse agricultural practices such as ploughing or the application of fertiliser. The plant's NVC classification is mainly restricted to the CG2

and CG10 calcareous grasslands. Typical associates may include *Anacamptis morio, Asperula cynanchica, Festuca ovina, Galium sterneri, Gentianella amarella, Sherardia arvensis* and *Thymus polytrichus.*

Spiranthes spiralis is easily recognised in the field, the only possible confusion being with *S. aestivalis*, which is now extinct in the British Isles (see p.144). From *S. aestivalis* it is distinguished by the fact that at flowering time all the leaves are in a tight rosette adjacent to the base of the stem, the stem itself having only reduced, scale-like leaves. In *S. aestivalis* the leaves not only surround the stem base but also occur some way up it. *Spiranthes spiralis* also flowers much later, and occupies a very different habitat. Populations are most easily found by searching short calcareous turf in the southern counties of England and, further north, in close-grazed limestone grassland on the coast of north Lancashire.

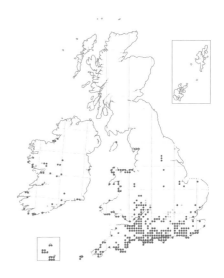

Pollination is thought to be mainly effected by bees. Subsequent to the pollinia being removed the position of the rostellum changes to expose the stigma, and this ensures that cross-pollination occurs. Seed-set is efficient, but on germination a period of up to 14 years is thought to be required before flowering can be achieved in the wild (Lang 1980). Cultivation experiments have found, however, that under controlled conditions this can be reduced to as little as five years (Lang 1980). Wild plants are often found in tight groups, and in such cases they are likely to have originated from lateral buds on a single stem, these producing separate tubers when the connecting root dies back. Large groups of plants can form in this way. Inconsistencies in flowering probably result from varying climatic conditions, as well as competition with cohabiting species, the mycorrhizal fungus probably being most susceptible to these factors. Hybrids and variants appear to be unknown in the British Isles.

Plate 146. The leaf-rosette of *Spiranthes spiralis* develops in autumn and is photosynthetically active through winter into spring; it withers in early summer before the flowers emerge. Dorset, April 1999.

10.3. *Spiranthes aestivalis* (Poir.) Rich.

Summer Lady's-tresses

Perennial herb with elongated tubers; *stems* 10–40 cm, erect; *leaves* linear-lanceolate, rounded at the apex, entire, bright green, shiny, mostly basal, but also with a few cauline; *inflorescence* a spike of 3–10 cm, with flowers in a single spiral row; *bracts* lanceolate; *flowers* small, 6–8 mm, tubular, white, faintly scented at night; *outer perianth segments* linear-lanceolate, obtuse, 6–7 mm, forming a tube with the labellum; *inner perianth segments* slightly smaller, linear; *labellum* 6–7 mm, oblong, denticulate distally; *column* horizontal, green; *anther* at upper surface of column, acute; *pollinia* two, yellowish, attached to upper surface of the viscidium; *stigma* green, rounded below, truncate above; *rostellum* deeply bifid; *ovary* sessile, usually glandular; *flowering* July to August; 2n = 30.

The past and current distribution of this plant in north-west Europe has recently been described (Foley 2004). In the British Isles it has only been recorded from the Channel Islands and the New Forest in Hampshire, and it is now extinct in both these areas. Elsewhere in Europe it is also rare, and decreasing as its damp, marshy or heathy habitat is threatened by drainage or by land improvement schemes. Populations on the Dutch–Belgian border, now possibly extinct, together with old ones in southern England and Germany, appear to represent the northern limit of its range. Even just across the Channel in north-west France, where formerly there were many populations, numbers are now greatly reduced. While there is concern for the plant's survival throughout most parts of central Europe, further to the south, especially in the Mediterranean area – in Spain, for example – there are still some good populations, so that its survival chances there should be better. Widely recorded across Europe, as far east as the Balkans (and also, though very doubtfully, in Asia Minor), it is also found in North Africa. In the Alps populations are known at altitudes up to 1200 m, but in general this is a lowland plant.

Its typical habitat in the New Forest was in boggy ground amongst *Sphagnum*, sometimes growing alongside streamlets. In the Channel Islands it occupied similar ground, as well as growing along a sandy lake margin. In France, however, it is found in a wider range of habitats, including valley bogs, damp heathland, dune slacks, and surprisingly, in rich, alkaline *Schoenus* fens. It is also found in damp grassland and mountain pastures in other parts of Europe.

It was first recorded for the British Isles at St Ouen's Pond, Jersey by Charles Babington, in July 1837. A specimen collected by him was sent to James Sowerby, who reproduced a drawing of it in his *English Botany* (Sowerby 1838), and this, or a duplicate, is now preserved in the herbarium of the Natural History Museum, London. Even in those days the plant was said to be far from plentiful, and was not found elsewhere on the island. It was then grossly over-collected, as evidenced by the number of specimens in various herbaria, and by the end of the century it had become very rare. Up to 1917 it was still recorded by a local botanist, T.W.

Attenborough, but afterwards he found none until a single plant in 1925, which he did not officially record, presumably for conservation reasons. This seems to be the last definite record for Jersey, since that of Louis-Arsène for 1928 is subject to doubt, as are many of the other specimens of rarities in his collection. The actual site at St Ouen's Pond where the plant grew is still natural but has become overgrown by reeds, these not now being cut back as formerly. Recently it has been suggested that the site be regenerated, in the hope that plants might reappear from dormant seed; or, alternatively, that an attempted reintroduction be made from a foreign source.

The plant also occurred on Guernsey at the Grand Mare. It seems to have first been recorded here in the 1850s, but an earlier undated record by W.W. Newbould may precede it (McClintock 1975). It was fairly abundant in the early years but by 1906 had become quite rare owing to habitat drainage and excessive collecting. It has not been recorded since 1914 and the site is now greatly reduced, although a small amount of suitable habitat remains.

The New Forest in Hampshire was the single mainland British locality for *S. aestivalis*, one record in 1854 at Bewdley, Worcestershire having been an aberrant form of *Gymnadenia conopsea*, and another from Devon also an error. It appears to have been discovered in the New Forest by Joseph Janson in 1840, since one of his specimens in the Natural History Museum, London bears that date. There seem to have been five separate localities in the area to the south-west of Lyndhurst, including one by a pond at Brockenhurst, some distance away from the others. The other sites were in *Sphagnum* bog and along streamsides, with rather small populations. One discovered by J. Cross prior to 1900 had up to 200 plants, but numbers were much reduced by the 1920s; figures of up to 50 plants were sometimes quoted for another site. As time passed it appears that, at all the known localities, the *Sphagnum* habitat became gradually reduced through drainage, while tree-planting and scrub and carr encroachment also contributed to the loss of suitable habitat. On the whole the plant was generally scarce at all the New Forest sites, a view supported by comments on herbarium specimen labels; here as elsewhere collection no doubt also

Plate 147. The upright leaves of Summer Lady's-tresses *Spiranthes aestivalis* easily distinguish it from *S. spiralis*; the plants also occupy quite different habitats. Peaty damp heathland with pines, Normandy, France, 25 July 1998.

played its part in hastening its demise. It appears to have been last recorded at a New Forest site in 1959, or maybe even as late as 1961, and is now extinct in the British Isles. The legacy of 236 British specimens, some with tubers attached, in three of our major national herbaria, is itself a testament to the general lack of consideration for the plant's conservation.

In the course of preparing this book there have been rumours of an illicit re-introduction to the New Forest and of plants flowering there. The rumours remain unsubstantiated, but a discovery of *S. aestivalis* in the New Forest cannot now be assumed to be a natural reappearance.

The specific name *aestivalis* refers to its flowering time (summer), no doubt to differentiate it from its relative, the autumn-flowering *S. spiralis*. Owing perhaps to its rarity no other common or colloquial English names have been recorded, but in France it is referred to as *Spiranthe d'Eté*. It is most readily distinguished from *Spiranthes spiralis* by the fact that the flowering stem emerges from and not adjacent to the basal rosette, the leaves are linear-lanceolate not ovate-elliptical, and also occur part way up the stem. To see the plant most conveniently it will be necessary to visit a population in northern France; one of the most accessible is to the south of Cherbourg and is of great international importance.

It has been suggested that *S. aestivalis* is pollinated by nocturnal insects, since observations indicate that its scent is stronger in the evening; but so far this appears to be unproven (Summerhayes 1968). The pollination mechanism is similar to that for *S. spiralis*, and vegetative reproduction can also occur, lateral root buds producing separate detached tubers. In the British Isles no records of hybrids or varieties have been traced.

Plate 149 (opposite). The only native orchid known to have become extinct in the British Isles. *Spiranthes aestivalis* – a plant at the edge of its range in Britain, and harried by collectors for its rarity. Peaty damp heathland with pines, Normandy, France, 25 July 1998.

Plate 148 (below). The last known British site for *Spiranthes aestivalis*: its latest record here was in 1959. Should it be reintroduced? Float bog, New Forest, South Hampshire, 26 July 2002.

11.1. *Herminium monorchis* (L.) R. Br.

Musk Orchid

Perennial herb with one fully developed root tuber at anthesis and several immature tubers borne on slender rhizomes; *stem* 5–15(–25) cm, erect, green; *main leaves* two to three, positioned low on the stem, to 7 × 2 cm, broadly lanceolate to oblong, entire, green, with a few smaller, bract-like leaves higher up the stem; *inflorescence* a lax to quite dense, one-sided spike, with many small, greenish, subcampanulate, sweetly scented flowers; *bracts* lanceolate, usually shorter than the ovary; *outer perianth segments* to 3 mm, connivent, lanceolate to ovate; *inner perianth segments* slightly longer and narrower than the outer, converging; *labellum* to 4 mm, trilobed, green, the middle lobe the longest, the lateral lobes divergent or ± forward-pointing; *spur* absent; *column* small, broad; *anther* rounded; *pollinia* two; *stigma* bilobed; *ovary* sessile, slightly twisted; *flowering* June to July; 2n = 40.

The genus *Herminium* comprises about 30 species world-wide, mainly occurring in the northern temperate areas of Europe and Asia. Only one of these species, the Musk Orchid *Herminium monorchis*, is present in Europe, with a range extending eastwards from Britain across southern Scandinavia, central Europe and Asia, as far as China; it is also found in the Himalayas. It often prefers calcareous grassland, and can be found at altitudes of up to 2000 m in mountain areas; outside Britain it can also be found in non-calcareous soils, and frequently occurs in damp habitats.

The generic name *Herminium* derives from the Greek *hermis*, 'buttress', referring to the plant's pillar-like tubers, whilst the specific epithet *monorchis* relates to the single root tuber present at flowering (*orchis*, 'testicle'). It was first recorded in Britain in Cambridgeshire by John Ray, in 1663, '*Orchis pusilla odorata* … In the chalk pit close at Cherry Hinton' – a locality where it has long been extinct.

In the British Isles the Musk Orchid is now restricted to southern England. It was formerly recorded in East Anglia as far north as northern Norfolk, and in Herefordshire and south Wales, but is now extinct in these areas. Its current northern limit is in the Chilterns and in the Cotswolds near Cheltenham. In many parts of southern England it is scarce. This is especially so in Dorset, where it reaches its current western limit in England, as well as in Wiltshire and Hampshire, although the Wiltshire colony at Ham Hill is a strong one, with a population of several hundred flowering plants. It is also quite frequent on the chalk downs of Kent and Sussex, where several large populations are known; one population in the latter county had in excess of 20,000 flowering plants in 1966 (Lang 1980). Numbers of flowering spikes may fluctuate extremely widely, however, so their presence or absence may not be a true reflection of a population's size, or even of its existence.

In Britain it is mainly restricted to short *Festuca* turf of chalk or limestone grassland. Natural banks and terraces and the sides of earthworks are especially favoured, as are the sloping sides of raised greens on golf courses. Path borders where competition is reduced, quarry floors and spoil heaps are other places where it is known to occur, and on the coast of south Wales it has been found on dune grassland. Its NVC classification includes the *Festuca ovina – Avenula pratensis* (CG2) and

Plate 150 (opposite). The sweetly scented flowers of the Musk Orchid *Herminium monorchis* are a bright yellowish green. Short turf over ancient chalk workings, North Hampshire, 21 June 2003.

the *Brachypodium pinnatum* (CG4) grassland communities; one unusual association in which it is also recorded is the *Hedera helix – Urtica dioica* woodland subcommunity (W21a). Typical associates are other orchids that also favour the warm short-grazed calcareous turf of the southern counties.

Despite this plant's common English name its flowers are rather honey-scented than musk-like, but nevertheless attract small flies and beetles. Owing to the construction of the floral parts, pollinators must enter sideways, and in so doing make contact with the viscidium which, together with its attached pollinium, is removed. This adheres to the insect's body and legs so that the pollinium is subsequently transferred to the stigma of the next flower visited. Since the stigma protrudes below the pollinia, fragments of the latter can fall onto the stigma and so lead to self-fertilisation.

Vegetative reproduction, however, is thought to be the method by which most populations are maintained, because seedlings are rarely observed. The two or more tubers produced each year are separated at some distance below ground, as they are borne at the tips of slender stolons up to 20 cm in length. In the following year each of these tubers produces a shoot. Nutrient, in the form of photosynthates from the parent plant, is usually sufficient for only one of them to flower, but strong plants may be succeeded by two or more new flowering plants. As the tubers are borne on such long stolons, each year's plants appear in a slightly different place, and this has led to the species being considered somewhat migratory. Since seed-set and vegetative reproduction are efficient, it is perhaps surprising that the plant is not more widespread in the British Isles. Prevailing climatic conditions and lack of suitable habitat would appear to be the limiting factors for a species at the extremes of its geographical range. Hybrids or varieties appear to be unknown in Britain.

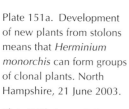

Plate 151a. Development of new plants from stolons means that *Herminium monorchis* can form groups of clonal plants. North Hampshire, 21 June 2003.

Plate 151b (opposite). Although seen here standing above very short turf on ancient chalk-workings, in slightly taller vegetation the Musk Orchid can be extremely hard to detect. N. Hampshire, 2 July 1999.

12. *Orchis* L.

Perennial herbs with two globose to ellipsoid tubers; *stem* glabrous; *leaves* basal, rosulate, spotted or not; *inflorescence* few- to many-flowered, lax or dense, emerging from a sheathing spathe-like leaf; *bracts* thin, membranous, often coloured; *flowers* usually purple or pink and white, sometimes yellowish or greenish; *perianth segments* sometimes connivent to form a galea, or with outer sepals spreading to deflexed, the sepals and two inner petals ± equal in length, or the latter shorter, glabrous; *labellum* entire to trilobed, often with the central lobe divided into lobules with a tooth between, porrect to deflexed, glabrous or papillose, usually spurred, spur occasionally absent; *column* with a trilobed rostellum; *pollinia* two, each with free caudicle and viscidium, occasionally viscidia connate in a single bursicle; *ovary* sessile, cylindrical, twisted, glabrous.

Orchis is the type genus of the family Orchidaceae, and appropriately, is one of the best known genera in the British Isles. The genus as a whole comprises about 33 species which are widely distributed throughout much of Europe, the Mediterranean and temperate Asia to the Caucasus and Caspian areas, and in southern Siberia. The name derives from the Greek *orchis*, 'testicle', owing to the appearance of the two ovate tubers.

The recent dismemberment of the broad genus *Orchis*, involving the transfer of many familiar '*Orchis*' species into other genera, will be surprising to many. It has come about as a result of extensive and ongoing researches into the phylogeny of the European orchids, being conducted by botanists throughout Europe (for a fuller discussion see *Chapter 2. Orchid Taxonomy and Classification*). These researchers have demonstrated that *Orchis*, in its old sense, was made up of many rather distantly related groups, so to achieve a classification that truly reflected ancestry, *Orchis* had to be redefined (Pridgeon *et al.* 1997, Bateman *et al.* 1997).

In its new delimitation *Orchis* includes five species in the British Isles, falling into two groups. The Early Purple Orchid *Orchis mascula*, the type species of the genus, is the sole British and Irish example of the mascula group, and by far the most common member of the genus. All the others belong to the militaris group, characterised as the 'anthropomorphic species' on account of the suggestion in their flowers of the human form, also reflected in their names: the Man, Lady, Monkey and Military Orchids. These are generally scarce, and some are extremely rare. The Lady, Monkey and Military Orchids, *O. purpurea*, *O. simia* and *O. militaris*, are confined to southern England and are at the edge of their range here.

The flowers in *Orchis* are well adapted for pollination, although they offer no reward in the form of nectar. Insects are deceived into visiting by the bright colours of the flowers and their fragrance, but the spur is empty. As the insect hopefully probes the flower the rostellum is touched and the sticky pollen-bearing viscidia become exposed; these then attach themselves to the proboscis. Variations in floral morphology within the genus are considered to be adaptations to different types of pollinator. Pollination is usually efficient, resulting in good seed-set and, where species meet, the formation of occasional hybrids. Hand-pollination has, however, been used to boost the fortunes of the English rarities *O. simia* and *O. militaris*, and results in almost 100 per cent seed-set.

Plate 152 (opposite). The flowers of the Early Purple Orchid *Orchis mascula*, like those of all *Orchis* species, deceive pollinators into visiting but offer no reward. Derbyshire, 31 May 2001.

12.1. *Orchis anthropophora* (L.) All.

Syn. *Aceras anthropophorum* (L.) W.T. Aiton

Man Orchid

Plate 153. Two colour forms of the Man Orchid *Orchis anthropophora* growing in rough grassland on chalk, East Kent, 21 May 1999.

Perennial herb, glabrous, with two ovoid root tubers; *stem* 10–30(–40) cm, erect; *leaves* several, those below oblong-lanceolate, entire, somewhat keeled, dark green, glossy, those above diminishing in size; *inflorescence* a long, narrow, rather lax, many-flowered spike; *bracts* membranous, shorter than the ovaries; *flowers* greenish yellow, streaked and margined with red; *outer perianth segments* 6–7 mm, ovate-lanceolate, incurved and connivent with the inner segments; the latter shorter and narrower, linear; *labellum* 12–15 mm long, yellow-green, often tinged or edged with red, trilobed and 'man-like', the lateral lobes long and narrow, the median also long, and further divided into narrow sublobes with a small tooth in between; *spur* essentially absent but replaced by two small nectar-secreting depressions; *column* short; *anther* ovate, yellow-green; *pollinia* two, yellowish; *stigma* positioned in the space formed by the labellum base and the column; *rostellum* very small; *ovary* sessile, cylindrical, green; *flowering* June to July; 2n = 42.

Originally placed by Linnaeus in his genus *Ophrys,* which contained orchids without a spurred labellum, this plant was transferred to the monotypic genus *Aceras* by W.T. Aiton (1766–1849), and then to *Orchis* by C. Allioni (1728–1804). Until recently the majority of botanists considered it to be most appropriately included in *Aceras,* on the basis of its not having a spur (*Aceras,* Greek, 'without a spur'). Darwin (1877) differed, however: 'The separation of this genus is evidently artificial. It is a true *Orchis,* but with a very short nectary [spur].' This insight has been amply confirmed by recent DNA analysis and objective morphological comparison (Bateman *et al.* 1997, Bateman 2001), which conclusively establishes the plant as a member of the anthropomorphic-flowered group of the newly more narrowly defined genus *Orchis.* The Greek name *anthropophora,* literally 'man-bearing', clearly refers to the shape of the labellum, which approximately resembles a human figure. Surprisingly, colloquial English names for this plant seem to be rare, but the human likeness is recognised in other parts of Europe. In France it is referred to as *L'Homme Pendu* ('the hanged man'), in Germany as *Puppenorchis* ('marionette orchid') and *Menschentragendes* ('man-bearing') as well as *Ohnhorn* ('lacking a spur'), and in Italy as

Ballerino. The first British record appears to be that published by Ray in 1696. This was made by a Mr (probably Samuel) Dale in a disused gravel pit at Dalington [Ballingdon] in Essex: '*Orchis anthropophora oreades ... flore nudi hominis effigiem repres-entans ...*' An even earlier record given by Christopher Merrett in 1666, for '*O. antrophora autumnalis*', is thought likely to have been an error for the Frog Orchid *Dactylorhiza viridis*.

Orchis anthropophora is most frequent in western Europe and North Africa, with a northern limit in southern England, but it is also distributed through parts of the Mediterranean as far east as Cyprus. It is a plant of calcareous soils, in the north and west of its range occurring especially in downland, but elsewhere in hill pastures, woodland margins, olive groves, and open stony ground and phrygana. It is recorded in the Alps to an altitude of 1500 m.

In the British Isles it is a lowland plant with a Continental type of distribution, mainly restricted to the south-east of England, and especially to Kent. Scattered occurrences have been recorded as far north as Lincolnshire and Warwickshire, and west into Somer-set, but in these areas it is on the very edge of its range and populations are small, often surviving for only a short time, and frequently under threat. The Somerset records exemplify this. The plant was found at South Stoke in 1933, with the record supported by a herbarium specimen. It has not been seen there since then, so the population is assumed to be extinct. A late-nineteenth century discovery near Cleve-don resulted in all the plants being dug up and transferred to a garden, the native

Plate 154. Although often found in short chalk grassland, *Orchis anthropophora* can also be found amongst scrub or even in woodland. Roadside verge, East Kent, 8 June 1996.

population never being seen again. At its northern limit in Lincolnshire, where it still survives, numbers are usually small and the population size fluctuates appreciably. This behaviour is typical of this and other orchids, especially when at the limits of their geographical range.

British habitats for the Man Orchid include chalk pastures and downland, old limestone- and chalk-quarry workings, and roadside verges. The plant can tolerate a certain amount of shade and so is also found in scrubby areas amongst coarser grasses and at woodland margins. An unusual Sussex site was on stabilised shingle, but this population was unfortunately later destroyed. In its typical downland habitat it may be accompanied by other orchids such as *Anacamptis pyramidalis, Dactylorhiza fuchsii, Gymnadenia conopsea* and *Neottia ovata*, and typical downland plants such as *Briza media, Centaurea nigra, Polygala calcarea* and other *Polygala* species. The NVC system classifies it mainly within the CG2 and CG3 calcareous grassland communities. Over-grazing and ploughing as well as other forms of intensive farming, including herbicidal spraying, will lead to its elimination. Many East Anglian populations were lost to ploughing in the late-nineteenth century, and most of the remainder suffered the same fate during the Second World War. Rabbits can be a serious menace, nibbling off the flowering spikes in successive years. The use of quarries and chalk-pits for landfill and refuse disposal poses another threat, but at some of the protected localities populations can exceed 10,000 flowering plants in a favourable season. As a rapidly declining species it is listed as Endangered in the 2005 Red List.

Plate 156 (above). Both the common and scientific names for the Man Orchid *Orchis anthropophora* are derived from the flower shape. A heavily pigmented plant, on a roadside verge, East Kent, 8 June 1996.

The Man Orchid is quite readily recognised in the field, and although of perhaps a rather drab appearance, its characteristically shaped labellum suffices for identification. Always very local, living plants are most likely to be found by making a trip to Kent, preferably to one of the known protected sites.

The flowers have a slight scent, reminiscent of freshly mown hay; they also contain nectar, readily accessible in the depression at the base of the labellum, which attracts small insects, including ants. The precise method of pollination is not fully understood but a large proportion of plants set seed, and it is thought that both self- and cross-pollination are likely to occur. Despite this, seed germination must be very poor, since new populations are only rarely established. The plants, which can live for up to ten years and flower for five, reproduce vegetatively by tuber replacement on an annual basis, and so the population is maintained. New leaves emerge in the autumn but die back by the time the plant flowers.

Hybrids with the Monkey Orchid *Orchis simia* have been recorded in Kent and are discussed in the account of that species, below. In continental Europe other hybrids with various species of *Orchis* are also known.

Plate 155 (opposite). The spurless flowers of *Orchis anthropophora* led to its being placed in a separate genus, *Aceras*, but in all other characters it is a typical *Orchis*. East Kent, 23 May 2002.

12.2. *Orchis simia* Lam.

Monkey Orchid

Perennial herb with two rounded tubers; *stem* 30–45 cm; *leaves* rather few, sheathing above, oblong-lanceolate to oblong-ovate, shiny grey-green, unspotted, obtuse to acute at apex, folded and keeled; *inflorescence* a fairly dense, ovoid to cylindrical, rather amorphous spike, the flowers opening from the top downwards; *bracts* tapering to an acute apex, greenish to pink or paler; *flowers* of medium size, faintly scented; *outer perianth segments* c.10 mm, in the form of a longish, loose connivent hood, whitish to pale violet, finely spotted; *inner perianth segments* shorter, whitish with a violet margin, ± linear, acute; *labellum* 14–16 mm, longer than wide, trilobed, pinkish white or deeper pink, the upper lobes ('arms') slender, violet, the middle lobe much longer than the laterals, spotted purplish with small papillae, bilobed distally into two long, narrow, ± flexuous segments ('legs'), with a small tooth between; *spur* flattened, sometimes notched, pointing downwards, pinkish white; *column* short, whitish; *anther* oblong; *pollinia* two; *stigma* placed above the spur; *rostellum* downpointing; *ovary* cylindrical, twisted, with violet ridges; *flowering* May to June; 2n = 42.

The specific name *simia* (Latin for 'ape' or 'monkey'), relating to the shape of the labellum of this plant, is apt, since the somewhat upcurved, narrow lobes are very reminiscent of the arms and legs of a performing monkey. An early reference to what may be *O. simia*, along with the Military Orchid *O. militaris*, is given for the Thames valley and Chilterns area by Merrett (1666), whilst a more definite one is provided by Morison (1699) for Henley. The plant was first discovered in Kent in 1777, near Faversham.

Plate 157. Plants of the Monkey Orchid *Orchis simia* from Oxfordshire tend to be shorter, with more compact inflorescences and paler flowers, than those found in Kent (see Plate 159, p.160). Grassland on chalk, Oxfordshire, 21 May 1997.

Plate 158 (opposite). The inflorescence of *Orchis simia* opens from the top downwards. Chalk hillside overlooking River Thames, Oxfordshire, 25 May 1996.

The Monkey Orchid is another member of this genus with a very limited area of distribution in the British Isles; it is now known in only three populations, two in Kent and one in Oxfordshire, at Hartslock. It was formerly more widespread, and occurred more commonly in Kent and the Thames valley area, as well as in Surrey, Sussex and south-east Yorkshire. After the mid-nineteenth century, however, it underwent a severe decline in Britain and became extremely rare, by 1950 being known from only one locality in Oxfordshire (Summerhayes 1968). In 1951 one plant appeared in Kent, and in 1955 a much larger population was found in that county. Following hand-pollination at the new site the population increased in size, and seed from there was subsequently introduced at other potential habitats in the county, with another population becoming established as a result. The Hartslock site was almost completely lost through ploughing in about 1950, but following careful management of the few remaining plants the population has since increased considerably, with 200 flowering in 2001 (Sumpter *et al.* 2004). Other than at these extant localities, the Monkey Orchid has also occurred in recent times near Aston

Rowant on the Oxfordshire/Buckinghamshire boundary, where a few plants survived until becoming overgrown in 1974, and on coastal grassland on Spurn Point, Yorkshire, from where it was lost in about 1983 owing to the site becoming too saline when the sea encroached (Fisher 1987). The plant is at its northern geographical limit in Britain but is widespread throughout much of southern and central Europe, occurring especially in France, Italy and the Balkans, and is scattered eastwards to western Russia and the Middle East, and south to North Africa.

Although tolerating sparse scrub and light shading, *O. simia* prefers a more open habitat than its close ally *O. militaris*, and favours warm, grazed and well-drained, herb-rich chalk turf. Typical associates include *Cirsium acaule, Festuca ovina, Knautia arvensis, Leontodon hispidus, Linum catharticum* and *Sanguisorba minor*. It has been identified as a component of the *Festuca ovina – Avenula pratensis* (CG2) grassland community of the NVC classification.

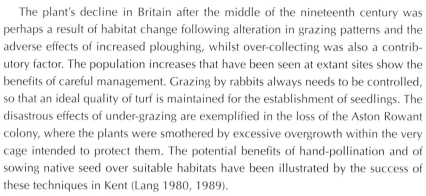

Plate 160 (opposite).
The extremely rare hybrid
*Orchis anthropophora ×
O. simia* ('*×Orchiaceras*'
bergonii); the parents of
this one may have been
given a helping hand.
East Kent, 23 May 1988.

Plate 159 (below).
More robust, darker-
flowered plants characterise
the Kentish populations of
Orchis simia. Chalk grassland, East Kent, 7 June 1996.

The plant's decline in Britain after the middle of the nineteenth century was perhaps a result of habitat change following alteration in grazing patterns and the adverse effects of increased ploughing, whilst over-collecting was also a contributory factor. The population increases that have been seen at extant sites show the benefits of careful management. Grazing by rabbits always needs to be controlled, so that an ideal quality of turf is maintained for the establishment of seedlings. The disastrous effects of under-grazing are exemplified in the loss of the Aston Rowant colony, where the plants were smothered by excessive overgrowth within the very cage intended to protect them. The potential benefits of hand-pollination and of sowing native seed over suitable habitats have been illustrated by the success of these techniques in Kent (Lang 1980, 1989).

Although in many ways *O. simia* is rather close to *O. militaris* in appearance, the lobes of the labellum, especially the narrow, slightly sinuate 'legs' of the lower portion, are sufficient to distinguish it. To see *O. simia* in the wild it is necessary to obtain permission from the authorities at one of its three extant sites.

The flowers, which often open from the top downwards, are faintly scented and so are visited by a variety of insects, including butterflies. Fertilisation occurs by natural means, and seed-set seems to be quite readily achieved. Experimentation elsewhere, along with experience in Kent, indicates a minimum period of seven years from seed germination to flowering (Lang 1980). Research in Belgium (Willems & Bik 1991, Willems 1992) has shown that some plants can be relatively long-lived – one plant flowered for 19 successive years – and that such well-established plants can play an important part in maintaining the overall strength of the population.

Variation between the two naturally occurring populations has been noted, those in Kent being considered to be more robust, with deeper coloured flowers that bear more strongly spotted labella. However, recent morphometric work (Bateman & Farrington 1989) has indicated only minor morphological differences between the two populations, along with low intrapopulation variation. This is thought to reflect recent establishment of the Kent population from Continental sources, and a depleted gene pool in the Oxfordshire plants. As isolated populations, both may well be under long-term threat from genetic deterioration. Formerly *O. simia* grew in association with *O. miltaris* at various Thames valley sites, and from there, in the past, the hybrid between the two has been recorded (see the account for *O. militaris*, below). A very attractive and interesting hybrid with the Man Orchid *O. anthropophora* ('*×Orchiaceras' bergonii*) was recorded for a few years in Kent, around 1985. Although this was in a quite natural habitat it is thought to have been artificially produced, by hand-pollination; elsewhere in Europe, however, the same hybrid does occur naturally. Hybridisation with other species also occurs on the Continent.

12.3. *Orchis militaris* ʟ.

Military Orchid

Plate 161. The most thriving
British population of the
Military Orchid *Orchis
militaris* (var. *militaris*) is
in an old chalk-pit in West
Suffolk, where it is probably
a colonist from Continental
populations. 23 May 1997.

Plate 162 (opposite).
Papillae on the labellum of
Orchis militaris var. *militaris*
suggest buttons on a soldier's
tunic. The alternative English
name of Soldier Orchid was
perhaps more apt than the
current standard name,
Military Orchid. Old chalk-
pit, W. Suffolk, 23 May 1997.

Perennial herb with two rounded tubers; *stem* 20–60 cm; *leaves* rather few, sheathing above, oblong-lanceolate to oblong-ovate, shiny yellow-green on upper surface, paler beneath, unspotted, obtuse to acute at apex; *inflorescence* a dense to fairly lax, ovoid to cylindrical spike up to 14 cm long; *bracts* shorter than the ovary, triangular-ovate, tinged pink to violet; *flowers* large, scented; *outer perianth segments* 10–15 mm, greyish or pink externally, whitish, with purple lines on the inside, ovate, connivent; *inner perianth segments* 10–12 mm long, similar in colour to the outer segments, linear-lanceolate, acute; *labellum* 12–18 mm long, trilobed, the lateral lobes comparatively short, to 8 mm, pale to deeper purple but whitish in the centre and spotted, the middle lobe usually much longer than the laterals, to 18 mm, whitish in the centre and spotted purplish with small papillae, bilobed distally but with a small tooth between the lobes; *spur* to 8 mm, narrow-cylindrical, pointing downwards; *column* obtuse; *anther* purplish, ovoid; *pollinia* two, dark blue-green; *stigma* cordate, shiny; *rostellum* three-lobed; *ovary* linear, sessile, twisted, green, tinged with violet; flowering May to June; 2n = 42.

The specific name *militaris* originates from the shape and spotting of the labellum, which has been considered to bear resemblance to an upright soldier-like figure with a buttoned tunic. An early British record was given by Merrett (1666), who stated that the plant occurred in several places on the chalk between Wallingford and Reading. A later record was that of Dale for a now extinct site at Belchamp Walter, Essex, where *O. militaris* grew with the Man Orchid *O. anthropophora*. It is also recorded, even earlier, by the British herbal writer Gerard (1597), who referred to it as 'Soldiers Cullions [testicles]', but his description may have been based on foreign material.

The Military or Soldier Orchid is another plant that has become very rare in the British Isles, now occurring regularly at only two, widely separate localities, in Suffolk and in Buckinghamshire. It was formerly much more frequent and was known from many sites on the chalk of southern England, especially in the Chilterns. As with the Monkey Orchid *O. simia*, it appears to have started to decline about the middle of the nineteenth century, and by 1914 it was considered to be extinct in Britain. A long period followed without further records, and it was not until 1947 that the plant was rediscovered, somewhat serendipitously, in Buckinghamshire, by J.E. Lousley. On this now legendary occasion Lousley temporarily diverged from a picnic party and found 18 flowering plants on nearby chalk downland. In the same general area of the Chilterns there are at least two other localities where the plant occurs, although somewhat intermittently and in small numbers. Additionally, and

well away from these sites, a new locality was discovered in Suffolk in 1954; this, protected in the Rex Graham Reserve, is now much the largest British population, with up to 2000 flowering spikes recorded in a single season. The Military Orchid was also formerly known in Berkshire, Essex, Hertfordshire, Middlesex and Surrey, but is now extinct in all of these counties. There was a record from Sussex in 1924; old records from Kent, however, are thought to be errors.

Outside Britain *O. militaris* is very widespread. With western limits in France and Spain, it occurs eastwards in a broad band across Europe into central Asia. It has its northern limit in the Baltic islands of Sweden and Estonia, and reaches as far south as central Spain and the Balkans.

Its British habitats all overlie chalk, where it is found in grassland, scrub and open woodland. Conditions are invariably dry, whereas on the Continent the plant exhibits a much wider ecological tolerance, being also known from wet pastures and marshes. Lousley never divulged the whereabouts of his Buckinghamshire find, nor would he let anyone else photograph the plants, but a population discovered in the 1960s at Homefield Wood, near Marlow, is thought to be the same one. Although this population is still surviving and indeed increasing, its open downland habitat has changed as trees and shrubs have taken over the site, and the plants are now confined to woodland glades. Associated species there include *Fragaria vesca, Hedera helix, Mercurialis perennis, Rubus fruticosus* and *Viola riviniana*. The Suffolk site is in a disused chalk-pit and has rather different associates, including *Daphne mezereum, Inula conyza, Ligustrum vulgare, Mycelis muralis* and *Torilis japonica*.

Plate 163 (below, left). The Chilterns populations of the Military Orchid have been named *Orchis militaris* var. *tenuifrons*, as they differ in slight ways from populations of var. *militaris* in Suffolk and in mainland Europe. Grassy valley on chalk, Buckinghamshire, 15 May 2002.

Plate 164 (below, right). The 'anthropomorphic' *Orchis* have a labellum that suggests a human body: *Orchis militaris* var. *tenuifrons*, Buckinghamshire, 6 June 1996.

Here the plants of *Orchis militaris* are somewhat different to those in the Chilterns and more representative of those in mainland Europe. This, together with their relatively disjunct British distribution, suggests a possible origin via wind-borne seed carried from abroad. Within the NVC communities *O. militaris* has not been readily classified, other than as a member of the *Geranium robertianum* subcommunity (W8c) of light *Fraxinus excelsior – Acer campestre – Mercurialis perennis* woodland.

The Military Orchid's decline in the late-nineteenth century has never been satisfactorily explained, but in recent years protection of the various sites and beneficial habitat management, especially by clearance of shrubs and trees, has led to a local increase in numbers, with more than 100 plants now flowering annually at Homefield Wood (Sumpter *et al.* 2004). It appears that excessive shading results in a reduction in both flowering and the production of aerial stems. New shoots of *O. militaris* have also been known to be bitten off by small mammals, damage that has been reduced by removing ground layers of mosses that formerly offered concealment to the rodents. Hand-pollination to increase seed-set is also considered to be important in boosting population numbers (Sumpter *et al.* 2004).

Orchis militaris is best recognised by the pale, rose to almost lilac coloration of the outer perianth segments and petals, which are paler in colour on the outside, and by the elongated, broad body of the lower part of the labellum, which is further divided into two broad lobes and a small median tooth. The plant can usually be viewed at either of the two main sites, subject to appropriate restrictions.

The flowers are faintly scented and are visited by flies and bees, apparently attracted by this fragrance and by the nectar in the spur. Natural seed-set is low, however, with an apparent maximum of only 30 per cent of the flowers setting seed and often very many fewer. A period of seven years may be required from germination to flowering. Vegetative reproduction is rare.

The Buckinghamshire and Oxfordshire plants show slight morphological differences from plants from Suffolk and mainland Europe (which conform to the type, var. *militaris*), and have been described as var. *tenuifrons* P.D. Sell. They differ from the type in being smaller, with shorter, narrower leaves and a smaller, fewer-flowered spike. Recent genetic analysis shows, however, that the populations at the three principal sites are all distinct from each other, and may represent separate colonisation events from Continental parents (Qamaruz-Zaman *et al.* 2002). In the Chilterns *O. militaris* shows considerable genetic variation within and between populations, but plants at the Suffolk site show little genetic variation. This suggests that this colony has developed from a very small number of founder plants, possibly even only a single individual, and probably by recent long-distance dispersal (Fay *et al.* 2004). Genetic analysis also reveals that the genome of *O. militaris* in northern Europe contains elements from *O. simia*, suggesting historical introgression, possibly during the last glaciation (Fay *et al.* 2004). The recent hybrid with *O. simia* (*O.* ×*beyrichii* A. Kern.) was recorded in the mid-nineteenth century from several localities in the mid-Thames valley and Chilterns where the parents coexisted. At the present time, however, the relatively wide geographical separation of the two species appears to preclude any opportunity for hybridisation.

12.4. *Orchis purpurea* Huds.

Lady Orchid

Perennial herb with two rounded tubers; *stem* to 50(–100) cm; *leaves* few, elliptic-oblong to oblong-lanceolate, bright to grey-green, unspotted, the upper acute and clasping; *inflorescence* a dense to fairly lax, ± oblong spike to 15 cm long; *bracts* narrow, ovate, purplish; *flowers* large, many, with a dark red hood and paler labellum, faintly scented; *outer perianth segments* 12–14 mm, ovate, reddish purple, heavily blotched red-brown and darker-veined; *inner perianth segments* narrow, linear, while-lilac with violet spots; *labellum* 10–15 mm, whitish, many- and finely spotted with violet papillae, broad and flat, three-lobed, the lateral lobes narrow, linear, the median broader, widening below and divided into two rounded, crenate lobes with a minute tooth between; *spur* short, cylindrical, curved forwards, notched; *column* very short; *anther* ovoid; *pollinia* two; *stigma* cordate, shiny; *rostellum* three-lobed; *ovary* 10–18 mm long, linear or curved, sessile, twisted, green, sometimes tinged purple; *flowering* May (to June); 2n = 40, 42.

Plate 166 (above). The Lady Orchid *Orchis purpurea* is a robust plant with broad leaves, well adapted to its woodland habitat. Grassy clearing in deciduous woodland, Chilterns, Oxfordshire, 25 May 1996.

The Lady Orchid is largely restricted to south-east England, and especially to Kent, but with occasional outlying localities to the north and west; it also occurs in Sussex where it is very scarce, but is otherwise absent from the British Isles. Outside its normal British range, a single plant was discovered in *Fagus* woodland in south Oxfordshire in 1961 (Kemp 1987), and other plants have occurred there intermittently since. Its range was further extended when an isolated flowering plant was found at a new site in the Avon Gorge, Somerset in 1990 (Willis *et al.* 1991), and another plant was found at Porton Down, Wiltshire in 2004. There are also records in 1967 from a hazel coppice in Herefordshire, which appear not to have been confirmed since, and from north Essex during the eighteenth century (Hall 1935). The Kent populations can often be large, and it is estimated that there are more than 100 separate localities, some of which comprise over 1000 plants. In mainland Europe it is widespread, occurring from Spain and France eastwards through central Germany, Poland and into Russia, as well as southwards from Holland and Denmark to North Africa.

This is a plant of dry, calcareous soils, usually found in open *Fagus*, *Corylus* or *Fraxinus* woodland and scrub, but also occasionally occurring out in the open. It is mainly a constituent of the *Fagus sylvatica – Mercurialis perennis* woodland community (W12) of the NVC classification. Most localities are on chalk but a few are on clay and ragstone, whilst the Somerset locality is on Carboniferous limestone and the Herefordshire site is on Lower Old Red Sandstone. Typical associates include *Daphne laureola*, *Helleborus foetidus*, *Neottia ovata*, *Orchis mascula*, *Platanthera spp.* and *Primula vulgaris*. However, the most constant and characteristic associate in Britain is *Mercurialis perennis*.

Plate 165 (opposite). The 'heads' of the anthropomorphic *Orchis* are formed of the three sepals and the two lateral petals held closely together to form a hood, or galea, over the column. *Orchis purpurea*, beech woodland, East Kent, 9 June 1996.

The relative abundance of the Lady Orchid in Kent, compared to its great rarity elsewhere, is perhaps indicative that a warmer, drier and more continental type of climate is necessary for it to thrive. It is likely that the Kent populations originated or have been reinforced by wind-borne seed carried across the Channel from nearby areas of France, where the plant is frequent, and that this occurred in relatively recent times. Similarly, seed carried on the wind from Kent might explain the origin of other scattered populations in the south of England. It is thought that the plant in the Avon Gorge may have developed from seed escaping from the University of Bristol Botanic Gardens, where *O. purpurea* was cultivated during the early 1980s, or even that it may have been inadvertently introduced by visitors to this well-botanised area.

The Latin epithet *purpurea*, 'red-purple', relates to the colour of the dark red-brown sepals, and the common name comes from the overall impression of a small 'lady' given by the compact shape

Plate 168 (opposite).
A perfect pair of white ladies; anthocyanin-free *Orchis purpurea*, E. Kent, 23 May 1994.

Plate 167 (below). Relatively frequent in its main area of distribution in Kent, *Orchis purpurea* can even be found on some roadside verges. East Kent, 8 June 1996.

of these as they overtop the divided labellum. A very early record, which may be the first for Britain, is from Northfleet near Gravesend, where the plant was found by John Sherard in 1724 (Ray 1724); an earlier one reported by Merrett in 1666 for Gads-hill is doubtful. Although *O. purpurea* shows some similarities to the very much smaller Burnt Orchid *Neotinea ustulata* it is unlikely to be confused with this down and pasture plant, *O. purpurea* having deep reddish crowded sepals and characteristically shaped, pinkish white labella with fine crimson spots. The Lady Orchid is most easily observed at one of the large populations in open *Fagus* woodland in eastern Kent.

The plant is faintly scented and visited by small flies, including those of the genus *Odynerus*. These act as pollinators but the process is not very efficient, since many capsules fail to set seed. Bee pollinators have also been recorded in France. A period of up to ten years is thought necessary for seedlings to reach flowering. Although most populations will have a rather high proportion of non-flowering plants, a higher incidence of flowering may be achieved in the year following a very dry summer. This gives the tubers the opportunity to dry out, which seems to be favourable to flowering, and overall dry conditions seem to be generally good for the plant. As with many mainly woodland orchids, an optimum balance between shade and light is important so a relatively open canopy, achieved either by coppicing or by natural means, will be beneficial.

Perhaps appropriately, hybrids ('×*Orchiaceras' melsheimeri*) between the Lady and the Man Orchid – 'the happy couple', according to Lang (2001) – were found in Kent in 1998. Appreciable variation in labellum shape and flower colour can also occur. Ettlinger (1987) reported peloric and duplex forms amongst an otherwise normal population in Kent. Occasionally the labellum may be variously divided, resulting in lobes of differing shapes, and the flowers may also range between albino (var. *albiflora* A. Camus) and dark-coloured. Some of this colour variation may be due to changes in the level of shading. Two morphological forms were detected in Kent, by F. Rose (Rose 1948). Those to the west were said to be smaller, with a dense inflorescence, small ovaries and blunt, well-spotted labella, whilst those to the east were reputedly taller, with a lax inflorescence and flowers with markedly lobed, but less spotted labella, but any real distinction is hard to discern.

Plate 169. The Lady Orchid gains its common name from the suggestion of a figure in a voluminous dress given by the labellum; here the lady is clad in white (var. *albiflora*). Beech woodland, E. Kent, 9 June 1996.

12.5. *Orchis mascula* (L.) L.

Early Purple Orchid

Perennial herb with two rounded tubers; *stem* 15–60 cm, erect; *leaves* oblong-lanceolate, acute at the apex, keeled, shining green, especially below, often spotted, the lower spreading, the upper more erect and clasping; *inflorescence* a spike, somewhat lax, ovoid to cylindrical; *bracts* linear-lanceolate, acute, tinged purple; *flowers* rather large, usually reddish purple but also sometimes much paler pink, or rarely white, sometimes with an unpleasant odour; *outer perianth segments* 6–8 mm long, the laterals ovate-lanceolate; *inner perianth segments* ± ovate, shorter and paler than the outer segments; *labellum* 8–15 mm long, trilobed, about as broad as long, with reflexed sides, red-purple, sometimes paler or rarely white, with a whitish, spotted central area, the middle lobe slightly longer than the laterals; *spur* 10–15 mm long, cylindrical, slightly curved upwards, widening towards the apex; *column* short; *anther* ovate, purplish; *pollinia* two, dark green; *stigmas* two, purple-edged; *rostellum* three-lobed; *ovary* sessile, tinged purple; *flowering* April to June; 2n = 42.

Plate 170. The Early Purple Orchid *Orchis mascula* on limestone pavement in the Burren, Co. Clare, where colour variants are very common. 6 May 2003.

The 'Early Purple', whose descriptive name is sometimes inappropriately hyphenated, is one of the most widespread and best-known of all British orchids. Whilst never common, and probably decreasing, it can still be found in good numbers in suitable habitats throughout most of the mainland. Although avoiding the highest ground, it is recorded as far north as the islands of northern Scotland, as well as in the Channel Islands and the Isle of Man. In Ireland it is widespread and forms a conspicuous element of the spring-flower display of the Burren. Outside the British Isles it is similarly wide-ranging, with a northern limit within the Arctic Circle on the western Norwegian coast. It occurs eastwards throughout most of mainland Europe and into western Asia, as well as south to North Africa.

The Early Purple Orchid is a plant particularly of lime-rich soils but can also occur in neutral or slightly acid areas. It occupies a wide variety of habitats, ranging from shaded woodland and hedgerows, and the grikes in limestone pavements, to open downland, pastures, sand dunes and roadside verges. Such a broad habitat tolerance, which no doubt accounts for its relative abundance and wide distribution in the British Isles, is reflected in the large number of communities in which it has been identified in the NVC system. Although it has been recorded from *Sphagnum* mires it seldom grows in marshes and other wet places, but can withstand a certain amount of dampness. As an early-flowering plant, in woodlands it is often associated with other spring flowers such as *Anemone nemorosa*, *Hyacinthoides non-scripta* and *Primula vulgaris*, as well as *Geranium robertianum*, *Glechoma hederacea*, *Mercurialis perennis* and *Teucrium scorodonia*. In more open, grassland habitats *Anacamptis morio*, *Asperula cynanchica*, *Cirsium*

Plate 171. '... and far descried, High tower'd the spikes of purple orchises'. An image from Matthew Arnold's *Thyrsis* (1867), invoked in Derbyshire: *Orchis mascula* in limestone grassland, 31 May 2001.

acaule, Galium verum, Hieracium pilosella and *Primula veris,* and sedges such as *Carex caryophyllea, C. flacca* and *C. panicea*, will often be present. Mountain cliff ledges are a rare and unusual habitat, where occasionally the plant can be found growing with *Dryas octopetala* and *Silene acaulis*, and in the Burren with *Gentiana verna* and *Neotinea maculata*.

The plant does not appear to be under any particular threat at present, other than that of habitat destruction. Woodland clearance appears to have little adverse effect, since populations will persist in the open after this has taken place. Like all orchids it is very prone to being dug up or picked, but its comparative abundance is likely to deter plant collectors, and its rather offensive odour, reminiscent of tom-cats, deters its use as decoration within the home.

The specific name *mascula* means 'male' or 'masculine', and refers to the plant's paired, testicle-like underground tubers. Probably because of this, and its perceived possibilities as an aphrodisiac, no other British orchid has had such a large number of common names applied to it. Ninety-six are listed by Grigson in his *Englishman's Flora* (1955). In the past the sexual association led to the tubers being recommended by apothecaries for a wide range of related complaints, the dying tuber being dispensed to cool ardour, the developing one to improve it. *Orchis mascula* is also thought by some to have been the plant referred to by Shakespeare in *Hamlet* (Act IV, Scene 7), when describing Ophelia's garland as containing 'long purples' or 'dead men's fingers', although it seems probable that there is a confusion here with the finger-tubered *Dactylorhiza*. Another name for the Early Purple Orchid is 'Gethsemane', alluding to an association with the crucifixion according to which the plant is said to have been growing below the cross, gaining its spotted leaves when splashed with Christ's blood. It has also been called 'Adder Grass', presumably because of the similarity of the spotting on the leaves to the patterning on the

Plate 172. As the distribution map shows, few parts of the British Isles lack the Early Purple Orchid *Orchis mascula.* Grassy coastal hillside, Berwickshire, 9 May 1998.

snake; it was under this name that the plant was first recorded in Britain, in the north of England around the middle of the sixteenth century, by William Turner (1562): an orchid which '... hath many spottes in the leafe and is called adder grasse in Northumberland'.

Orchis mascula is easily recognised in the field but is rather similar to the Green-winged Orchid *Anacamptis morio*. It differs from the latter in its rather taller habit, in having no green veins on the lateral sepals and in having, usually, dark spots on its leaves, although in Scotland the leaves are more likely to be unspotted. It can be readily found, especially in a search of its favoured habitats of open woodland and scrub over calcareous soils. Plants can vary considerably in stature, however, from tiny depauperate individuals in coastal turf to large, lush specimens in rich woodland conditions.

As mentioned above, the Early Purple Orchid possesses a rather repugnant cat-like scent, but small insects are attracted to the flowers and very successfully effect pollination, shown by the resulting high quantity of seed that is set. As with most orchids, several years elapse before seedlings attain flowering. Vegetative reproduction is relatively infrequent. Plants may persist for several years in a vegetative state if the habitat becomes overgrown and light is excluded, but usually flower again after felling or coppicing.

Variation is mostly exhibited by differences in flower colour. The usual red-purple may be replaced by a lighter shade of pink; pure-white flowered plants can also be found occasionally. The hybrid with *Anacamptis morio* is sometimes encountered ('*Orchis*' ×*morioides*), especially where *Orchis mascula* grows in open pastures along with the other parent. This hybrid occurred for a couple of years in south Cumbria in the mid-1980s (Foley 1986) but unfortunately died out soon afterwards. Morphological characters are intermediate between the two parents.

13.1. *Pseudorchis albida* (L.) Á. & D. Löve

Syn. *Gymnadenia albida* (L.) Rich.; *Leucorchis albida* (L.) E. Mey.

Small White Orchid

Perennial herb with divergent, palmate root tubers; *stem* 10–35 cm, glabrous, erect, with two or three membranous, scaly leaf sheaths at the base; *leaves* three to five at base of the stem, broadly lanceolate, pointed, entire, shiny green, those above ± bract-like; *inflorescence* a dense, cylindrical, somewhat one-sided spike; *bracts* lanceolate; *flowers* c.2–3 mm in diameter, numerous, ± tubular, whitish to greenish white throughout, faintly scented; *outer perianth segments* ovate, connivent with the inner whorl, the segments of which are also similar in shape; *labellum* forward-pointing, trilobed, the lateral lobes shorter than the median; *spur* to 2.5 mm long, slightly thickened at the apex, downcurved; *column* erect; *anther* broad, greenish-white; *pollinia* two, very small; *stigma* ± reniform; *rostellum* long; *ovary* ridged, slightly twisted; *flowering* (May to) June to July; 2n = 42.

The genus *Pseudorchis* contains three species worldwide, but in Europe there are only two, *P. albida* and *P. straminea* (Fernald) Soják. Molecular studies show that '*Pseudorchis' frivaldii* (Hampe ex Griseb.) P.F. Hunt, restricted to the mountains of the Balkans, belongs in the genus *Gymnadenia*, while *Pseudorchis* proper is more closely related to *Platanthera* (Bateman 2005, in press). *Pseudorchis albida* var. *albida* itself is widespread but rather local in Europe, occurring up to altitudes of 2500 m, from the Pyrenees eastwards through much of central Europe to Turkey and the Caucasus, as well as in western Scandinavia and Iceland. It is also recorded from southern Greenland and northern parts of the American continent westwards to Alaska, and some of these records, together with the Icelandic ones, have been referred to var. *subalpina* (Neuman) Hyl. The plant is also found in Siberia, and parts of eastern Asia.

The generic name *Pseudorchis* (Greek, 'false' orchis) presumably originates from the plants' rather similar appearance to members of the genus *Orchis*, but they differ in the shape of their underground tubers and in many other characters. The nomenclature of the species has undergone several rather confusing changes, it having also been variously placed under *Biochia, Entaticus, Gymnadenia, Habenaria, Leucorchis, Orchis, Peristylus, Platanthera* and *Satyrium*. The specific epithet *albida*, however, is quite straightforward, referring to the white flowers. The first definite British record appears to have been made by John Ray in Wales: '*Orchis pusilla odorata radice palmata* found on the back of Snowdon-hill by the way leading from Llanberis to Carnarvan' (Ray 1670). A description of Ray's various botanical itineraries

Plate 176. The generic affinities of the Small White Orchid have often been debated but its distinctness has been confirmed by DNA analysis. Unimproved grassy hillside, Roxburghshire, 25 June 2002.

Plate 175 (opposite). Not the most spectacular of orchids, the inconspicuous *Pseudorchis albida* can be hard to locate amongst taller vegetation. Unimproved grassy hillside, Roxburghshire, 2 June 1997.

also states that he saw 'a species of *Orchis palmatâ* with an odorate flower' at Llanberis on 26 May 1662 (Clarke 1900). The plant still occurs within this general area.

In the British Isles the Small White Orchid is a distinctly northern and western plant, more or less restricted to upland areas. It is very scarce in western Wales, Derbyshire, Yorkshire and Cumbria, but becomes more frequent in Scotland, and especially so in the north-west. Perhaps surprisingly, there are old records for southern England on the Weald, especially near the border of Sussex and Kent, where it used to occur in heathy areas. In Ireland, where it is now a Red Data Book species and classified as 'Vulnerable', it was formerly recorded from 23 counties. There have been only about seven individual or county records since 1970, however, and this sharp decline is attributed to over-grazing and pasture reclamation.

The habitat of *P. albida* is more restricted than that of many other British orchids. Typically it is a plant of upland pastures, occurring either on soils that are neutral to acidic or, if calcareous, in places where there has been appreciable leaching of the base-rich component, the soils being consequently rather poor in nutrients. Grazing in such localities is often light and the plant can survive, at least temporarily, amongst taller vegetation, but will be lost if this becomes too overgrown. It has also been recorded in more heathy habitats at lower altitude, such as on the Sussex Weald. Typical associates include *Galium saxatile*, the milkworts *Polygala vulgaris* and especially *P. serpyllifolia*, and also *Potentilla erecta*. NVC groupings include the H14a *Festuca ovina* heath subcommunity and the U17b *Geranium sylvaticum* grassland subcommunity. Apart from some species of *Dactylorhiza*, other orchids are not often found in close association with *P. albida*. It can also occur on mountain ledges up to an altitude of 600 metres or so, where it sometimes grows with *Galium boreale* and *Sedum rosea*. In the west of Scotland it has been recorded down to almost sea-level.

Plate 177. Upland grassland is the favoured habitat of *Pseudorchis albida*, here growing with *Gymnadenia borealis* and *Platanthera chlorantha* in Roxburghshire, 25 June 2002.

As mentioned above, *Pseudorchis albida* is now under considerable threat in Ireland and perhaps to a lesser extent elsewhere. Adverse farming practices, especially 'improvement' by the use of artificial fertilisers, annexation of upland areas for other agricultural purposes, and excessive grazing of these pastures, have variously contributed to losses and reduction of population sizes. Even in the last 20 years or so the more accessible populations in northern England appear to have declined, although the situation appears rather better in the Scottish Highlands.

Not too easy to detect in the field, the plant is readily recognised, once found, by its fairly dense spike of rather dingy, whitish-green, somewhat drooping flowers; Small White Orchid is not an unfair name. The flowering period is quite short, however, and the flowers wither quickly, which can make it still more difficult to find. To see the living plant a visit should be paid to one of its Scottish strongholds. One such, near Loch Tay in Perthshire, has recently become almost a *locus classicus* for the plant. Make a visit there and success should be almost assured; to find it in one of its rather few English populations, however, will need a greater deal of patience and perseverance.

The time of flowering depends on a combination of factors, especially latitude and altitude. The flowers themselves produce ample nectar and also emit a pleasant scent, attracting a variety of day-flying insects which readily remove the pollinia and effect cross-pollination. When the flowers start to wither, however, the pollinia of those unvisited by insects tend to detach and fall onto the stigma, bringing about self-pollination. Examination of fruiting plants suggests that in most cases a high proportion of seed is set. Following germination, aerial stems are produced in about four years. Reproduction by vegetative means, if it occurs at all, is rare.

The hybrid with the Heath Fragrant-orchid *Gymnadenia borealis* (×*Pseudadenia schweinfurthii* (Hegelm. ex A. Kern.) P.F. Hunt), intermediate in perianth and spur characters, and with pale pink flowers (see Plate 334, p. 314), has been recorded from several places in the north and is not infrequently found growing with both parents in north-west Scotland. The hybrid with the Heath Spotted-orchid *Dactylorhiza maculata* has been recorded from Orkney and Skye.

Plate 178. A less common, drier habitat for *Pseudorchis albida* – a slope with *Juniperus communis* and *Calluna vulgaris*. East Inverness-shire, 30 June 2003.

14. *Platanthera* Rich. nom. cons.

Butterfly-orchids

Perennial herbs with tuberous, tapering roots; *stem* bearing ovate main leaves, positioned towards the stem base, those above bract-like, sheathing; *flowers* in a moderately dense spike, white to greenish, fragrant; *lateral perianth segments* patent, the dorsal and inner segments ± connivent and forming a hood; *labellum* linear-oblong, lingulate, entire; *spur* long, slender; *anther* positioned at the top of the column; *pollinia* two; *stigma* ± oblong; *rostellum* inconspicuous; *capsule* fusiform.

The genus *Platanthera* contains about 85 species, distributed throughout most of the temperate and tropical regions of the northern hemisphere. Eight species occur in Europe, if *P. micrantha* (Hochst. ex Seub.) Schltr. and *P. azorica* Schltr., endemic to the Azores, are included. The name originates from the Greek *platos*, 'wide', and *anthera*, 'anther'.

The two species that occur in Britain, *P. bifolia* and *P. chlorantha*, are very closely related, being almost indistinguishable at the genetic level, which suggests that they diverged as species comparatively recently. Bateman *et al.* (2003) consider that *P. chlorantha* diverged from *P. bifolia*, with sufficient morphological change through mutation to cause a shift in pollinating hawk-moth species – an evolutionary model that would have fascinated and delighted Darwin. The flowers of the butterfly-orchids are highly fragrant, especially in the evening, and are pollinated

Plate 179 (opposite). *Platanthera chlorantha*, Kinross-shire, 7 July 2002.

The two butterfly-orchids are very similar, but may be distinguished by the alignment of the pollinia. In the Greater Butterfly-orchid *Platanthera chlorantha* (far left) they are placed diagonally on a broad column, while in the Lesser Butterfly-orchid *P. bifolia* (near left) they are parallel on a narrower column. The flower shape is also subtly different; plant size, however, is not a useful character. Plate 180 (far left): *P. chlorantha*, unimproved pasture, Kinross-shire, 7 July 2002; Plate 181 (near left): *P. bifolia*, coastal grassland, N. Uist, O. Hebrides, 15 June 1990.

by night-flying moths, whose long proboscis are able to access the nectar in the long, narrow spur. In doing this they detach the pollinia, which attach themselves to the insect's head and are carried over to a neighbouring flower to bring about cross-pollination. The paleness of the flowers also helps the moths to locate them in the poor light.

14.1. *Platanthera bifolia* (L.) Rich.

Lesser Butterfly-orchid

Perennial herb with two ovoid root tubers; *stem* 15–30(–50) cm, erect, slender, with membranous sheaths at the base; *leaves* two, placed near stem base, large, up to 10 × 3 cm, elliptical to oval, subopposite, veined, pale green, the upper stem leaves small and bract-like, sheathing; *inflorescence* a rather compact cylindrical spike, sometimes more lax; *bracts* lanceolate or ovate-lanceolate, veined, green; *flowers* to about 18 mm in diameter, whitish, smaller than in *P. chlorantha*, with less of a greenish tinge and less strongly scented; *outer perianth segments* with the laterals to 10 mm, lanceolate, patent, white, the upper slightly shorter, ovate; *inner perianth segments* shorter than the outer, linear-lanceolate, curved, white or greenish white; *labellum* to 12 mm, lingulate, white, tipped green; *spur* to 25–30 mm long, narrow, ± horizontal; *anther* with two pollinia, the lobes parallel vertically; *stigma* positioned on lower front of the column, not extending below the entrance to the spur; *rostellum* only comprising the viscidia; *ovary* linear, twisted; *flowering* May to July; 2n = 42.

The Lesser Butterfly-orchid *Platanthera bifolia* has a wide distribution, being recorded throughout most of Europe from 70° N in Scandinavia southwards to the Mediterranean islands and east through the Balkans to the Caucasus, Russia, and northern Asia, including the Himalayas. It is also found in North Africa. Throughout its range it occurs in more open habitats than its close relative *P. chlorantha*, and on both acidic and calcareous soils. It favours heathland, moorland, scrub margins and open woodland. In Europe it may be found from almost sea-level to high altitudes in the mountains.

The specific name *bifolia* quite obviously refers to its two main leaves. Its common English name 'Lesser' Butterfly-orchid, however, is something of a misnomer, as size often fails to distinguish *P. bifolia* from *P. chlorantha*, the 'Greater' Butterfly-orchid. The first British record appears to be that given by John Ray in 1696, '*Orchis alba bifolia minor calcari oblongo* … The lesser Butterfly Orchis. *In pascuis* [fields]'; but, for once, Ray is not specific about a location.

The Lesser Butterfly-orchid is recorded throughout much of the British Isles. Although widespread in southern England it is not especially abundant there, but to the west and north it becomes much more frequent. It also occurs across much of

Plate 182 (opposite). Plants of *Platanthera bifolia* growing in open grassland situations are more compact in habit and inflorescence than those growing in woodland habitats. The diffference is probably no more than an environmental response to differing light and nutrient levels. Coastal grassland, North Uist, Outer Hebrides, 15 June 1990.

Ireland, especially the west. It can be found on both basic and acidic soils. In the British Isles it occurs in two slightly different morphological forms, plants found in woodland being taller, with narrower leaves and a relatively lax inflorescence, compared to those occurring in open, more acidic habitats which are shorter, with ovate leaves and a denser inflorescence.

In the south, although known from damp, acidic localities such as the New Forest, *P. bifolia* occurs most frequently as a woodland plant, often under *Fagus*, and sometimes in deep shade. Here the soil is usually basic. The plants are of similar size to *P. chlorantha*, and are of the narrower-leaved form. Associated species can include *Cephalanthera damasonium*, *Neottia ovata*, *N. nidus-avis* and *Orchis mascula*. Further northwards this form becomes less frequent, but is still occasionally met with in the Scottish Borders. In the north and west of the British Isles *P. bifolia* favours a much more open habitat, often occurring in upland pastures, flushed heaths and moorland, where more acidic conditions exist. Here the plants are the smaller, shorter-stemmed, more densely flowered form, more appropriately reflecting the name Lesser Butterfly-orchid. The immediate habitat is often damp, and the plant is often accompanied by *Caltha palustris*, various *Dactylorhiza* species, especially *D. maculata*, *Gymnadenia borealis*, *Pinguicula vulgaris* and *Succisa pratensis*. Sometimes plants are also rooted in *Sphagnum*. Alternatively, in drier habitats, they may grow amongst *Calluna*, *Nardus stricta* and *Pteridium*, and in some localities *Pseudorchis albida* may be close by. One strong population in Cumbria occurs unusually on the grassed-over surface of a covered reservoir. In the west of Ireland

Plates 183 (below left) and 184 (below right). A looser inflorescence and longer leaves are features of the so-called 'woodland form' of *Platanthera bifolia*. *Betula/Salix* bog, Berwickshire, 8 July 1997.

Plate 185. The Lesser Butterfly-orchid is often a plant of unimproved grassland, as here on the coast of North Uist, Outer Hebrides, 15 June 1990.

peaty grassland, cut-away bog and bog margins are favoured. This wide range of habitats is reflected in the plant's NVC records, which include at least eight mire associations as well as *Erica vagans – Schoenus nigricans* heath (H5), woodland (W10), and several other minor communities. The species is declining and is currently regarded as Vulnerable (Cheffings & Farrell 2005). In southern England it is now scarce, populations having been lost through habitat change. In its northern upland habitat, however, it seems to be under less pressure.

Recognition of *Platanthera bifolia* as a member of the genus is confirmed by its quite distinctive flower shape. Identification to species level is achieved by examination of the column, where the pollinia are found to lie close together and vertically parallel, not sloping as in *P. chlorantha*. To search out a population of *P. bifolia* a visit could be made to any of the habitats described above, but the upland pastures of the hills of northern England and western Scotland may be the most rewarding.

As mentioned in the account for the genus, pollination occurs by night-flying moths attracted by the flowers, the fragrance of which increases after dark. The viscidia are close together, such that an insect attempting to access nectar in the spur is sure to touch them. They adhere to the base of the proboscis, and when the insect flies off, the pollinia are removed. Very quickly the pollinia then swing forward to a position where they will contact the stigma when another flower is visited. Cross-pollination is achieved in this way, often with a high rate of seed-set. Vegetative reproduction, if it occurs at all, is very rare.

Hybrids have been recorded with *P. chlorantha* but are difficult to detect as the intermediates differ only slightly from one or other of the parents. Hybridisation is likely to be rare, as although the parents share a habitat and flowering period, flower morphology and pollinators differ, reducing the chances of interspecific pollination. Claims for hybridisation may therefore derive from aberrant forms of one or other species. The two species have, however, been artificially crossed. A hybrid with the Frog Orchid *Dactylorhiza viridis* was recorded in 1949 from South Uist but has not been found since. More recently, a hybrid with *Gymnadenia borealis* has been recorded in Sutherland. Variants are rare, although peloric forms have been observed.

14.2. *Platanthera chlorantha* (Custer) Rchb.

Greater Butterfly-orchid

Perennial herb with two ovoid root tubers; *stem* 25–50 cm, erect, yellow-green, sheathed at the base; *leaves* basal, usually two, large, to 15 × 5 cm, elliptical to oval, subopposite, keeled and veined, pale green, glossy beneath and often similarly so above, the upper stem leaves bract-like, linear-lanceolate; *inflorescence* a lax spike; *bracts* lanceolate, green; flowers relatively large, *c.*20 mm diameter, white to greenish white, fragrant; *outer perianth segments* ovate-lanceolate, patent, to 11 × 6 mm, white, tinged green; *inner perianth segments c.*8 mm long, linear-lanceolate, curved; *labellum* to 16 mm, lingulate, greenish white; *spur* to *c.*30 mm long, narrow, ± downward-pointing; *anther* with two pollinia, the lobes widely diverging below; *stigma* concave, positioned at the entrance to the spur; *rostellum* merely comprising the viscidia; *ovary* sessile; *flowering* May to July; 2n = 42.

The Greater Butterfly-orchid is one of the more widespread of our orchids, being recorded from much of Britain and Ireland, including many of the islands, though not the Channel Islands. It is especially frequent in southern England and western Scotland; in other areas, however, although present in suitable habitats, it can be quite scarce. Elsewhere its range extends from 63° N in Scandinavia southwards to Spain and then east throughout much of the rest of Europe to the Balkans, Turkey, the Caucasus and Siberia. In mainland Europe it has a preference for similar habitats to those described below for the British Isles, and has been found at altitudes up to 2000 m in the Alps.

The specific name *chlorantha* refers to the greenish-tinged colour of the flowers; the common name 'Greater' Butterfly-orchid, as already mentioned, is not necessarily always appropriate (see the account for the Lesser Butterfly-orchid *Platanthera bifolia* above, p.182). The 'Butterfly' reference would seem to refer to the flower shape, since butterflies are not thought to be regular pollinators. Gerard (1597) described the plant as 'That kinde which resembleth the white Butter-flie'; although Curtis later remarked in his *Flora Londinensis* (1775–1787) that 'the English name of Butterfly Orchis is scarcely warranted by the appearance of the flowers'. Other local names include the Night Violet (Wiltshire) and White Angel (Somerset). Early-sixteenth century records for the plant were made by Gerard 'upon the declining of the hill at the North ende of Hampsteed heath …' and [as *Orchis hermaphroditica*] '… in the wood belonging to a worshipfull gentleman of Kent named Master Sedley of Southfleete'. Gerard considered the plant (along with others of the genus *Ophrys*) to be of little use in medicine but to be 'regarded for the pleasant and beautifull flowers, where with nature hath seemed to plaie and disport hir selfe'.

The Greater Butterfly-orchid is usually a plant of base-rich or calcareous soils but can also occur in much less basic conditions, growing with its close relative *P. bifolia*. It is often a plant of moist, deciduous woodland and scrub, being especially found over heavier clayey soils in the south. It will flower in quite deep shade but generally prefers a more open situation. If shading becomes too great it can remain in the vegetative state for a considerable length of time, in one case for up to 20 years (Lang 1980). There are several instances where a spectacular population

Plate 186. In flower the butterfly-orchids are un-mistakeable, but the unwary could mistake the paired basal leaves for those of a Common Twayblade *Neottia ovata*. Greater Butterfly-orchid *Platanthera chlorantha*, unimproved pasture, Kinross-shire, 7 July 2002.

Plate 187 (above). The pale flowers of the Greater Butterfly-orchid *Platanthera chlorantha* are visible to night-flying moths, which are also attracted by the strong fragrance of the flowers and the nectar in their spurs. Grassy hillside, Roxburghshire, 6 July 1997.

Plate 188 (opposite). A loose, few-flowered spike of *Platanthera chlorantha*: the resemblance to a butterfly is rather fanciful. Grassy hillside, Roxburghshire, 22 June 1997.

explosion has occurred as soon as woodland has been cleared or coppiced. It is also found in damp pastures, on grassy slopes, in marshy areas and, in Scotland, on heath moorland. Its main NVC classification is within the *Fraxinus excelsior – Acer campestre – Mercurialis perennis* woodland (W8). Frequent associates are those typical of such habitats, such as *Anemone nemorosa, Deschampsia cespitosa, Geranium robertianum, Glechoma hederacea, Neottia ovata, Orchis mascula, Primula vulgaris* and *Stellaria holostea*. In the southern part of its range *Cephalanthera damasonium* is also an associate, and in the more open, grassland habitats *Dactylorhiza fuchsii, Gymnadenia conopsea* and *Platanthera bifolia* may grow with it. Populations are normally not dense, the plant often having a rather scattered local distribution.

Platanthera chlorantha is very readily distinguished from the superficially similar *P. bifolia* since in the latter the pollinia, which in both cases are placed close to the mouth of the spur, lie parallel and vertical, whereas in *P. chlorantha* they slope towards each other at the top, giving the impression of a loosely inverted V-shape. Whilst the plant can be found growing in many areas where the habitat is suitable, searches are likely to be most productive if made in the wooded chalk downs of the south, in the limestone scrub of south Cumbria, or in western Scotland.

The flowers' sweet scent and their apparent luminosity, which makes them especially noticeable in poor light, attract night-flying insects; several species of night-flying moth have been caught with pollinia of *P. chlorantha* attached to them (Summerhayes 1968). The method of pollination is quite similar to that for *P. bifolia*, and seed-set occurs in 70 to 90 per cent of the flowers. Vegetative reproduction may happen occasionally when additional lateral buds form at the base of the stem, giving rise to new tubers which eventually separate as independent plants. Generally, however, population increase and colonisation depends almost entirely on successful seed-set and dispersal. Declining populations through habitat loss have led to its being considered Near Threatened in the 2005 Red Data List (Cheffings & Farrell 2005).

Abnormal flower structure may sometimes occur. A plant with three lips and three spurs has been recorded from the Isle of Skye. Similar peloric forms are also known. One of these resulted in an erroneous Scottish record for the intergeneric hybrid with the Small White Orchid *Pseudorchis albida*. The more likely hybrid with *P. bifolia* (*P. ×hybrida*) has been recorded on several occasions in Britain, but putative hybrids must be examined very carefully.

15. *Gymnadenia* R. Br.

Fragrant-orchids

Perennial herbs with palmate root tubers; *stem* 15–70 cm, glabrous, erect, with two or three membranous, scaly leaf sheaths at base; *leaves* three to five, ± erect, broad- to linear-lanceolate with subcucullate apices, entire, green, those above small, lanceolate, ± bract-like; *inflorescence* a fairly dense, ± cylindrical spike; *bracts* lanceolate; *flowers* fairly large, 8–14 mm across, pinkish or sometimes of a deeper red, occasionally white, strongly scented; *outer perianth segments* having laterals to 7 mm long, oblong-ovate, with rolled margins, spreading and forming a hood with the upper segment; *inner perianth segments* broader and shorter, connivent; *labellum* 4–7 mm long, ± equally trilobed, the lobes rounded, occasionally incised; *spur* relatively long, to c.16 mm, slender, downcurved; *column* short; *anther* pyriform; *pollinia* two, each attached to a viscidium; *stigmas* two, on the anther base; *rostellum* long, projecting between the viscidia; *bursicle* absent; *ovary* ridged, twisted and curved; 2n = 40, 80, with various higher values also recorded.

As traditionally delimited, the genus *Gymnadenia* comprises about 10 species world-wide, its overall distribution ranging through temperate Eurasia. In this view there are just two species in Europe, the widespread *G. conopsea*, and *G. odoratissima* (L.) Rich., a plant of the more mountainous regions of mainland Europe and western Asia. Ongoing studies by R. Bateman and colleagues suggest, however, that the genus should also include the similar '*Pseudorchis*' *frivaldii* and *Nigritella*, and that the widely distributed *G. conopsea* (*sensu lato*) is, at least within the British Isles and western Europe, actually a complex of three distinct species. Taken as a broad entity, *G. conopsea* is widely distributed, occurring through most of Europe, western and central Asia, China and Japan, south to the Himalayas, with its northern limit in northern Scandinavia. In the British Isles it is one of the most frequently met and best-known orchids, occurring as it does (in one or other of the segregate species) in most mainland counties, as well as throughout much of Ireland except the far south-west. An old record of *G. odoratissima* from Durham is generally considered to be erroneous.

The introductory description given above covers the range of variation evident in British and Irish populations of *G. conopsea* (*s.l.*). Within this broad species, three distinct taxa are well characterized by both morphology and ecological preference. The taxonomic level at which they are recognised is, however, a subject of

Plate 190. *Gymnadenia conopsea*, easily identified by its long narrow spike. Limestone pavement, the Burren, Co. Clare, 3 July 2002.

Plate 189 (opposite). A newly recognised species, the Marsh Fragrant-orchid *Gymnadenia densiflora*. Small fen, North Hampshire, 11 July 2002.

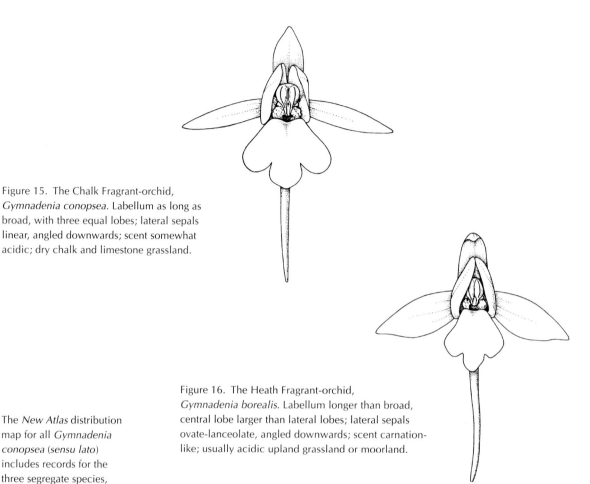

Figure 15. The Chalk Fragrant-orchid, *Gymnadenia conopsea*. Labellum as long as broad, with three equal lobes; lateral sepals linear, angled downwards; scent somewhat acidic; dry chalk and limestone grassland.

Figure 16. The Heath Fragrant-orchid, *Gymnadenia borealis*. Labellum longer than broad, central lobe larger than lateral lobes; lateral sepals ovate-lanceolate, angled downwards; scent carnation-like; usually acidic upland grassland or moorland.

The *New Atlas* distribution map for all *Gymnadenia conopsea* (*sensu lato*) includes records for the three segregate species, which are under-represented in their individual maps.

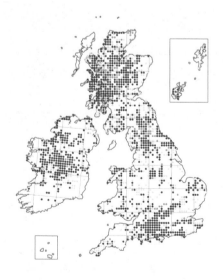

debate. On the strength of ITS sequence analysis, and other criteria, Bateman and colleagues (Bateman *et al.* 1997, Bateman 2004) have treated them as distinct species, *G. conopsea* (*sensu stricto*), *G. borealis* and *G. densiflora* – a view that we follow here. Others, considering their great morphological similarities, prefer to treat them at subspecific level. The following descriptions of the three plants (pp.194–198) highlight the morphological differences in their flowers and their ecological preferences.

In addition to the various distinctions noted below, it is worth mentioning that although all three taxa are sweetly scented there are subtle differences between them in fragrance. This is difficult to describe, and may also vary between individual populations.

The generic name *Gymnadenia* originates from the Greek *gymnos*, 'nude', and *aden*, 'gland', and relates to the flower structure, the viscidia at the base of the pollinia having no bursicle to cover them. The epithet *conopsea* is from the Greek *konops*, 'mosquito', and *opsis*, 'similar to', referring to the shape of the flower; *borealis*, 'northern' in Latin, reflects the primarily northern distribution of these plants. The first mention in the literature of fragrant-orchids

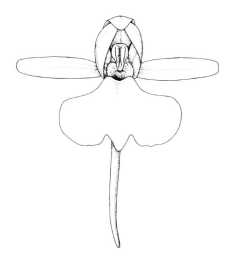

Figure 17. The Marsh Fragrant-orchid, *Gymnadenia densiflora*. Labellum broader than long, lateral lobes larger than central lobe; lateral sepals blunt, held horizontally; scent spicy, clove-like; damp calcareous or basic grassland or marshes.

occurring in the British Isles appears to be that of Thomas Johnson in his *Mercurius Botanicus* of 1634, where he records what is probably *G. borealis*: 'Orchis palmata minor calcaribus oblongis ... In montosis [in mountainous areas]'. Fragrant-orchids are easily recognised in the field, the coral-pink or deeper-coloured, sweet-scented flowers, with their long slender spurs, being characteristic. Closer inspection, and consideration of the habitat, will be needed to determine the individual taxa. At generic level the only likely confusion is with the Pyramidal Orchid *Anacamptis pyramidalis*, but this can be distinguished from *Gymnadenia* by the two upright ridges on the labellum, one on each side of the spur mouth. Fragrant-orchids are frequent throughout much of the British Isles, and can be readily located on calcareous grassland in the south or on the hill pastures of northern England and Scotland.

The sweetly scented flowers attract a range of insects, and those with long probosces are able to access the nectar in the long, narrow spur (see Figure 9, p. 4; Plate 11, p. 5). The vertically positioned pollinia become attached to the proboscis; they then reorientate to point forward in the best position to make contact with the stigma of the next flower visited, and achieve efficient pollination. Not only moths and butterflies but also bees, beetles and spiders are recorded from the flowers, although the role of these in pollination is unclear. The relatively frequent occurrence of hybrids with species of *Dactylorhiza*, which have shorter spurs, has led to the suggestion that pollination may be occurring by such insects with shorter probosces. On the whole fertilisation is efficient, with seed being set in an estimated 50 to 90 per cent of flowers. This is the main method of reproduction, as vegetative propagation is apparently unrecorded.

As mentioned above, hybrids occur frequently, especially with the Frog Orchid *Dactylorhiza viridis* and other species of *Dactylorhiza*, the Small White Orchid

Plate 191. *Gymnadenia borealis* has the deepest pink flowers of the three species of fragrant-orchid. The weak lateral lobes of the labellum are characteristic. Peaty upland hillside, Roxburgh-shire, 25 June 2002.

Pseudorchis albida, and between the various subspecies. The segregate species of *Gymnadenia* involved in any given hybrid is not likely to be recorded in the literature, but may in some cases be deduced from the locality. Albino plants are also quite common, especially in *G. conopsea*.

15.1. *Gymnadenia conopsea* (L.) R. Br.

Syn. *Gymnadenia conopsea* subsp. *conopsea*

Chalk Fragrant-orchid

Flowers rose-pink, 9–12 mm across; *lateral outer perianth segments* 5–6 × *c*.1 mm long, bent downwards; *labellum* 5–6 × 5–6 mm, with obvious lobes; *spur* 12–14 mm; *flowering* June to July.

Gymnadenia conopsea (*sensu stricto*) is largely a plant of the southern half of Britain as far north as Durham and Cumbria, frequent on dry calcareous downland and pastures (see Plate 46, p. 40) and often growing in large populations along with other orchids such as *Dactylorhiza fuchsii*, *Neottia ovata*, *Ophrys apifera* and *Neotinea ustulata*. It is also found on some of the drier limestone areas of Ireland, although the majority of fragrant-orchids found in Ireland seem to be referable to *G. densiflora*. The Chalk Fragrant-orchid is very rare in Scotland but has been recorded from the north-west mainland, the Hebrides and Banff, with one unconfirmed record from Orkney.

Plate 192 (near right). An abnormal inflorescence of *Gymnadenia conopsea* with malformed, non-resupinate flowers. Chalk downland, Dorset, 27 June 2002.

Plate 193 (far right). White-flowered variants of *Gymnadenia conopsea* are not unusual. Chalk downland, Dorset, 27 June 2002.

Plate 194 (opposite). A loose inflorescence of pale pink flowers is typical of *Gymnadenia conopsea*. Chalk downland, Dorset, 27 June 2002.

15.2. *Gymnadenia borealis*

(Druce) R.M. Bateman, Pridgeon & M.W. Chase

Syn. *G. conopsea* subsp. *borealis* (Druce) F. Rose

Heath Fragrant-orchid

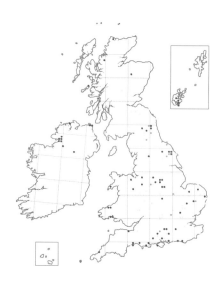

Flowers dark pink to purple, 8–10 mm across; *lateral outer perianth segments* 4–5 × *c.*2 mm, bent downwards; *labellum* 4–5 × 3.5–4 mm, rather indistinctly lobed; *spur* 11–14 mm; *flowering* June to July.

Gymnadenia borealis is a plant of hill pastures, heathy areas and *Molinia* grassland, sometimes to a considerable altitude, and is found mainly in the north of the British Isles. Scotland and parts of northern England are its stronghold, although it is also recorded further south on the Sussex Downs, in south-west England and in Wales. The habitat can be base-rich, but is often more acidic than that of *G. conopsea* and *G. densiflora*, with *Dactylorhiza purpurella* and *Platanthera bifolia* often present. It is later-flowering (July) than *G. conopsea*.

ITS sequence analysis performed by Bateman and colleagues (Bateman *et al.* 1997) demonstrated, as they say, to their surprise, that despite the great morphological similarities between this and *G. conopsea*, there is a marked molecular disparity between the two taxa, justifying their ranking as separate species.

Plate 195 (right).
The Heath Fragrant-orchid *Gymnadenia borealis* in coastal grassland, West Sutherland, 28 July 1991.

Plate 196 (opposite).
Gymnadenia borealis, the commonest fragrant-orchid in northern Britain, appears to be under-recorded in the *New Atlas* map. Critical recording of the distribution of the segregate species is needed. Peaty upland hillside, Roxburgh-shire, 26 June 1990.

15.3. *Gymnadenia densiflora* (Wahlenb.) A. Dietr.

Syn. *Gymnadenia conopsea* subsp. *densiflora* (Wahlenb.) E.G. Camus, Bergon & A. Camus

Marsh Fragrant-orchid

Flowers rose-pink, 11–14 mm across; *lateral outer perianth segments* 6–7 × 1 mm, positioned horizontally; *labellum* 3–4 × 6–7 mm, distinctly lobed; *spur* 14–16 mm; *flowering* July.

Individuals of *Gymnadenia densiflora* are usually more robust plants than those of the other two species, and have inflorescences that are markedly densely packed, as the name implies. The plant is predominantly one of damp calcareous areas, especially marshes, fens and dune slacks, but does also sometimes occur on dry north-facing grassy banks. It is mainly restricted to an area from southern England to north Wales, and to parts of northern England (where it can be quite common), sometimes on calcareous grassland. It is also somewhat later-flowering (July) than *G. conopsea*, and is usually found in small populations, with *Dactylorhiza incarnata* and *Epipactis palustris* being frequent associates. In Scotland it is very rare, presently known only from sites in Ross-shire and Roxburghshire, although there do appear to be old records from central Scotland and the Borders. In Ireland it is the commonest fragrant-orchid.

Bateman and colleagues restored it to specific level on the basis of 'strong and reliable allozyme divergence from *G. conopsea*' (Bateman *et al.* 1997, citing the work of Scacchi and de Angelis 1989). They had not at that point conducted their own ITS analysis, but more recent work, indicated in an article by Bateman (2004), suggests that the molecular data do indeed confirm such a taxonomic decision.

Plate 197 (right).
Two very different orchids sharing a preference for moist calcareous sites: *Gymnadenia densiflora* growing with *Epipactis palustris* in damp ground alongside a chalk stream in N. Hampshire, 11 July 2002.

Plate 198 (opposite).
The broad, strongly three-lobed labellum with a paler patch at its base will help to identify *Gymnadenia densiflora*. (The entire spike is seen in Plate 189, p.190.) Marshy area by chalk stream, N. Hampshire, 11 July 2002.

16. *Dactylorhiza* Neck. ex Nevski

Syn. *Dactylorchis* Verm.

Spotted-orchids, Marsh-orchids, Frog Orchid

Perennial herbs, with two or three deeply and palmately two- to five-lobed root tubers; *stem* glabrous, solid or ± hollow, erect; *leaves* frequent, those below sheathing the stem, those above non-sheathing and grading into the bracts; *inflorescence* a lax to dense spike; *bracts* leafy; *outer perianth segments* erect or spreading; *inner perianth segments* connivent, so forming a helmet over the column; *labellum* entire to trilobed; *spur* usually broad and pointing downwards; *column* erect; *anther* adjacent to the column; *pollinia* two, each attached by a caudicle to a viscidium in a simple bursicle, or bursicle rudimentary; *stigma* ± bilobed, positioned at the entrance to the spur; *rostellum* trilobed; *capsule* erect.

Dactylorhiza is widely acknowledged to be a taxonomically difficult genus and there have been various interpretations of the delimitation of taxa within it, probably because the genus is evolving rapidly, with active speciation occurring; Hédren has succinctly noted (1996a) that 'evolution in *Dactylorhiza* is highly reticulate'. Recently much work has been done using molecular techniques coupled with morphometry (e.g. Hédren 1996a, 1996b, 1996c, Hédren *et al.* 2001, Pillon *et al.* subm.), and this has helped to clarify the situation considerably. In particular, the demonstration that many species of marsh-orchid are allotetraploids enables us to see the group in a truer perspective.

Allotetraploidy is the state where an organism's genotype is made up of the union of two distinct sets of chromosomes originating from different species, through hybridisation. The total number of chromosomes is therefore twice as great as in the

Plate 200. In suitable conditions *Dactylorhiza* can occur in enormous numbers, providing some of the greatest floral displays in the British Isles. *Dactylorhiza praetermissa* and *D. incarnata* in dune slack, Lincolnshire, 5 June 1987.

Plate 199 (opposite). A richly coloured Common Spotted-orchid *Dactylorhiza fuchsii* subsp. *fuchsii*, growing with Ragged Robin *Lychnis flos-cuculi* in base-rich grassland, Midlothian, 6 July 1990.

Plate 201 (below left). Hybridisation is frequent in Dactylorhiza, resulting in plants that can be difficult to identify, but parentage can often be deduced from the surrounding population. *Dactylorhiza fuchsii* subsp. *fuchsii* × *D. praetermissa* (D. ×*grandis*). Wet pasture, Guernsey, 13 May 2001.

Plate 202 (below right). An albino *Dactylorhiza maculata* (sometimes called forma *candidissima* (Krock.) Landwehr). Acid heathland, New Forest, South Hampshire, 17 June 2003.

Plate 203 (opposite). Recent research has shown that many marsh-orchids are allotetraploids with independent origins. Did H.W. Pugsley guess this when naming *Dactylorhiza traunsteinerioides*? Wet hillside flush, W. Ross, 23 June 1996.

putative parents. (For example, *D. fuchsii* and *D. incarnata* both have a diploid chromosome number, 2n = 40; their hybrid derivative *D. purpurella*, however, is an allotetraploid, with 2n = 80.) Such hybrids are fully fertile, as the two sets of chromosomes can fully recombine at meiosis. Allopolyploidy is considered to be an important cause of plant speciation. In *Dactylorhiza* it was first suspected, in *D. praetermissa*, by Heslop-Harrison (1953), and this was confirmed by Hédren (1996c) several decades later. In this case the principal diploid parents are *D. incarnata* (*sensu lato*) and a member of the *D. maculata*/*fuchsii* group (although *D. maculata* itself is usually an autotetraploid, in which the same set of chromosomes is doubled). Allotetraploid hybrids resulting from this parentage have appeared, and continue to appear, at different times and in different places. The older the allotetraploid the more clearly distinguished in ecology and morphology it is likely to be, as selection pressures will have had longer to 'refine' it as a species. A consequence of this process is that populations of plants of apparently similar morphology may have arisen completely independently of each other, as can be demonstrated by molecular analysis. As Hédren and colleagues have noted (Hédren *et al.* 2001), for circumscription of a species within this allotetraploid group morphology is not enough; genetic, ecological and geographical information is also essential. This is exemplified by recent work by Bateman (2005, in press) in connection with the broad morphological taxon *Dactylorhiza traunsteineri*, which has been shown to contain taxa of independent genetic origins: the type, *D. traunsteineri*, is centred on the Alps, while the British taxon known under the same name is of different origin, and should be termed *D. traunsteinerioides*. Similarly, modern comprehension of allotetraploidy and its origins makes it possible finally to lay to rest the spectre of the

name *Dactylorhiza majalis*, which has appeared in various combinations in the British flora, often as a 'dumping ground' for taxa it had been found difficult to place elsewhere. The Continental *D. majalis* (Rchb.) P.F. Hunt & Summerh. is not known to occur in the British Isles.

Even with the assistance of molecular techniques there can still be argument as to whether particular taxa deserve full specific status, or indeed in some cases as to which species they belong within. Recognizing taxa in the field is also not currently assisted by the new technology, although in due course it may be possible to sample more populations to assign them to individual taxa. In *Dactylorhiza* there is a tendency to variation within individual species, and the considerable propensity of these species to hybridise (without necessarily forming tetraploids), and to introgress, further complicates the picture. Individual plants can often cause problems with identification, and in the field it is probably best first to form an opinion on the identity of the population as a whole and then separate out any putative hybrids, for which one parent (or even both) may not always be present. Such hybrids may sometimes exhibit hybrid vigour and this may help to locate them within the population; but individuals may still be impossible to identify, even as putative hybrids. Backcrossing to one or other parent occurs frequently, resulting in populations comprising hybrid swarms, and this can cause additional problems in accurate identification.

The former classification of *Dactylorhiza* in *Orchis* and then in *Dactylorchis*, added to the taxonomic difficulties inherent to the genus, has led to a proliferation of synonyms as taxa have been transferred from genus to genus, species to species and infraspecifically up and down! In the following accounts, therefore, we provide

Plate 204. The flattened, lobed tubers of *Dactylorhiza* suggested the generic name, which means 'finger-root'. Cultivated tubers of *Dactylorhiza elata*, September 1997.

details of synonymy only in cases where confusion with currently available texts might otherwise occur.

It is generally accepted that there are about 40 to 50 species of *Dactylorhiza* world-wide (Meikle 1985, Pridgeon *et al.* 2001). These are mostly native to the Old World and especially to Eurasia and North Africa, but also occur in Alaska. Most members of the genus occupy damp habitats such as fens, marshes, damp grassland and dune slacks but others, such as *Dactylorhiza fuchsii*, are normally found in drier places, including calcareous grassland.

Of the British and Irish *Dactylorhiza* species, *D. fuchsii* and *D. maculata* are the only two representatives of the 'spotted-orchids' as distinct from the others, usually known as 'marsh-orchids'. As well as being distinguished by the spots on their foliage, the spotted-orchids tend to occur in somewhat drier habitats than those normally occupied by the marsh-orchids, and tend to have fewer sheathing leaves. All are sometimes referred to as 'dactylorchids'. The Frog Orchid *'Coeloglossum' viride* has recently been placed in *Dactylorhiza*, as *D. viridis*, and occupies a separate group within the genus. It favours drier habitats.

Compared with other orchids, members of this genus are amongst the fastest to reach maturity, and plants may colonise new sites rapidly and in great numbers. Pollination is very effective, as indicated by the high proportion of mature capsules developing in most populations. Plants also have a tendency to multiply vegetatively through the development of new tubers from lateral buds. A consequence of this is that they may occur in clumps. The name *Dactylorhiza* derives from the Greek *dactylos*, 'finger-like', and *rhiza*, 'root', in reference to the tuberous root system.

Key to *Dactylorhiza*

1a. Flowers green to red-brown .... *D. viridis* p.219
1b. Flowers pink to purple, occasionally white or pale
    yellow, not green 2

2a. Stems solid, leaves spotted, flowers pale to dark pink
    (spotted-orchids) 3
2b. Stems hollow, leaves spotted or often unspotted,
    flowers pale to dark pink, purple, red, occasionally
    cream or flesh-coloured (marsh-orchids) 5

3a. Labellum with lobes equal or middle lobe largest
    or longest; on calcareous or neutral soils 4
3b. Labellum with lateral lobes much larger than small
    middle lobe; on acidic soils .... *D. maculata* p.233

Plate 205 (opposite).
The lateral lobes of the labellum of *Dactylorhiza incarnata* subsp. *incarnata* are reflexed, making the flower appear rather narrow. Labellum markings are always confined within a central loop, but may also occur on the lateral sepals. Water meadow, West Suffolk, 20 May 2002.

4a. Flowers pale pink, occasionally white
        or darker; widespread .... *D. fuchsii* subsp. *fuchsii* [1] p. 225

4b. Flowers dark pink, leaves heavily spotted;
        coastal grassland in Scotland ...... *D. fuchsii* subsp. *hebridensis* [2] p. 231

5a. Labellum with sides strongly reflexed, usually with
        two distinct parallel loop-markings; flowers pink
        to purple, sometimes pale cream-yellow .... *D. incarnata* [3] p. 208

5b. Labellum usually flat, sides not strongly reflexed,
        usually with more irregular loop- and spot-
        markings; flowers usually purple 6

6a. Sheathing leaves usually more than five, mostly
        more than 2 cm wide at maximum width 7

6b. Sheathing leaves usually fewer than five, mostly
        narrower than 2 cm wide at maximum width 9

7a. Leaves spotted or not, labellum usually with distinct
        central lobe; flowers pink to purple 8

7b. Leaves usually unspotted, labellum diamond-shaped,
        with indistinct central lobe; flowers deep
        purple; northern and western distribution .... *D. purpurella* [4] p. 251

8a. Leaves unspotted or with ring-spots; labellum with
        distinct or indistinct central lobe; flowers pink
        to purple; southern half of Britain .... *D. praetermissa* p. 239

8b. Leaves unspotted or with solid spots; labellum
        with distinct central lobe; flowers pale purple;
        Ireland only .... *D. occidentalis* p. 257

9a. Leaves two (to three to four), narrow, arching, unspotted
        to spotted; labellum usually with elongated central lobe;
        flowers pale to dark pink; rare, in base-
        rich fens throughout British Isles .... *D. traunsteinerioides* p. 243

9b. Leaves two to three, broader, rosette-forming, heavily
        spotted; labellum with distinct but not elongated central
        lobe; flowers dark purple; North Uist only .... *D. ebudensis* p. 247

Notes

1 White- or pale-flowered populations in western Ireland may be var. *okellyi* (p. 230).

2 Darker-flowered populations in Cornwall or upland Scotland may be *D. fuchsii* subsp.
     fuchsii var. *cornubiensis* (p. 227) or var. *alpina* (p. 229), respectively.

3 See below (p. 209) for a key to the subspecies of *D. incarnata*.

4 Var. *cambrensis* on western and northern coasts has heavily spotted leaves/bracts (p. 254).

16.1. *Dactylorhiza incarnata* (L.) Soó

Early Marsh-orchid

Perennial herb with thick palmate tubers tapering into long, rooted segments; *stem* to *c*.60 cm, broad, rigid, ± hollow, pale green; *leaves* elliptical to lanceolate, usually hooded at the tip, sheathing and often crowded below, spaced along the stem above and becoming non-sheathing and smaller, yellow-green to green, unspotted, or spotted purple-brown on one or both surfaces; *inflorescence* a fairly dense, ± cylindrical spike; *bracts* lanceolate, tapering, frequently exceeding the flowers, green, sometimes tinged or spotted purple; *flowers* relatively small, variously coloured (depending upon the subspecies) white, cream-yellow, pink, bright red, crimson or purple, unmarked, or spotted or marked with short lines or loops in a darker colour; *outer perianth segments c*.6 mm long, erect or reflexed, ± lanceolate, veined, sometimes spotted; *inner perianth segments* shorter than the outer, broad-lanceolate, connivent; *labellum* to *c*.8 mm long, ovate to rounded, entire to trilobed, the margins often strongly reflexed giving a narrow appearance; *spur* to 8 mm long, tapering; *column* short; *anther* ovate; *pollinia* two; *stigma* longer than broad, sticky; *rostellum* pink to violet; *ovary* sessile, ridged; *flowering* May to August; 2n = 40.

In the British Isles the Early Marsh-orchid *Dactylorhiza incarnata* is represented by five subspecies: *incarnata, ochroleuca, coccinea, pulchella* and *cruenta*, each marked by its characteristic ecology, habitat and distribution, as well as morphological characters. Their taxonomic status is often challenged, and in Scandinavia, for instance, subsp. *ochroleuca* and subsp. *cruenta* are considered to be full species. Hédren and his colleagues have suggested (Hédren *et al.* 2001) that these infraspecific taxa may in fact have arisen independently on more than one occasion, and that outward morphological similarities are the result of selection pressures in certain habitats. Morphological variation is not, however, matched by molecular variation (Bateman 2005, in press). It is now well documented that in the formation of allotetraploid marsh-orchids, one of the principal diploid parents will be a member of the *D. incarnata* complex (Hédren 1996a, 1996b, Hédren *et al.* 2001, Pillon *et al.* subm.). No doubt much of the differentiation seen in the allotetraploids is derived from the subspecific taxon of *D. incarnata* involved in the parentage, although this at present cannot be distinguished for certain. The range of variation found in the British Isles is fully discussed by Bateman & Denholm (1985).

Key to subspecies of *D. incarnata*

1a. Leaves spotted on both surfaces .... subsp. *cruenta* p.216
1b. Leaves usually unspotted 2

2a. Flowers always cream, unmarked, the
    labellum distinctly trilobed .... subsp. *ochroleuca* p.211
2b. Flowers pink, red-purple or bright vermilion-
    red (very rarely cream in subsp. *pulchella*)
    and marked with dots, loops, etc.,
    the labellum entire to shallowly trilobed 3

3a. Plant with a slender stem, flowers purplish
    (very rarely cream), bracts tinged purple .... subsp. *pulchella* p.214
3b. Plant robust or squat, flowers pink to
    vermilion-red, bracts not tinged purple 4

4a. Plant fairly robust, flowers pale to deep pink,
    lateral lobes of labellum strongly
    reflexed .... subsp. *incarnata* below
4b. Plant squat, flowers bright vermilion-red,
    lateral lobes of labellum not strongly
    reflexed .... subsp. *coccinea* p.212

The map for the broad species *Dactylorhiza incarnata* (see opposite) combines records for all subspecies. Maps for the individual subspecies may under-represent their true distribution.

(a) subsp. *incarnata*

Stem to 40 cm; *leaves* unspotted; *bracts* leafy, usually exceeding the flowers; *labellum* to 8 mm long, pale to deep pink, loop- and spot-marked reddish, shallowly trilobed, the margins strongly reflexed; *flowering* early, May to mid-June, rather later in the north and at altitude.

This can be a quite variable subspecies, which has resulted in it being inconsistently recorded. It is widely scattered throughout the British Isles, where it is probably the commonest subspecies overall, although much less frequent in Ireland. It

Plate 206 (opposite). The normal colour form of *Dactylorhiza incarnata* subsp. *incarnata*. The hooded leaf-tips are a feature of this species. Water meadow, West Suffolk, 20 May 2002.

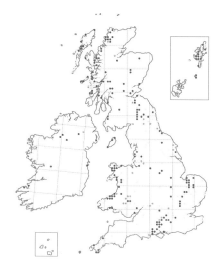

also occurs throughout much of Europe, eastwards into Asia and southwards to North Africa. It is a plant of calcareous to neutral damp habitats such as fens, marshes, dune slacks, damp meadows, ditch margins and upland base-flushed grassland. Although generally a lowland plant, it has been recorded up to an altitude of at least 440 m. In the NVC classification it is allotted to a wide range of mire, fen and dune communities. In view of it normally occupying damp habitats, drainage of such sites and agricultural upgrading is a constant threat, and many populations have been lost in this way.

The specific name *incarnata* derives from the Latin *caro* or *carneus*, 'flesh' or 'fleshy', relating to its flesh-pink coloured flowers. It appears to have been first noticed in the British Isles in 1833 in Cambridgeshire, by Babington, but was not distinguished as a separate plant until Leighton published an account of it a little later in his *Flora of Shropshire* (1841). It is not a difficult plant to locate in the field, and a search of its typical habitat should be rewarding. Its usually sharply reflexed labellum lobes, pink flowers and unspotted leaves will confirm its identity. An occasional variant with a few small spots on the upper surface of the leaves has been named f. *punctata* (Vermeul.) R.M. Bateman & Denholm, but Vermeulen's original concept of f. *punctata* included both subsp. *incarnata* and subsp. *pulchella* (R. Bateman, pers. comm. 2005) and the epithet is sometimes also applied to spotted variants of subsp. *pulchella*. Hybrids with other *Dactylorhiza* taxa also occur. Robust plants with large labella and spurs, found in eastern England and in Ireland, have been described as a variety (subsp. *incarnata* var. *gemmana*) by Pugsley but are of dubious status, and are now discounted as being of little taxonomic significance. White-flowered plants occasionally occur within populations of the normal coloured form.

Plate 207 (near right). Pale forms of *Dactylorhiza incarnata* subsp. *incarnata* should not be confused with subsp. *ochroleuca*. Such pale variants are found in most subspecies. Wet coastal grassland, Fife, 16 June 2002.

Plate 208 (far right). The rare pure-white *D. incarnata* subsp. *incarnata* var. *leucantha* R.M. Bateman & Denholm. West Ross, 31 May 2004.

(b) subsp. *ochroleuca*

(Wüstnei ex Boll) P.F. Hunt & Summerh.

Plant robust; *stem* to 60 cm; *leaves* relatively large, unspotted; *bracts* long, usually exceeding the flowers; *labellum* to *c*.7 mm long, cream, deepening in colour towards the spur entrance, unmarked, trilobed, the outer lobes often notched; *flowering* late May to early June.

The subspecific epithet *ochroleuca* relates to the flower colour and derives from the Greek *ochro*, 'pale yellow', and *leuco*, 'white'. The plant was first recorded in Britain relatively recently, Lousley having collected it from Blo Norton Fen in 1935. This was soon followed by its discovery at further sites close by and also within the Waveney valley. In the British Isles it is very rare, and many records have been the result of confusion with white- or cream-flowered forms of subspp. *incarnata*, *pulchella* or *coccinea*. It has only been recorded with certainty from a few localities in eastern England, mainly in East Anglia in the Waveney valley; one supposedly reliable record from Kidwelly, South Wales in 1919 has been shown to be a misidentification (Foley 2000). This is a plant of a very specific habitat within calcareous fens, where it shows a preference for moist but not permanently inundated areas, especially those parts which are slowly but only partially drying out and which may have originated through sedimentation. The level of the water-table appears to be critical, so that drainage of the area occupied by a population, or even in its vicinity, can have a disastrously adverse effect. In mainland Europe the plant is found, locally but widely scattered, from Scandinavia to central Europe, and there too it is rare and endangered.

Most of the few known British populations of subsp. *ochroleuca* have been lost in recent years; it is undoubtedly extremely rare, and is extant at just two localities.

Plate 209 (below left). The very rare *Dactylorhiza incarnata* subsp. *ochroleuca* has creamy-yellow flowers. Wet alkaline fen, West Suffolk, 10 June 2002.

Plate 210 (below right). *Dactylorhiza incarnata* subsp. *ochroleuca* in a Bavarian fen: the British population may have fewer individuals than this. Murnauer Moos, 1 June 1999.

Both of these populations have declined drastically and are close to extinction. Drainage is the main cause of loss, but at some sites grazing by deer and scrub encroachment have also contributed to the plant's decline. It is now so rare that recommendation of a suitable site at which it can be seen is not appropriate, although both extant sites offer some form of legal protection. If located, its rather robust stature, its long leafy bracts and its pale-yellow coloured, unmarked flowers, which have deeply trilobed labella and notched lateral lobes, will distinguish it from other subspecies occupying the same habitat.

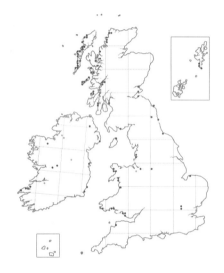

(c) subsp. *coccinea* (Pugsley) Soó

Stem to 20 cm, usually short and stout; *leaves* usually also short, unspotted; *bracts* relatively short; *labellum* to *c*.7 mm long, usually of a distinctive bright vermilion-red colour, especially when fresh, line- or dash-marked, shallowly trilobed; *flowering* later than subsp. *incarnata* when growing in the same habitat, normally from June to early July.

This very distinctively coloured subspecies is normally found close to the coast and is especially a plant of damp dune slacks in the west of the British Isles; it also occurs on the machair grassland of northern Scotland. More rarely it has been recorded inland, in calcareous fens and in upland flushes, as well as at sites that have originated from the disposal of base-rich or saline industrial waste. It frequently occurs in large populations, such as on the Lancashire and Anglesey coasts, where it may grow alongside subsp. *incarnata*. In its dune-slack habitat its associates include *Epipactis palustris, Salix repens* and, very rarely in south Wales, *Liparis loeselii*.

Dactylorhiza incarnata subsp. *coccinea* is possibly endemic to the British Isles, although some records from the Netherlands may be of the same plant. Its population status appears to be stable despite some sites having succumbed to human

Plate 211 (right). The short-statured *Dactylorhiza incarnata* subsp. *coccinea* can be abundant in coastal grassland with other orchids. Cardiganshire coast, June 1997.

Plate 212 (opposite). The rich red flowers of *Dactylorhiza incarnata* subsp. *coccinea* are easily recognised. Dune slack, South Glamorgan, 26 June 2002.

activities and to coastal development. It was first recognised as a distinct taxon at varietal level in the mid-twentieth century, by Pugsley. It is easily recognised by its short, rather squat stature and its bright red flowers, and can readily be found in many of the coastal dune slacks of north-west England. The name derives from the Latin *coccineus*, 'scarlet', and obviously refers to the striking colour of the flowers.

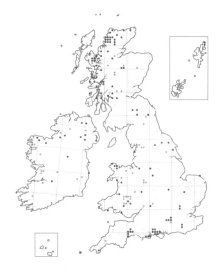

(d) subsp. *pulchella* (Druce) Soó

Stem to 40 cm, often slender; *leaves* unspotted (or occasionally finely spotted on upper surface: f. '*punctata*'); *bracts* short, usually noticeably purple-tinged; *labellum* to *c.*7 mm long, purplish (very rarely cream), loop- and spot-marked in a deeper colour, ± entire to shallowly trilobed but often variable in shape and markings; *flowering* June to July.

Dactylorhiza incarnata subsp. *pulchella* has a scattered distribution throughout Britain and Ireland, with populations especially concentrated in the New Forest area of southern England and in the Isle of Skye and Sutherland. Its occurrence in mainland Europe and elsewhere has been doubted and it may well be endemic to the British Isles. It normally prefers acidic habitats such as marshes, valley bogs, wet hillsides and heaths, but can also occur in more neutral conditions, and occasionally even in base-rich fens. In consequence of this it has a wider range of associates than the other subspecies of *D. incarnata*. In one atypical habitat in Cumbria it grows on the raised tussocks of *Schoenus nigricans* above bare, highly base-rich fen sediment. As the

Plate 213. A variable population of *Dactylorhiza incarnata* subsp. *pulchella*, in characteristic wet, peaty habitat. New Forest, South Hampshire, 7 June 2002.

plant has been under-recorded in the past, through confusion with other marsh-orchids, it is difficult to determine whether or not it has declined; if so this is likely to have occurred in the more populated areas where commercial development or agricultural improvement have taken place.

The plant was first described by Druce as a variety of *D. incarnata*; the epithet originates from the Latin *pulchellus*, 'beautiful'. Seen in its natural habitat it is sometimes confused with other taxa, especially subsp. *incarnata, D. purpurella,* or even *D. traunsteinerioides,* in each of whose typical habitats it can grow, sometimes in close association with them. It is best distinguished from these others by its slender habit, its normally unspotted leaves and its distinctively coloured purplish-spotted,

Plate 214. Richly coloured flowers help distinguish *Dactylorhiza incarnata* subsp. *pulchella*, but it has been confused with subsp. *incarnata*. Peaty deposits over limestone at edge of turlough, the Burren, Co. Clare, 2 June 2001.

Plate 215 (top left).
The spotted-leaved variant
of *Dactylorhiza incarnata*
subsp. *pulchella*, sometimes
called forma *punctata*.
Wet acid hillside, West Ross,
26 June 2003.

Plate 216 (top right).
A pale *Dactylorhiza
incarnata* subsp. *pulchella*:
the name var. *ochrantha*
Landwehr has been used for
all such variants of the broad
species *D. incarnata*. Peaty
heathland, New Forest,
S. Hampshire, 7 June 2002.

Plate 217 (bottom left).
A potentially confusing
plant if the parents were
not present: *Gymnadenia
borealis* × *Dactylorhiza
incarnata* subsp. *pulchella*.
Acid moorland, West Ross,
26 June 2003.

Plate 218 (bottom right).
The narrow inflorescence
and tall, thin plant suggest
a fragrant-orchid hybrid:
Gymnadenia borealis ×
Dactylorhiza incarnata
subsp. *pulchella*, acid moorland, W. Ross, 26 June 2003.

almost entire to shallowly-lobed, reflexed labella. It should be searched for in the
habitats, and especially in the geographical areas, indicated above. Hybridisation
with other marsh-orchids does sometimes occur.

(e) subsp. *cruenta* (O.F. Müll.) P.D. Sell

Stem to 40 cm, usually distinctly purplish-tinged; *leaves* spotted or more strongly blotched on
both surfaces, often appreciably so; *bracts* relatively short, tinged purple and spotted; *labellum* to *c*.7 mm long, purplish, dot- and loop-marked, usually shallowly trilobed; *flowering*
late May to June.

Plate 219. Both sides
of the leaf are spotted in
the intensely coloured
Dactylorhiza incarnata
subsp. *cruenta*. West Ross,
16 June 1991.

This is a plant of very restricted distribution in the British Isles, recorded first in 1949 from western Ireland by Heslop-Harrison, more recently in 1984 by Kenneth & Tennant from Ross-shire, and later still from a locality in Sutherland. These are the only known records so far but it is anticipated that other populations remain to be discovered in the more remote areas of the Scottish Highlands. On the Continent, however, it is much more frequent, especially in Scandinavia and in central-western Europe. In the Swiss Alps it occurs up to an altitude of 1800 m but in the British Isles its limit is reached at less than 500 m. At the 1984 locality on the Scottish mainland it occurs in sloping, more or less neutral flushed grassland; it is very local and its populations are of limited size. Associates here include several species of *Carex, Molinia caerulea, Pinguicula vulgaris, Schoenus nigricans, Tofieldia pusilla* and

Trichophorum cespitosum. Dactylorhiza incarnata subsp. *pulchella* and *D. maculata* are also to be found nearby. The Sutherland site, which is the other known mainland location, occupies a *Carex lasiocarpa* mire, but only one plant was seen here. Both these habitats contrast with the much more calcareous ones of Scandinavia and the Irish Burren. In the latter area plants are frequent and occur close to the margins of lakes and fens, as well as in and around the strongly base-rich turloughs typical of the region. Here they are accompanied by other rarities such as *Potentilla fruticosa, Teucrium scordium* and *Viola persicifolia*. It has recently been suggested (Carey & Dines 2002) that the Irish plants are spotted-leaved variants of subsp. *pulchella*, but their similarity to the Scandinavian plant, in morphology and choice of habitat, indicates that this is not so.

Threats to the survival of the various populations do not seem to be severe, although the Ross-shire population is close to a major cross-country road, and at all the sites the habitat is fragile and therefore easily damaged. The subspecific epithet derives from the Latin *cruentus*, 'bloody', presumably referring to the plant's blotched leaves or to the colour of its flowers. The best place to see it in its natural habitat is in western Ireland, where it can readily be identified by its spotted, streaked bracts and its leaves spotted and blotched on *both* surfaces.

Plate 220. Two Burren specialities: *Dactylorhiza incarnata* subsp. *cruenta* growing with *Potentilla fruticosa* at the edge of a turlough. The Burren, Co. Clare, 1 June 2001.

16.2. *Dactylorhiza viridis*

(L.) R.M. Bateman, Pridgeon & M.W. Chase

Syn. *Coeloglossum viride* (L.) Hartm.

Frog Orchid

Perennial herb with two segmented root tubers; *stem* 5–35 cm, glabrous, erect, with one to two membranous, scaly leaf sheaths at the base; *leaves* two to five, those below rounded to broadly oblong, blue-green, those above smaller and lanceolate; *inflorescence* a fairly lax, cylindrical spike; *bracts* ± lanceolate, the lower often greatly exceeding the flowers; *flowers* small, green, tinged brown, with a faint scent; *outer perianth segments* 4–6 mm, ± ovate, forming a hood, *inner perianth segments* linear-lanceolate; *labellum* up to 9 mm long, narrowly oblong, downpointing, green but usually edged reddish brown, trilobed near the tip, the middle lobe much the shorter; *spur* short, to 2 mm long, ± flattened, pale-coloured, containing nectar; *column* short; *anther* broader than long, positioned adjacent to the top of the column; *pollinia* two, pale greenish-yellow; *stigma* reniform; *rostellum* comprising two well-separated protuberances positioned each side of the upper edge of the stigma; *ovary* ridged, twisted; *flowering* June to August; 2n = 40.

Molecular studies by Bateman and his colleagues (Bateman *et al.* 1997) have revealed that despite some apparent morphological dissimilarities the Frog Orchid occupies a position well within the *Dactylorhiza* clade and is therefore most aptly treated as a member of *Dactylorhiza*. As it hybridises freely with several *Dactylorhiza* species and shares with them many similarities, this reclassification is perhaps less surprising than it might at first seem.

Dactylorhiza viridis is distributed throughout most of the temperate latitudes of the northern hemisphere. On the Continent it is widespread and fairly frequent, found northwards to northern Scandinavia and also in southern Europe, though here mainly confined to the mountains, where it reaches altitudes of 2500 m or more. It is scarce or absent from much of the Mediterranean. Plants at high altitude are often stunted and, together with those from the more northern areas, occur in a darker colour form, with stems and flowers strongly marked purple-brown.

Plate 221. The dull green flowers and short stature of the Frog Orchid *Dactylorhiza viridis* can make it difficult to spot, especially in longer grass. Dry coastal machair, Island of Vatersay, Outer Hebrides, 16 July 2003.

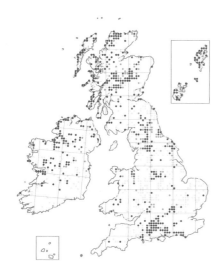

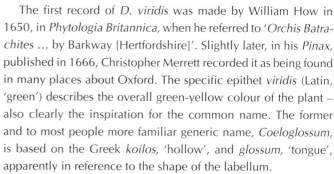

The first record of *D. viridis* was made by William How in 1650, in *Phytologia Britannica*, when he referred to '*Orchis Batrachites* ... by Barkway [Hertfordshire]'. Slightly later, in his *Pinax*, published in 1666, Christopher Merrett recorded it as being found in many places about Oxford. The specific epithet *viridis* (Latin, 'green') describes the overall green-yellow colour of the plant – also clearly the inspiration for the common name. The former and to most people more familiar generic name, *Coeloglossum*, is based on the Greek *koilos*, 'hollow', and *glossum*, 'tongue', apparently in reference to the shape of the labellum.

In the British Isles the Frog Orchid is widely distributed, frequently occurring in short grassland, especially in calcareous pastures, as well as up to considerable altitude in the mountains of the north. Whilst it is nowhere especially frequent, its strongholds are the downs of southern England (excepting Kent), the limestone pastures of northern England and north Wales, as well as much of western Scotland and the Hebrides. In all of these areas its preferred habitat is short turf. In the Hebrides the coastal machair holds populations of considerable size. Plants are also found in dune slacks and on dune grassland, on road verges, railway embankments, earthworks, quarry floors, golf courses, and even in montane flushes and on base-rich cliff talus in parts of Scotland. Some lowland populations can be large but sizes often fluctuate dramatically from year to year;

Plates 222 (below) and 223 (opposite). Heavily red-tinted plants of *Dactylorhiza viridis* are most frequently found in northern areas. Coastal grassland, Fife, 22 July 2002.

at higher altitudes the plant occurs much more sparsely. It is also widespread in Ireland and is especially frequent on the limestones of the Burren. Orchid associates are mainly *Dactylorhiza fuchsii* and other species of *Dactylorhiza*, *Gymnadenia conopsea* and *Neottia ovata*. The NVC classification for *D. viridis* includes many of the recognised calcareous grassland (CG) communities as well as sand dune (SD8) and, surprisingly, the *Empetrum nigrum* heath. The Frog Orchid appears to be a declining species, for reasons that are not clear, although agricultural improvement and road-verge disturbance have obvious disadvantageous effects. As the plant is quite small and inconspicuous, and of fluctuating incidence, it is difficult to make an accurate estimate of its current status.

Although it is not an easy plant to locate, as for many other orchids of the British Isles spotting it is much easier once one's eye is 'in'. A search of the habitats described above will yield the best chance of success.

The flowers are only faintly scented but the short spur contains nectar and this attracts small insects, including ichneumons. As the insects alight on the labellum and approach the spur entrance they are forced somewhat off-centre owing to the structure of the labellum. They therefore contact just one of the viscidia (which are positioned just above the stigma) and one of the pollinia is thereby removed. Over a period of minutes the detached pollinium hinges forward, although initially it retains its more or less original upright configuration. During this period self-fertilisation of the plant is avoided. As the insect moves on to another plant

Plates 224 (above left) and 225 (above right). The Frog Orchid frequently hybridises with other *Dactylorhiza* species, which supports its inclusion within the genus. Its parenthood is clearly visible in this plant: *Dactylorhiza fuchsii* subsp. *hebridensis* × *D. viridis*, dry machair grassland, Island of Vatersay, Outer Hebrides, 16 July 2003.

the attached pollinium moves forwards to a position in which it can make contact with the stigma of a new flower and so achieve cross-pollination. Not all the pollen is removed on first contact, so the insect can move on to fertilise the flowers of other plants as well. Seed-set is efficient, and mature fruit is produced quickly. Growth from seed seems to be quite rapid, and Willems & Melser (1998) have discovered that the plant can produce an inflorescence on its first appearance above ground. Vegetative reproduction is apparently very rare, although individual plants do occasionally survive for several years. The flowering period can be quite long, and in the north plants can be found in flower well into the autumn.

Hybrids with other species of *Dactylorhiza* are often reported. That with *D. fuchsii* ('×*Dactyloglossum' mixtum*) is quite frequent in Britain and Ireland wherever the parents come into close contact. More rare is that with *D. maculata* ('×*Dactyloglossum' drucei*), whilst another hybrid with *D. purpurella* ('×*Dactyloglossum' viridella*) is thought to be a British endemic, known from Durham, Sutherland, and the western isles of Scotland. A further unconfirmed British record is of what appears to be a hybrid with *D. praetermissa*. In the British Isles *D. viridis* also hybridises with *Gymnadenia conopsea*, the progeny ('×*Gymnaglossum' jacksonii*) being similar in appearance to *G. conopsea* but with green-tinged flowers and a labellum shape intermediate between the parents.

16.3. *Dactylorhiza fuchsii* (Druce) Soó

Common Spotted-orchid

Perennial herb, glabrous throughout, tubers flat-tened, roots short and thick; *stem* to 50(–70) cm, solid, erect, pale green but sometimes tinged purple above; *leaves* deeper green, normally distinctly spot- and blotch-marked on upper sur-face but occasionally unmarked, the sheathing leaves lanceolate to oblong-lanceolate, 5–15 × 0.5–5.0 cm, crowded towards the stem base, cauline leaves similar but decreasing in size up the stem; *inflorescence* a fairly dense, cylindrical, many-flowered spike; *bracts* linear-lanceolate, green, often tinged with violet, veined, approxim-ately equal in length to the ovaries; *flowers* pale pink to deep pink, less often red-purple, occasion-ally white, often scented; *outer perianth segments* to 9 mm, lanceolate, veined, the laterals spotted; *inner perianth segments* shorter, ± lanceolate, con-nivent, usually unspotted; *labellum* to 9 × 12 mm, white, pale pink or darker coloured, dash- and loop-marked in a deeper colour, occasionally un-marked, deeply trilobed, the central lobe as wide as, and equal to or longer than the laterals; *spur* to 10 mm long, straight or slightly curved, tapering; *column* erect; *anther* erect, purple; *pollinia* two, green; *stigma* tinged violet; *rostellum* trilobed; *ovary* sessile, ridged, tinged violet; *flowering* late May to August; 2n = 40.

Considered in its broadest sense *Dactylorhiza fuchsii* well earns its name the Common Spotted-orchid, being by far the most abund-ant orchid in Britain and Ireland. It is found throughout almost the whole of the British Isles, although it is much rarer in south-west England, south-west Ireland and north-ern Scotland than in other areas. It has been divided into a range of infraspecific taxa, some of which are delimited on relatively subtle morphological differences as well as on ecological and geographical grounds. It is also a common species in much of mainland Europe, extending eastwards into Russia and northwards into Scandinavia, though absent from parts of the south; as in the British Isles, additional infraspecific taxa occur.

The first record of this species and other members of the genus *Dactylorhiza* seems to have been made by John Gerard in his *Herball* of 1597. Gerard recog-nized the distinction from *Orchis* in the palmate roots, although his descriptions, while implying a spotted-orchid, seem to be confused with marsh orchids. He re-corded the plants from marshy places and wet woods in Kent and Hampstead. The

Plate 226. *Dactylorhiza fuchsii* subsp. *fuchsii* is usually pale to mid-pink. Disused limestone quarry, Co. Durham, 29 June 2002.

specific name *fuchsii* commemorates Leonard Fuchs, the German Renaissance botanist (1501–1566), whose name was later given also to the rather more exotic plant *Fuchsia*.

In the British Isles *D. fuchsii* is a plant of base-rich to neutral substrates where it occupies a wide range of habitats, especially calcareous grasslands, meadows, woodland margins, scrub, fens, marshes, heaths and dune slacks. Importantly, it also readily colonises man-made habitats such as roadside verges, railway embankments, quarry floors and other disused ground. It is usually one of the first orchids to appear in such places, and may become very abundant in these sites. As it occupies such diverse habitats it is associated with a wide range of species, and in consequence is also represented by a large number of NVC communities. Other orchids, especially *Neottia ovata* and grassland species such as *Anacamptis pyramidalis*, *Dactylorhiza viridis*, *Gymnadenia conopsea*, *Ophrys apifera* and *O. insectifera*, may also be present. In damper areas and dune slacks *D. fuchsii* often cohabits with (and hybridises with) other species of *Dactylorhiza*.

The faintly scented flowers attract bees and flies which feed on the sugars in the spur. The two pollinia, which are attached to separate viscidia, are readily removed on contact with an insect and are then carried over to the next flower. Pollination is very efficient and most plants soon bear well-developed capsules. Seed appears to be easily and widely dispersed, as shown by the tendency for *D. fuchsii* to establish itself quickly on recently disturbed ground. After germination, leaves begin to develop in the second year, the number increasing annually until flowering commences, sometimes within three years. Flowering then continues for several more years, with the plant gradually building up its stature. At this time some individuals also

Plate 227. The Common Spotted-orchid *Dactylorhiza fuchsii* subsp. *fuchsii* is often the most conspicuous orchid in many habitats throughout the British Isles. Chalk grassland, North Hampshire, 8 July 1996.

reproduce vegetatively, so that small clumps are formed. Plants also seem to be able to remain in a vegetative state for many years, awaiting the return of more favourable conditions before flowering. *Dactylorhiza fuchsii* is especially promiscuous, readily forming hybrids with other marsh-orchids with which it comes into reasonably close proximity, especially *D. incarnata*, *D. maculata*, *D. praetermissa* and *D. purpurella*. With these it can form complex hybrid swarms through backcrossing. It sometimes also hybridises with *Gymnadenia*.

Several infraspecific variants have been described, treated at different rank by different authors. Of these variants we prefer to recognise just one at subspecific level, *D. fuchsii* subsp. *hebridensis*, on account of its distinct morphology and colouring as well as its definable geographical range. The others we consider to be varieties of subsp. *fuchsii*, as in all cases the populations tend to grade into nearby populations of the nominate plant.

(a) subsp. *fuchsii*

Stem to 50(–70) cm, usually green; *leaves* usually spotted, sometimes heavily; *inflorescence* often more than 4 cm long, ± pyramidal, moderately dense; *flowers* usually pale to deep pink, very occasionally almost white or pure white; *labellum* up to 12 mm wide; *spur* 5–7 mm long, about 2 mm wide at mouth; *flowering* May to early July.

As subsp. *fuchsii* this plant has been considered by Sell (Sell & Murrell 1996) to occur in two varieties, var. *fuchsii* being a taller, longer-spiked plant with a leafy

Plate 228 (below left). A pale-flowered *Dactylorhiza fuchsii*: pure-white forms also occur. In this species the central lobe of the labellum is always the longest. Rough coastal grassland, Argyll, 28 June 1990.

Plate 229 (below right). The other end of the spectrum: the purple labellum of *Dactylorhiza fuchsii* subsp. *fuchsii* var. *rhodochila*. Rough grassy area in public parkland, Fife, 7 July 2003.

stem and with the central lobe of the labellum appreciably exceeding the laterals, normally to be found in light woodland and scrub. The other variety, var. *trilobata* (Bréb.) P.D. Sell, is said to be shorter, less leafy, with a shorter spike and labellum lobes all about equal in length; this a plant of more open habitats such as calcareous grassland. Bateman & Denholm (1989), however, reject the name *trilobata* on grounds of morphological indistinction, as well as taxonomic confusion, and it seems best to view the broad sweep as subsp. *fuchsii* without subdivision.

This is by far the most widespread variant of *D. fuchsii* within the British Isles. Occasional albino plants occur, with pure white flowers, which should not be confused with var. *okellyi* (see p. 230). Plants with exceptionally heavily pigmented flowers have been distinguished as *D. fuchsii* subsp. *fuchsii* var. *rhodochila* Turner Ettl., although the rank of *forma* would probably be more appropriate. This is a strikingly attractive variant and occurs quite widely, if occasionally, in populations of *D. fuchsii* subsp. *fuchsii*.

We treat the following taxa as varieties of subsp. *fuchsii*, as they show only minor morphological differences and geographical distinction from the wider populations of subsp. *fuchsii*, in many sites intergrading with plants indistinguishable from the norm.

The infraspecific taxa of *Dactylorhiza fuchsii* are not differentiated in this map.

Plate 230. When conditions are right, huge numbers of *Dactylorhiza fuchsii* can be found; this population has dwindled, however, as the site has become more shaded. Edge of *Salix* woodland on clay, East Berkshire, June 1988.

var. *cornubiensis*   (Pugsley) Soó

Stem usually less than 20 cm, usually suffused purple; *leaves* usually heavily spotted; *inflores-cence* 4 cm or less; *flowers* deep pink to reddish purple; *labellum* usually more than 9.5 mm wide; *spur* 7–8.5 mm, more than 2 mm wide at mouth; *flowering* June.

So far known only from Cornwall, plants with large dark flowers found in grassland and stabilised dunes on the coast near Tintagel and Lelant are considered to be a local variant and take their name from the Latin name for Cornwall, *Cornubia*. Although this has been treated as a variety of subsp. *hebridensis* (Sell & Murrell 1996), it seems more likely to be a separate development from subsp. *fuchsii*, marked by slightly larger and darker flowers. When searching for plants to photograph Sid Clarke found that individuals of '*cornubiensis*' were scarcely distinct from typical plants in the same area.

Plate 231. Darker flowers and a broader than normal labellum distinguish the local *Dactylorhiza fuchsii* var. *cornubiensis*. Coastal grassland, West Cornwall, 16 June 1998.

var. *alpina*   (Landwehr) R.M. Bateman & Denholm

Stem occasionally more than 20 cm, usually suffused purple; *leaves* usually heavily spotted; *inflorescence* usually less than 4 cm; *flowers* deep pink to reddish purple; *labellum* usually less than 9.5 mm wide; *spur* 7–8.5 mm, seldom more than 2 mm wide at mouth; *flowering* late June to July.

Bateman & Denholm (1989) equate small, dark-flowered plants from upland mainland Britain with similar material from continental Europe, and apply the epithet *alpina* to all these populations. This variant is known from Scotland and northern England, with possible occurrences in Wales and Ireland, and is morphometrically distinct from all other varieties. It differs from subsp. *hebridensis*, with which it is most likely to be confused, in having narrower, non-recurved leaves, a less dense inflorescence and a rather smaller labellum. Coastal plants attributed to this taxon are very close to subsp. *hebridensis*, while inland populations are not easy to distinguish from normal plants of subsp. *fuchsii*.

Plate 232 (opposite). Small, dark-flowered plants of the Common Spotted-orchid from upland and northern areas are known as *Dactylorhiza fuchsii* var. *alpina*. Perthshire, 19 July 1996.

Plate 233 (below). Coastal populations of *Dactylorhiza fuchsii* var. *alpina* are not easy to distinguish from subsp. *hebridensis*. Coastal machair, West Sutherland, 25 July 2003.

var. *okellyi* (Druce) R.M. Bateman & Denholm

Syn. *D. fuchsii* subsp. *okellyi* (Druce) Soó

Stem usually less than 20 cm, occasionally suffused purple; *leaves* narrow, rarely more than 2 cm wide, unspotted or faintly spotted; *inflorescence* usually not more than 4 cm long, cylindrical, not especially dense; *flowers* white or creamish, unmarked or with pinkish markings, strongly scented; *labellum* to about 9 mm wide; *spur* 5.5–6.5 mm, usually less than 2 mm wide at mouth.

This small, very attractive, white- or pale-flowered plant, endemic to the British Isles, is restricted to western and northern Ireland and to the western coast of Scotland in Kintyre; there is also one old, unconfirmed record from Sutherland. It is known from the South Ebudes and from a single record on the Isle of Man, but is rare in all its non-Irish localities. It is especially a plant of short, calcareous coastal turf and of the limestone pavement of the Irish Burren. It was named after P.B. O'Kelly of Bally-

Plate 234. *Dactylorhiza fuchsii* var. *okellyi* may be white or very pale pink; it is not an anthocyanin-free albino. Limestone pavement, the Burren, Co. Clare, 3 July 2002.

vaughan, Co. Clare (*fl*.1890–1930), who made his living selling rare plants from the Burren! It is often assumed that var. *okellyi* is entirely anthocyanin-free, but Summerhayes (1968) and Bateman & Denholm (1989) agree that some or many plants in each population show pigmentation of flowers and leaves, as a normal part of the variation of the taxon. Occasional white-flowered individuals of other subspecies should not be considered to be var. *okellyi*, except in the localities mentioned.

(b) subsp. *hebridensis* (Wilmott) Soó

Syn. *D. fuchsii* var. *hebridensis* (Wilmott) R.M. Bateman & Denholm

Stem 15–20(–30 cm), often suffused purple; *leaves* usually heavily spotted; *inflorescence* rarely more than 4 cm, often pyramidal; *flowers* deep pink to reddish purple; *labellum* usually more than 9.5 mm wide (to 15 mm); *spur* 7–8.5 mm, about 2 mm wide at mouth; *flowering* late June to July.

Plate 235. The short, dark-flowered *Dactylorhiza fuchsii* subsp. *hebridensis* differs significantly from subsp. *fuchsii* in both morphology and geographical distribution. Coastal machair, Vatersay, Outer Hebrides, 16 July 2003.

Plate 236. 'And we in dreams behold the Hebrides.' The Hebridean Spotted-orchid *Dactylorhiza fuchsii* subsp. *hebridensis* can be incredibly abundant on the shell-sand machair grassland of the Outer Hebrides. Barra, 17 July 2003.

This darkly pigmented taxon is known only from the British Isles, where it is largely restricted to western districts, especially to the Outer Hebrides and a few other islands. It is also known from the nearby coastal mainland of Scotland, and from similar areas of western Ireland. It is a plant of machair grassland and short coastal turf and can often be found there in large populations, frequently with other *Dactylorhiza* species in the vicinity and sometimes hybridising with them.

Plate 237 (near right). The labellum of *Dactylorhiza fuchsii* subsp. *hebridensis* is broader than in the type, and heavily marked with lines and spots. Barra, 17 July 2003.

Plate 238 (far right). The diploid hybrid between *Dactylorhiza incarnata* subsp. *coccinea* and *D. fuchsii* subsp. *hebridensis*, with bright colours and bold markings inherited from its parents. *D. ebudensis* is the allotetraploid derivative of the same cross. Machair, W. Sutherland, 25 June 2003.

16.4. *Dactylorhiza maculata* (L.) Soó

Heath Spotted-orchid

Perennial herb, glabrous throughout, tubers palmate, with short, thick roots; *stem* to 50 cm, solid, erect, pale green but sometimes tinged purple above; *leaves* bright to dark green, normally distinctly spot- and blotch-marked on upper surface, sheathing leaves being ± lanceolate, recurved, 5–15 × 0.5–2.0 cm, crowded towards the stem base, cauline leaves narrower but decreasing in size up the stem; *inflorescence* lax to dense, a pyramidal, rather few-flowered spike; *bracts* linear-lanceolate, green, often tinged with violet, veined, in length equal to or longer than the ovaries; *flowers* from almost white to pale pink or deeper lilac-pink, faintly scented; *outer perianth segments* to 11 mm, narrowly lanceolate; *inner perianth segments* shorter, ± lanceolate; *labellum* to 9 × 13 mm, white to pale pink, dash- and loop-marked in a deeper colour, shallowly trilobed, the lateral lobes broad, rounded, the middle lobe much smaller and shorter than the laterals, ± triangular; *spur* to 9 mm long, straight or slightly curved, slightly tapering; *column* erect; *anther* erect, purplish; *pollinia* two, green; *stigma* edged violet; *rostellum* trilobed; *ovary* sessile, ridged; *flowering* late May to August.

Along with *Dactylorhiza fuchsii*, in the British Isles the Heath Spotted-orchid *D. maculata* is one of the most frequently encountered members of the orchid family. It shows a preference for damp but not waterlogged upland habitats, and is especially frequent throughout the north of England as well as most of Scotland, Wales and much of Ireland. To the south and east of England it is much scarcer but it is still relatively frequent in Norfolk, Sussex and Hampshire. *Dactylorhiza maculata* shows considerable morphological variation, especially in the shape, colour and markings of the flowers, and so has been considered to exist in several distinct taxonomic entities, although some of these have not been too clearly defined. Recent work by Bateman & Denholm (2003) suggests, indeed, that no justifiable infraspecific taxa can be detected when the full range of the species is considered. Viewed as a whole, *D. maculata* (*sensu lato*) reaches eastwards to central Asia, south to the Mediterranean, and north to northern Norway and Iceland. The British and Irish plant is generally known as subsp. *ericetorum* (E.F. Linton) P.F. Hunt & Summerh. In mainland Europe *D. maculata* occurs as several separate subspecies, including subsp. *maculata* and subsp. *elodes* (Griseb.) Soó; the former is absent from the British Isles, but both are frequent on the Continent. In the British Isles subsp. *elodes* has usually been included within subsp. *ericetorum*, although Grisebach's name *elodes* (1845) has priority over Linton's

Plate 239. A deep-pink Heath Spotted-orchid *Dactylorhiza maculata*. Plants with this colouring occur in several areas. Coastal acid heath, West Sutherland, 22 July 2000.

Plate 241 (opposite). A boldly marked *Dactylorhiza maculata*: the labellum markings are often spotted rather than looped, as seen in Plate 53 (p. 46). Acidic grassland, Selkirkshire, 1 July 1998.

ericetorum (1900). At least four other non-British subspecies have also been described: subsp. *schurii* (Klinge) Soó, from the Carpathians; subsp. *transilvanica* (Schur) Soó, mainly from Yugoslavia; subsp. *islandica* (Á. & D. Löve) Soó, from Iceland; and subsp. *lancibracteata* (C. Koch) Soó, from Turkey and the Caucasus. Lastly, plants from the Scottish island of Rhum and other nearby islets have been separated as subsp. *rhoumensis* (H.-Harr. fil) Soó, on the grounds of darker colour and a later flowering period. They are said to be more strongly marked than subsp. *ericetorum* and have a longer central lobe to the labellum, so showing an approach to *D. fuchsii*. Bateman & Denholm (1989, 2003) studied populations on Rhum and elsewhere in the Hebrides and mainland Britain and were unable to find convincing evidence that this can be regarded as a taxon distinct from subsp. *ericetorum*. They

Plate 240. Separated from its close relative *Dactylorhiza fuchsii* by its preference for acidic soils, *D. maculata* also has proportionately longer, narrower leaves with more intense dark spotting. Acidic grassland, Stirlingshire, 13 June 1992.

note, however, that dark-flowered populations occur both on Rhum and on Exmoor, probably having different origins. Pure white forms (f. *candidissima*) have been recorded (see Plate 202, p. 202), and Bateman & Denholm (1989) have observed that these occur most frequently where *D. maculata* grows above limestone. A variant with very heavy pigmentation in the flowers, *D. maculata* f. *concolor* (Vermeul.) Landwehr (Plate 54, p. 47), has appeared occasionally at sites scattered between the New Forest and West Ross.

The specific name is derived from the Latin *macula*, 'spot' or 'stain', and refers to the dot-marked leaves. The first British record for the plant may have been made by John Gerard in 1597 (but see the account for the Common Spotted-orchid *D. fuchsii* above, p. 223).

The habitat requirement for *D. maculata* is damp acidic conditions, such as are found in upland regions of the British Isles, to an altitude of at least 900 m. Moors, flushed grasslands and bogs are favoured. The plant is also frequent on lowland heaths, and even occurs in limestone areas where the substrate is locally overlain with a peat deposit; more rarely it occurs in open woodland. It occupies a wide range of NVC heath, mire and grassland communities, too numerous to detail here. Although there has been some loss of habitat this has largely been due to drainage, lack of grazing, or commercial development, mostly of lowland heath and bog, and as *D. maculata* is an upland plant most populations should be safe from similar threats.

The Heath Spotted-orchid is easy to locate, sometimes present in large numbers, at other times scattered, especially in damp spots on upland, rather acidic

Plate 242. The Heath Spotted-orchid *Dactylorhiza maculata* is the most abundant orchid across the acidic moors and heaths of the northern and western British Isles. Moorland, Isle of Lewis, Outer Hebrides, 14 July 1991.

grassland. It is rather similar in general appearance to *D. fuchsii* but an examination of the labellum will reveal its relatively broad lateral lobes between which is positioned a much smaller, often shorter central one. In *D. fuchsii* the lobes are more or less equal in size, or the central lobe is the longest.

A characteristic of *D. maculata* is its readiness to hybridise with other species of *Dactylorhiza* in situations where they grow close together. This is especially the case with *D. purpurella* in the north, where the hybrid is found to favour slightly less acidic conditions than *D. maculata*. The parents may not always be present, lost either through changing ecological conditions or, since the hybrid is at least partially fertile, through backcrossing to one or other of the parents. In consequence some populations exist as complex hybrid swarms. Hybrids and backcrossed swarms of *D. maculata* with *D. praetermissa* also occur sometimes, but much less frequently, since the parents differ appreciably in their relative tolerance of basic conditions and so are less likely to come into close contact. Where they overlap *D. maculata* also occasionally hybridises with *D. fuchsii*, but the offspring can be very difficult to detect among the parents, and some records of this hybrid may be errors for variants of one or other supposed parent. Hybrids with some of the subspecies of *D. incarnata* are not uncommon, and offspring of *D. maculata* with the much rarer *D. traunsteinerioides* are occasionally found. Intergeneric hybrids involving *Gymnadenia* are recorded from western Scotland, and one with *Pseudorchis albida* has been claimed for Orkney and Skye.

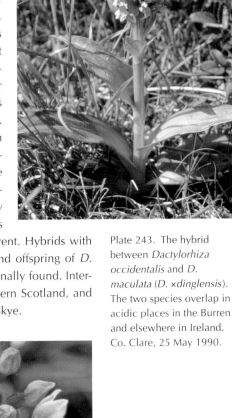

Plate 243. The hybrid between *Dactylorhiza occidentalis* and *D. maculata* (*D. ×dinglensis*). The two species overlap in acidic places in the Burren and elsewhere in Ireland. Co. Clare, 25 May 1990.

Plates 244 (far left) and 245 (near left). Two individuals from the cross between *Gymnadenia borealis* and *Dactylorhiza maculata* (×*Dactylodenia legrandiana*), showing how hybrid orchids can differ greatly and cause much confusion – and interest. Damp heath, east Inverness-shire, 30 June 2003.

16.5. *Dactylorhiza praetermissa* (Druce) Soó

Southern Marsh-orchid

Perennial herb, glabrous throughout, tubers palmate, roots long, thick; *stem* to 70 cm and often more than 5 mm in diameter, robust, thick-walled but hollow, erect, green; *leaves* grey-green or darker, unspotted or with large, elongated, ring-like spots, sheathing leaves at least four, to 15 × 3.5 cm, ± oblong-lanceolate, spreading, crowded towards the stem base, the cauline leaves similar but smaller; *inflorescence* a usually dense and many-flowered, cylindrical spike; *bracts* linear-lanceolate, acute, green, often tinged purple; *flowers* a rich pink-purple, sometimes paler; *outer perianth segments* to 15 mm, lanceolate, pink-purple, veined; *inner perianth segments* shorter, ovate-lanceolate, obtuse; *labellum* up to 12 × 14 mm, pink-purple to magenta, lightly dot- and line-marked, sometimes heavier, broadly elliptical, shallowly trilobed, the laterals rounded, the central short, rounded; *spur* to 9 mm long, slightly tapering; *column* short, erect; *anther* purplish; *pollinia* two, greenish; *stigma* edged purple; *rostellum* purplish; *ovary* fusiform, ridged; *flowering* late June to July; 2n = 80.

Plate 247. How could *Dactylorhiza praetermissa* have been overlooked by botanists until 1914? Marsh by chalk stream, N. Hampshire, 4 July 1994.

Plate 246 (opposite). The labellum of the Southern Marsh-orchid may be almost unlobed, as in this magnificent white-flowered specimen (var. *albiflora* (Druce) Harz). Marsh by chalk stream, North Hampshire, 9 July 1996.

Dactylorhiza praetermissa, known aptly (for the British Isles at least) as the Southern Marsh-orchid, occurs most frequently in the south and south-east, with an area of overlap with the Northern Marsh-orchid *D. purpurella* from south Wales through Cheshire and Lancashire to north-east Yorkshire. Except in central and north Wales it is a frequent plant to the south of this line, and also occurs in the Isles of Scilly and the Channel Islands. Outside the British Isles it is restricted to north-west Europe, where it is a local and uncommon plant of northern France, Denmark, Belgium and the Netherlands. It has been demonstrated that *D. praetermissa* is an allotetraploid derived from *D. incarnata* and *D. fuchsii* (Hédren 1996c), but more recent work (Pillon *et al.* in press) has detected elements of the genome of *D. saccifera* (Brongn.) Soó, a Balkan species closely allied to *D. fuchsii*, in some samples of *D. praetermissa*.

In Britain the Southern Marsh-orchid prefers a damp calcareous habitat such as is found in marshes, fens, water-meadows and dune slacks. Here populations are often large. In some cases the plant also occurs in slightly more acidic conditions in damp heathland. It shows a similarity to its close ally *D. purpurella* in also being quick to colonise quarry floors, disused industrial areas and other man-made habitats such as road verges. It is a lowland plant, rarely ascending to above 200 m.

Frequent associates are orchids such as *D. incarnata, Epipactis palustris* and *Gymnadenia densiflora*, and other occupants of damp meadows, grassland and marshes such as *Caltha palustris, Filipendula ulmaria, Menyanthes trifoliata* and various species of *Carex* and *Juncus*. Around fen and marsh margins it grows alongside *Equisetum palustre, Glyceria maxima* and *Phragmites australis*, and in sandy boggy areas with *Eriophorum latifolium* and *Molinia caerulea*. In sand-dune slacks *Dactylorhiza incarnata* subsp. *coccinea* may accompany it, along with *Epipactis palustris* and *Salix repens. Dactylorhiza praetermissa* also occasionally occurs in dry chalk and limestone grassland but there usually only as rather stunted depauperate plants and in populations which do not seem really to thrive. As will be gathered from the above, the plant is represented in a wide range of NVC associations, among which the mire (M13 and M22–M24), swamp (S24) and dune-slack (SD14–16) communities are the most important. As with most other marsh-orchids it is susceptible to losses through drainage or commercial development, but overall it appears to be stable, and there is even evidence of a possible increase as it colonises man-made habitats.

Plate 248. The Southern Marsh-orchid can be extremely abundant in suitable places, but it is sensitive to habitat change. Rough coastal grassland, N. Somerset, 17 June 1997.

The Southern Marsh-orchid is not a difficult plant to locate in the south of England. Its relatively robust stature, larger flowers and labellum lightly marked (rather than loop-marked) with small dots are sufficient to distinguish it from *D. incarnata* subsp. *incarnata*, to which it has a superficial resemblance. The specific name *praetermissa* is based on the Latin *praetermissio*, 'omission', since it was overlooked as a true species until described by Druce in 1914.

Plate 249 (far left). The labellum of *Dactylorhiza praetermissa* is finely speckled with markings. Deep-pink or light purple are the normal colours. Marsh by chalk stream, N. Hampshire, 28 June 2002.

Plate 250 (near left). Plants with looser spikes and more obviously lobed labella have been called *Dactylorhiza praetermissa* var. *macrantha* (Sipkes) R.M. Bateman & Denholm: they are rare and possibly of hybrid origin. Water meadow, Dorset, 5 June 1997.

In the south of England, especially in the area between Kent and Cornwall, there exist populations of plants that generally resemble typical *D. praetermissa* but have leaves that are very heavily spotted or ring-marked and flowers that are deeper coloured and more heavily marked. In the past these have been placed at various taxonomic levels. They were described as *Orchis pardalina* (from the Latin *pardus*, 'leopard') by Pugsley, but earlier as *Orchis latifolia* var. *junialis* by Vermeulen; nowadays, however, they are usually accepted as merely a form of *D. praetermissa*, forma *junialis* (Vermeul.) P.D. Sell. They remain recognisable within populations of

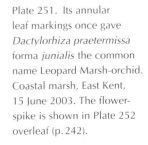

Plate 251. Its annular leaf markings once gave *Dactylorhiza praetermissa* forma *junialis* the common name Leopard Marsh-orchid. Coastal marsh, East Kent, 15 June 2003. The flower-spike is shown in Plate 252 overleaf (p. 242).

typical *D. praetermissa*, which in some cases they outnumber. *Dactylorhiza fuchsii* is often found to be present together with *D. praetermissa* wherever f. *junialis* is found, and it has been suggested (Summerhayes 1968) that the latter may have arisen through hybridisation between *D. fuchsii* and *D. praetermissa*. However, f. *junialis* exhibits a relatively high degree of uniformity between and within populations and also possesses relatively high fertility as judged by the number of seed capsules set, and these factors would seem to militate against the idea of a hybrid origin. Apparently confirming this, Pillon and

co-workers (Pillon *et al.* subm.) regard the plant as a variant of the allotetraploid *D. praetermissa*. The name *junialis* derives from the Latin *iunius*, 'June', after the month in which it begins to flower.

At the north-western limit of its range, in the area of overlap with *D. purpurella*, hybrids with this latter species have been recorded, especially in Wales. *Dactylorhiza praetermissa* also frequently hybridises with *D. fuchsii*, whilst in base-rich fens in East Anglia plants with narrower leaves, more lax inflorescences and intermediate labella have been considered to be the hybrid with *D. traunsteinerioides*. If true, this would be an endemic British hybrid.

Plate 252. *Dactylorhiza praetermissa* forma *junialis* is found among populations of unspotted plants. Coastal marsh, E. Kent, 15 June 2003.

16.6. *Dactylorhiza traunsteinerioides*

(Pugsley) Landwehr

Including *Dactylorhiza traunsteineri* auctt. non (Sauter ex Rchb. f.) Soó;
  Dactylorhiza traunsteineri subsp. *lapponica* (Laest. ex Hartm.) Soó

Narrow-leaved Marsh-orchid or Pugsley's Marsh-orchid

Perennial herb with short thickened tubers, roots thick, numerous; *stem* to *c*.30 cm, rarely more, somewhat hollow, flexuous, slender, pale green but often noticeably tinged purple above; *leaves* pale to medium green, unspotted or spotted, sheathing leaves few, usually two to four, narrow, oblong- to linear-lanceolate, sometimes ± recurved, 5–12 × 0.5–1.8 cm, cauline leaves very few, similar in shape but smaller; *inflorescence* a lax, few-flowered, ± one-sided spike; *bracts* linear-lanceolate, green, often tinged or spotted mauve-violet; *flowers* pale to deep lilac- or red-purple with darker markings; *outer perianth segments* to 8 mm, oblong-lanceolate; *inner perianth segments* ovate; *labellum* to 9 × 11 mm, pale to deep lilac- or red-purple with darker markings, very rarely white and unmarked, ± deltate, distinctly trilobed with the central lobe much the longer; *spur* to 10 mm long, straight or slightly curved; *column* small; *anther* elliptical, pink-violet; *pollinia* two, green; *stigma* tinged violet; *rostellum* trilobed; *ovary* sessile, ridged, tinged violet; *flowering* late May to June (to July); 2n = 80.

This rather scarce plant has received much attention over the years as its taxonomy and relationship with plants on the European mainland have been debated. Although Pugsley postulated, as long ago as 1936, a distinction between plants in the British Isles (which he named *traunsteinerioides*, meaning 'traunsteineri-like') and the Continental *D. traunsteineri*, and this distinction has been upheld by authorities such as Delforge (1995), others such as Roberts (1988) and Foley (1990a) found no morphological characters to support it. Recently, however, the group has been subjected to genetic analysis, and it has been shown that despite their morphological similarities the various populations do have different genetic origins and should therefore be regarded as distinct entities (Hédren *et al.* 2001, Bateman 2005 in press, Pillon *et al.* subm.). The name *Dactylorhiza traunsteinerioides* (Pugsley) Landwehr is therefore the appropriate one for use in the British Isles. The common name 'Pugsley's Marsh-orchid' commemorates the botanist who first recognised the plant's distinctiveness. *Dactylorhiza traunsteineri* (Sauter ex Rchb.) Soó should be regarded as a Continental taxon, centred on the Alps. Its name honours the Austrian amateur botanist Josef Traunsteiner (1798–1850).

Further complicating the situation is the Scandinavian taxon *Dactylorhiza lapponica* (Laest. ex Rchb.f) Soó. Plants resembling this are known from Scotland, and on their discovery in 1988 they were referred to as *D. lapponica*, but the consensus

Plate 253. Pugsley's Marsh-orchid *Dactylorhiza traunsteinerioides*. This individual has unspotted leaves, and would formerly have been called *D. traunsteineri*. Wet hillside flush, West Ross, 23 June 1996.

then developed that they were not greatly distinct from other British and Irish populations of '*D. traunsteineri*', leading to their treatment by Sell & Murrell (1996) as *D. traunsteineri* subsp. *lapponica* (Laest. ex Hartm.) Soó, at least within the British Isles. (The Scandinavian plants appear to be distinct from those found in Britain.) Recent morphological and molecular work by Bateman (2005 in press), however, failed to find any significant difference between supposed '*traunsteineri*' and supposed '*lapponica*' in Scottish populations and he considers it best to regard all British plants of this group as *D. traunsteinerioides*. Further work is needed to clarify the situation with regard to Scandinavian *D. lapponica*, which may have yet another independent origin as an allotetraploid.

In the British Isles *D. traunsteinerioides* is a scarce plant with a scattered, patchy distribution. Confusion with other marsh-orchids has, in some instances, led to doubtful records, and some of those shown in the *New Atlas of the British and Irish Flora* (2002) may include these. It does, however, have a concentration of populations in East Anglia, Yorkshire, North Wales (especially Anglesey), western Scotland and the Burren area of western Ireland. It is also recorded more locally in western and southern England, as well as elsewhere in Ireland. It is not yet clear if it occurs outside the British Isles: Delforge (1995) tentatively ascribes populations in the Somme area of northern France to this taxon.

Despite the recent agglomeration of the two taxa formerly recognised as *D. traunsteineri* subsp. *traunsteineri* and subsp. *lapponica* there is some merit in discussing them independently. The most commonly found form is 'subsp. *traunsteineri*', which is taller (up to 40 cm) and has unspotted or lightly spotted leaves. The bracts are suffused red-purple throughout and are not usually spotted.

This plant shows a marked preference for strongly base-rich flushes, especially localities where calcareous water percolates over a sparse ground cover and particularly where there is a build-up of tufa. It also occurs in and at the margins of fens, and occasionally in other wet but more neutral conditions. Records for slightly acidic conditions should be carefully scrutinised since it is easy to confuse this plant with aberrant forms and hybrids of *D. purpurella*, as well as with two of the subspecies of *D. incarnata* (subsp. *pulchella* and subsp. *cruenta*). Especially in its spring-flush community, *Schoenus nigricans* is an ever-present associate; other associates include *Carex* species which are typical of its habitat, *Menyanthes trifoliata*, *Pinguicula vulgaris*, *Valeriana dioica*, and in the north of England *Primula farinosa*. In the NVC system it is classified as being mainly present in mires, including *the Schoenus nigricans – Juncus subnodulosus* mire (M13), and within that the *Festuca rubra – Juncus acutiflorus*, *Briza*

Plates 254 (opposite) and 255 (below). First identified as *Dactylorhiza lapponica*, the small, heavily spotted plants of *D. traunsteinerioides* are found only in northern Scotland. No significant differences exist between populations, suggesting that they are best considered as a single allotetraploid species. Ardnamurchan crater, west Inverness-shire, 18 June 1996.

Plate 256. The rounded lateral lobes and well developed central lobe of the labellum are useful characters for recognising *Dactylorhiza traunsteinerioides*. '*D. traunsteineri*', wet hillside flush, West Ross, 23 June 1996.

media – Pinguicula vulgaris and *Caltha palustris – Galium uliginosum* subcommunities. Many of these habitats are especially fragile and easily damaged, and great care should be taken when visiting sites. The flush populations are often small, some having only a handful of plants. One unusual habitat occurs on the Durham coast where the plant is found in small numbers in a flush on steep magnesian limestone cliffs, overlooking the sea.

In its typical form the plant is not difficult to recognise, its slender habit, few unspotted leaves, and elegant, deeply trilobed labellum being diagnostic. Like most species of *Dactylorhiza*, however, it is subject to variation and hybridisation, and in such cases correct identification is more difficult. Most populations are in protected areas such as nature reserves or SSSIs, some in north-east Yorkshire and on Anglesey having a majority of typical plants. These will be the best places to search. Drainage and man-made disturbance are the main threats to the plant's survival, but lack of grazing, and conifer plantation, will also adversely affect some populations.

Populations and individual plants formerly treated as *D. traunsteineri* subsp. *lapponica* differ from 'subsp. *traunsteineri*' in being usually shorter (to 20 cm tall), with heavily spotted leaves and bracts. As Bateman (2005 in press) has shown, however, these characters are not reliable, and intermediates and examples of 'typical *traunsteineri*' can occur in the same populations. All such populations occur in Scotland, with scattered locations on the mainland from Kintyre northwards to Sutherland and occasionally in the Western Isles; the plant is not recorded for Ireland. It favours wet, base-rich hill

Plate 257. Habitat of *Dactylorhiza traunsteinerioides* ('*D. lapponica*'). Ardnamurchan crater, west Inverness-shire, 18 June 1996.

flushes within areas that are largely acidic and peaty. In the Scottish isles it occurs close to sea-level but on the mainland it can ascend to 300 m or so. On its discovery, when it was identified as *D. lapponica*, the plant was regarded as a rarity for which Schedule 8 protection was necessary, but this species-defined conservation category is likely to be downgraded when it is treated as a variant within the non-threatened *D. traunsteinerioides*.

Pollination of *D. traunsteinerioides* is by the same method as for other species of *Dactylorhiza*, and subsequent seed-set is usually good. Vegetative multiplication will occur where mature plants produce lateral shoots, which ultimately detach and so form separate plants.

16.7. *Dactylorhiza ebudensis*

(Wief. ex R.M. Bateman & Denholm) P. Delforge

Syn. *Dactylorhiza majalis* subsp. *scotica* E. Nelson; *Dactylorhiza comosa*
    subsp. *scotica* (E. Nelson) P.D. Sell; *Dactylorhiza majalis* subsp. *occidentalis*
    var. *ebudensis* Wief. ex R.M. Bateman & Denholm

Hebridean Marsh-orchid

Plate 258. Its intense coloration and heavy leaf-markings should make *Dactylorhiza ebudensis* easy to recognise among other Hebridean dactylorchids. Wet machair, N. Uist, Outer Hebrides, 12 June 2000.

Perennial herb, glabrous throughout, tubers palmate, roots numerous, thick; *stem* only 6–10(–18) cm, erect, flushed reddish brown; *leaves* dull green, heavily blotched and often purple-bordered, to 16 mm wide, sheathing leaves two to three, rosette-like at the base of the stem, spreading to erect, usually arched, cauline leaves usually only one; *inflorescence* a dense spike to 6 cm long; *bracts* suffused reddish brown, sometimes spotted, the lowermost leaf-like; *flowers* five to twenty, violet-purple; *outer perianth segments* to 10 mm, linear-lanceolate, obtuse, red-purple, marked; *inner perianth segments* oblong, red-purple; *labellum* 6–8.5 × 8–11.5 mm, weakly trilobed, lateral lobes usually reflexed; *spur* usually less than 8.5 mm long, usually not exceeding 3.0 mm wide, longer than ovary, conical, purple; *column* short, erect; *anther* pink-violet; *pollinia* two, greenish; *stigma* edged purple; *rostellum* red-violet; *ovary* slender, ridged, flushed purple; *flowering* late May to June (to July); 2n = 80.

The Hebridean Marsh-orchid, as it has come to be called, was first discovered in 1936 by M.S. Campbell, and was then attributed to *Dactylorhiza occidentalis* (Campbell 1937). Its nomenclatural history in the intervening years has recently been expounded in detail by Lowe (2003),

revealing an extraordinary saga of taxonomic errors (the epithet *scotica* having never been validly published) and confusion over the entities formerly included in '*D. majalis*'. Lowe himself published the combination *D. majalis* subsp. *ebudensis* (Wief. ex R.M. Bateman & Denholm) M.R. Lowe for this taxon, and it has also been referred to as *D. traunsteineri* (Carey & Dines, in Preston *et al.* 2002). The recent acceptance that *D. majalis* does not occur in the British Isles, and that the taxa formerly referred to it as subspecies are in fact allotetraploids of independent origin, enables the recognition of *D. ebudensis* as a full species. Molecular analysis has even demonstrated that its parentage is *D. incarnata* subsp. *coccinea* × *D. fuchsii* subsp. *hebridensis* (Bateman 2005, in press), one that befits an independent Hebridean origin.

The plant that has caused so much interest and taxonomic angst is limited in its distribution to one 10 km square in North Uist, and has a total population of about 2000 flowering plants (Lowe 2003). It grows in an unusual type of machair vegetation, in an extensive dune slack where a high water-table is perched not far below the surface. In NVC terms it may be characterized as *Festuca rubra* – *Galium verum* fixed-dune grassland (SD8), sub-community *Bellis perennis* – *Ranunculus acris*.

The majority of the population occurs in a single slack system stretching over 2 km, although there are a few satellite populations as well. In this area *D. purpurella* is scarce, but both it and *D. incarnata* subsp. *coccinea* become more frequent where wetter conditions prevail (Lowe 2003). Hybridisation with other *Dactylorhiza* taxa is suspected, especially since plants intermediate to *D. purpurella* are known. The site is a designated SSSI, which confers some protection, but threats may arise through loss of habitat as a consequence of agricultural 'improvement' or a change in grazing regime. The new Red List (Cheffings & Farrell 2005) rates *D. ebudensis* under the IUCN category 'Vulnerable', and Lowe (2003) proposes Schedule 8 protection for this endemic plant.

Plate 259. *Dactylorhiza ebudensis* is found only in one population, on North Uist, Outer Hebrides. 14 June 1990.

Plate 260 (opposite). The Hebridean Marsh-orchid is a genuine endemic that deserves full legal protection. Wet machair, North Uist, Outer Hebrides, 14 June 2000.

16.8. *Dactylorhiza purpurella* (T. & T.A. Stephenson) Soó

Northern Marsh-orchid

Perennial herb, glabrous throughout, tubers palmate with many thick roots; *stem* to 30(–45) cm and up to 5 mm in diameter, slightly hollow, erect, green; *leaves* dull green, unmarked or lightly spotted towards the apex to heavily blotch-marked on upper surface, sheathing leaves at least four, to 15 × 3 cm, ± lanceolate, slightly spreading, crowded towards the stem base, cauline leaves smaller, ± lanceolate; *inflorescence* a usually dense and many-flowered, ovoid to cylindrical, sometimes ± flat-topped spike; *bracts* linear-lanceolate, acute, green, often tinged purple; *flowers* usually a rich red-purple, sometimes paler; *outer perianth segments* to 8 mm, ovate-lanceolate, red-purple, dash-marked; *inner perianth segments* ovate, sometimes crenulate; *labellum* up to 9 × 11 mm, red-purple, loop- and line-marked, deltate to rhomboid, ± entire with only a short mid-lobe to shallowly tri-lobed, almost flat; *spur* to 9 mm long, conical, purple; *column* short, whitish; *anther* purplish, spotted; *pollinia* two, green; *stigma* shiny, edged purple; *rostellum* purplish; *ovary* erect, cylindrical, ridged, spotted; *flowering* late May to July (to early August); 2n = 80.

As with most of the allotetraploid marsh-orchids, *Dactylorhiza purpurella* was formerly treated as a subspecies of *D. majalis*, but the morphological and molecular consensus has long held it to be a distinct species. Hédren (1996b) and Pillon *et al.* (subm.) have demonstrated that it is a derivative of a cross between *D. incarnata*

Plate 261 (opposite). The deep-purple flowers of the Northern Marsh-orchid *Dactylorhiza purpurella* var. *purpurella* are a lovely and, fortunately, frequent sight in the northern half of the British Isles. Marshy coastal grassland, Fife, 16 June 2002.

Plate 262. The observant motorist will often spot *Dactylorhiza purpurella* var. *purpurella* on road-side verges in the north, as here in Berwickshire, 5 June 1998. A fruiting spike from the previous year is visible.

and *D. fuchsii*. In addition to the nominate var. *purpurella*, the somewhat different var. *cambrensis* has also recently been distinguished.

The Northern Marsh-orchid is principally found, as its common name implies, in the more northern parts of the British mainland, where it is a frequent plant in appropriate habitat. It is frequent too on the islands off the west coast of Scotland, as well as in Orkney, Shetland, the Isle of Man, Ulster and north-eastern parts of the Republic of Ireland. It also occurs at scattered localities elsewhere in Ireland. It is interesting to note that its near relative *D. praetermissa* replaces it in areas to the south and south-east of its territory but scarcely transgresses into it. Nevertheless, there is a band of overlap loosely dividing the two species, running north-eastwards from south Wales through Cheshire, Lancashire and into north-east Yorkshire, where the plants occasionally hybridise. There is also one anomalous population in Hampshire (Lang 2004). *Dactylorhiza purpurella* is also found in the countries of north-west Europe, especially the Faeroe Islands, the west coast of Norway and the Baltic island of Gotland, and as subsp. *majaliformis* it has been recorded from Denmark.

Plate 263. Unspotted leaves and an almost unlobed labellum are good characters for *Dactylorhiza purpurella* var. *purpurella*. Roadside verge, Berwickshire, 5 June 1998.

This is a plant of bogs, marshes and similar wet habitats. Although it often occurs in generally acidic, upland areas, a certain amount of calcareous ground water or base-rich flushing is a necessary requirement. It is also found in more or less neutral conditions such as in damp meadows and, on drier ground, sometimes in disused industrial areas. In more calcareous districts it can grow on quarry floors and in dune slacks.

Dactylorhiza purpurella var. *atrata* is heavily pigmented in both its leaves and its flowers. Rough coastal grassland, Co. Durham. Plate 264 (near right): 6 June 2002; Plate 265 (far right): 19 June 2002.

(a) var. *purpurella*

Leaves unmarked or with small spots, often restricted to the apical portion; *bracts* usually unspotted; *labellum* somewhat rounded, 5–8 × 6–10 mm, almost entire or very weakly lobed.

Widely distributed throughout the range of the species, this is one of the orchids most frequently encountered in the north of the British Isles. It is found from lowland dune slacks and coastal marshes to high-altitude hill flushes, reaching to at least 600 m in northern Scotland. Its associates include a wide range of *Carex* species, several species of *Juncus, Schoenus nigricans*, grasses such as *Briza media, Molinia caerulea* and *Nardus stricta*, and herbs including *Caltha palustris, Galium palustre, G. uliginosum, Pinguicula vulgaris* and *Primula farinosa*. It is represented in a wide range of NVC mire, grassland and sand-dune communities. Populations, especially in the lowlands, can be very large, and it seems to be a very efficient coloniser, readily setting viable seed.

It is also not averse to occupying what appear to be somewhat atypical dry habitats on roadside verges or derelict urban sites. Some of these populations may contain hybrids, especially with *D. fuchsii*, and frequent backcrossing may lead to the development of hybrid swarms from which both parents are eventually eliminated. As for all plants of damp habitats, sites are liable to destruction through drainage, and redevelopment and coastal leisure projects can also be a threat. This is, however, a common plant in the north, and its overall distribution appears to be stable.

The Northern Marsh-orchid is readily found in hilly areas, where besides the spotted-orchids and *D. incarnata* it is the most frequent member of the genus; its deep purple flowers, with deltate, more or less undivided labella, and unspotted or lightly spotted leaves should be adequate to differentiate it. The name *purpurella*

Plate 266 (far left). The rare *Dactylorhiza purpurella* var. *maculosa* (T. Stephenson) R.M. Bateman & Denholm has light spotting on the upper surface of the leaves. Rough coastal grassland, Co. Durham, 6 June 2002.

Plate 267 (near left). *Dactylorhiza purpurella* is as promiscuous as any other member of the genus: here it has contributed its dark colour to its offspring with *Dactylorhiza incarnata* subsp. *incarnata* (*D. ×latirella*). Lightly grazed field, Barra, Outer Hebrides, 17 July 2003.

Plate 268. The Northern
Marsh-orchid can occur in
large numbers in moist,
base-rich sites. Road verge,
Berwickshire, 5 June 1998.

Plate 268. The Northern
Marsh-orchid can occur in
large numbers in moist,
base-rich sites. Road verge,
Berwickshire, 5 June 1998.

originates from the colour of the flowers and is derived from the Latin *purpureus*,
'red-purple'. Remarkably, although this – like other species of *Dactylorhiza* – had
been observed in the past, it was not until the work of the Stephensons in the early
part of the twentieth century that it was formally named (as *Orchis*).

Hybrid swarms produced with other *Dactylorhiza* species can often lead to highly
complex populations, the individuals within which largely defy accurate identification on morphological grounds. As well as these, *D. purpurella* has also been known
to form hybrids with *D. viridis* and *Gymnadenia borealis*. A population in Co. Durham of exceptionally dark plants with heavily spotted leaves has been described as
var. *atrata* A.J. Richards.

Plate 269 (opposite).
Dactylorhiza purpurella
var. *cambrensis* is found
along the western and
northern coasts of the
British Isles, usually close
to the sea. This is the
Scottish form, described
as subsp. *majaliformis*.
Coastal grassland,
Caithness, 1 June 1990.

(b) var. *cambrensis* (R.H. Roberts) R.M. Bateman & Denholm

Syn. *D. majalis* subsp. *cambrensis* (R.H. Roberts) R.H. Roberts;
D. comosa subsp. *cambrensis* (R.H. Roberts) R.H. Roberts

Including *D. purpurella* subsp. *majaliformis* E. Nelson

A rather taller plant than var. *purpurella*, with *leaves* more heavily spotted
and with larger spots; *bracts* spotted; *flowers* also larger, especially the
labella; *labellum* 6–8 × 9–11 mm, rhomboid, shallowly to distinctly trilobed, lateral lobes ± flat; *spur* usually less than 3.0 mm wide.

As suggested by the (truncated) list of synonyms given above, the
taxonomic status of this plant has long been debated, it having
been placed at different times into both the catch-all '*D. majalis*'
and '*D. comosa*'. The current view (e.g. Bateman 2005 in press,
Pillon *et al.* subm.) is that it is best regarded as a variety of *D. purpurella*. These robust, deeply coloured orchids, first described

by Roberts as *D. majalis* subsp. *cambrensis*, and validated in this book (p. 373) as *D. purpurella* var. *cambrensis*, are found in wet dune slacks in west Wales, including Anglesey. At least one population, at Ynyslas, has been shown to contain the ITS allele of *D. saccifera*, probably transmitted from a *D. fuchsii* ancestor with this genotype, possibly itself a hybrid with *D. praetermissa* (Pillon *et al.* subm.).

Morphologically similar plants from Scrabster, Caithness, on the coast of northern Scotland, were described as *D. purpurella* subsp. *majaliformis* E. Nelson (1979); as the earlier name within *D. purpurella* this takes priority over *cambrensis* if the taxon is considered to be a subspecies, although *cambrensis* is the prior name and is valid at varietal level. Further work investigating the relationship of these taxa and populations would be desirable.

At all its known sites '*majaliformis*' is restricted to damp, coastal areas, including seaward-facing grassy slopes, usually within 100 m of the sea. These are all on the western and northern Scottish mainland and the Outer Hebrides, apart from two isolated localities in Cardiganshire (possibly confused with populations of var. *cambrensis*). Scottish records of '*D. majalis* subsp. *occidentalis*' are almost certainly referable to this taxon. Outside the British Isles it is has only been recorded in Denmark. The epithet *majaliformis* alludes to its morphological similarity to *D. majalis* (i.e. having the general physical shape of *D. majalis*); *cambrensis* is from the Latin *Cambria*, 'Wales'. A small population of marsh-orchids from a riverside fen near Wansford, east Yorkshire, has also been referred to this taxon, but represents a hybrid swarm derived from *D. purpurella* and spotted-orchids.

Being a slightly more robust, more heavily leaf-spotted plant than var. *purpurella*, with larger flowers and more divided labella, var. *cambrensis* should be readily identifiable if found in its coastal habitats.

Plate 270 (below left). *Dactylorhiza purpurella* var. *cambrensis* was described from coastal west Wales. Marshy grassland, Merioneth, 13 June 2002.

Plate 271 (below right). The robust plants of *Dactylorhiza purpurella* var. *cambrensis* are conspicuous in its habitat of damp grassland. Merioneth, 13 June 2002.

16.9. *Dactylorhiza occidentalis* (Pugsley) P. Delforge

Syn. *Dactylorhiza majalis* subsp. *occidentalis* (Pugsley) P.D. Sell; *Dactylorhiza comosa* subsp. *occidentalis* (Pugsley) P.D. Sell; *Dactylorhiza majalis* subsp. *occidentalis* var. *kerryensis* (Wilmott) R.M. Bateman & Denholm

Irish Marsh-orchid

Perennial herb, glabrous throughout, tubers palmate, roots numerous, thick; *stem* usually to 35(–50) cm, diameter usually less than 5 mm, slightly hollow, erect, green; *leaves* glaucous to bright green, sometimes unspotted but often heavily marked with rings, spots and blotches, sheathing leaves usually about four, to 12 × 2.5 cm, ± lanceolate, slightly spreading, sometimes curved, crowded towards the stem base, cauline leaves usually two, similar but smaller; *inflorescence* a usually dense, numerous-flowered, ovoid spike; *bracts* linear-lanceolate, acute, green, often tinged purple; *flowers* usually a deep red-purple, sometimes paler; *outer perianth segments* to 10 mm, linear-lanceolate, obtuse, red-purple, marked; *inner perianth segments* oblong, red-purple; *labellum* usually to 8 × 11 mm, red-purple, contrastingly and usually heavily loop-, line- or dot-marked, broader than long and broadest at the middle, trilobed, the laterals flattish, rounded, crenulate; *spur* usually less than 8.5 mm long, 3.0 mm or more wide, conical, purple; *column* short, erect; *anther* pink-violet; *pollinia* two, greenish; *stigma* edged purple; *rostellum* red-violet; *ovary* slender, ridged, flushed purple; *flowering* late May to June (to July); 2n = 80.

Dactylorhiza occidentalis appears to be a genuine Irish endemic, with populations throughout the island except in the north-east of Ulster, where it is replaced by *D. purpurella* var. *cambrensis*. An allotetraploid derived from *D. maculata* and *D. incarnata* (Pillon *et al.* in press), it has been much misunderstood and frequently confused with the other western allotetraploid marsh-orchids. Some of the confusion stems from its existence in two forms: 'f. *occidentalis*', with heavily spotted and blotched leaves, dark flowers and a heavily line- and dash-marked labellum, particularly from central and western Ireland; and 'f. *kerryensis*', with unmarked leaves, paler flowers and a dot- or dash-marked labellum, usually found in south-western and western Ireland. There are, however, populations in which both spotted and unspotted individuals occur.

The name of this species originates from the Latin *occiduus*, 'western', reflecting its distribution. It is a frequent plant in the west of Ireland, especially in and

Plate 272. A particularly impressive inflorescence of the Irish Marsh-orchid *Dactylorhiza occidentalis*, an Irish endemic allotetraploid. Coastal grassland, Co. Cork, 31 May 2001.

around the Burren. In the latter area it sometimes grows in peaty pockets on the limestone pavement, and has even been recorded in drier areas amongst *Dryas octopetala* (Webb & Scannell 1983). However, it is especially a plant of marshes, wet meadows and damp pastures, growing with *Iris pseudacorus*, *Molinia caerulea* and *Juncus* species. Sometimes it also occurs on heaths, as well as on roadsides and around cliff tops. It is an early flowerer, often forming large populations. Some of these show a degree of variation occasionally suggesting affinities with *D. purpurella* or *D. traunsteinerioides*.

The Irish Marsh-orchid also occurs in scattered localities elsewhere in the island, but some of these records may represent hybrids with *D. incarnata*, and need reconfirmation. Both forms described can be found in discrete populations, although others may contain a mixture of both.

With regard to threats, this plant will suffer from attempts to drain or otherwise alter its habitat, but evidence to date suggests that its position is currently stable.

Plate 273. Spotted-leaved forms of *Dactylorhiza occidentalis* are regarded as typical. Calcareous grassland, Co. Clare, 12 May 1997.

Plate 274 (opposite). The so-called Kerry Marsh-orchid is a variant of *Dactylorhiza occidentalis* with unspotted leaves, found most often in the south-west of Ireland. Coastal grassland, Co. Cork, 31 May 2001.

17. *Neotinea* Rchb. f.

Perennial herbs with two rounded or ellipsoid tubers; *stem* usually short; *leaves* two to four, in a basal rosette, one to two on stem, sometimes spotted; *inflorescence* dense, cylindrical to conical; *bracts* membranous; *flowers* small, green-white or cream to white or pink, sometimes with dark spots and markings; *lateral perianth segments* connivent, forming a hood; *labellum* three-lobed, with central lobe often forked, but lacking a central tooth; *spur* present, short and conical or longer and cylindrical; *column* short; *anther* prominent; *pollinia* two, each with a short caudicle attached to a viscidium; *stigmas* two, lateral, joined at base; *ovary* cylindrical to fusiform, glabrous.

The genus *Neotinea*, known in earlier times as *Tinea*, is named after the nineteenth-century Sicilian botanist Vincenzo Tineo (1791–1846) of Palermo. As redefined the genus contains six species, ranging from western Ireland southwards to North Africa, and from the Canary Islands to the Caspian Sea.

Neotinea was formerly a monospecific genus, containing only *N. maculata*, but as part of their wide-ranging phylogenetic studies of the Orchidinae, Bateman and his colleagues have demonstrated that certain species of *Orchis* (*sensu lato*) are more accurately regarded as belonging to *Neotinea* (Pridgeon *et al.* 1997, Bateman *et al.* 1997). In the British context, the inclusion of the Burnt Orchid in the genus *Neotinea* may come as a surprise to those to whom it is familiar as *Orchis ustulata*, especially given its close resemblance to a shorter form of the Lady Orchid *Orchis purpurea*, and apparent difference from the Dense-flowered Orchid *Neotinea maculata*. As discussed earlier, however, the phylogenetic studies of Bateman and his colleagues (Bateman *et al.* 1997) indicate that the genus *Orchis* (*s.l.*), as formerly understood, has several genetic origins, and therefore cannot continue to be recognized as a single taxonomic entity (see *Chapter 2. Orchid Taxonomy and Classification*, p. 28).

Within the Orchidinae a distinct clade is formed by *Neotinea maculata* and the more brightly coloured species '*Orchis*' *lactea*, '*O.*' *ustulata*, '*O.*' *tridentata* and '*O.*' *commutata*. Despite the link between these groups (the 'maculata group' and the 'ustulata group') being comparatively weak, Bateman *et al.* (1997) believe the clade to be sufficiently cohesive that all these species should be transferred to *Neotinea*. The creation of a new genus for them was considered, but Bateman and his colleagues claim that there are sufficient similarities in floral morphology to justify uniting these apparently disparate plants, and also mention that this is the simplest nomenclatural option. As defined by Bateman *et al.* (1997), members of the expanded genus *Neotinea* share a short stature with dense inflorescences of small flowers. In the flowers the outer and inner perianth segments form a hood, while the labellum is three-lobed. The central lobe may be further divided into two lobes, but the 'tooth' found between these in, for example, *Orchis simia* (rather long) and *O. purpurea* (rather small), is absent.

Pollination in the genus is poorly understood. The spurs of *N. maculata* are nectariferous, but the other species lack nectar and are probably pollinated by small flies and other insects deceived by their attractive flowers (Pridgeon *et al.* 2001).

Plate 275 (opposite). The pink-tinged form of the Dense-flowered Orchid *Neotinea maculata* is a rare variant in Ireland, but commoner in the Mediterranean. Such plants have spotted leaves. Limestone pavement, the Burren, Co. Clare, 6 May 2003.

17.1. *Neotinea maculata* (Desf.) Stearn

Syn. *Neotinea intacta* (Link) Rchb. f.

Dense-flowered Orchid

Perennial herb with two small ovoid root tubers; *stem* 10–30 cm, bearing a few membranous basal leaf sheaths; *leaves* two to six, the basal elliptical-oblong, entire, green, sometimes spotted, the upper small, narrow and bract-like, appressed to and partially sheathing the stem; *inflorescence* a distinctly compact, cylindrical, somewhat one-sided spike, typically 2–6(–10) cm long; *bracts* small, ± lanceolate, acute; *flowers* very small, only partially opening, pinkish or white, occasionally spotted, faintly scented, the flower colour apparently being related to the presence or absence of leaf spotting; *outer perianth segments* 3–4 mm, connivent, lanceolate to ovate-lanceolate; *inner perianth segments* very narrow, linear; *labellum* very small, trilobed, the central lobe the longest, the latter linear and notched at the apex; *spur* very short, conical, containing nectar; *column* very short, notched; *anther* placed at the top of the column and bearing two very small, pale green pollinia; *stigmas* two, large; *rostellum* in the form of a flat plate placed between the stigma lobes; *ovary* twisted, slightly ridged; flowering April to June; 2n = 42.

Neotinea maculata, the Dense-flowered Orchid, has a relatively restricted and phytogeographically interesting distribution. In Northern Europe it is only known from southern and western Ireland, and the Isle of Man. There is then a considerable gap, until it is found with greater frequency in south and south-west Europe, where it ranges from the Canary Islands, Madeira and Portugal, eastwards through much of the Mediterranean region

Plate 276. The normal greenish-white colour of the flower of *Neotinea maculata* in Ireland. Sand dunes, the Burren, Co. Clare, 7 May 2003.

to Cyprus, Turkey and Lebanon, and to North Africa. Its disjunct occurrence as relict populations in Ireland is thought to be due to its having survived through the last Ice Age from a previously warmer period, when it was much more widely distributed. It is possible that there was at one time a land connection between the Iberian peninsula and Ireland, situated well to the west of France, and that plants migrated northwards along the warmer, oceanic western border of this connection. This would explain the absence of *N. maculata* from western France, and similarly the absence of *Saxifraga spathularis*, another Iberian plant that also occurs in Ireland. The presence of the warm Gulf Stream off the west coast of Ireland may also have helped these and other Iberian species to survive in Ireland. The occurrence of *N. maculata* on the Isle of Man was only detected relatively recently, and plants here are likely to have originated from an Irish population, by wind-blown seed.

In Ireland, apart from an isolated locality in the south near Cork, *N. maculata* is confined to an area in the west and centre of the island. There it extends north to Lough Carra in Co. Mayo and to Enniskillen further to the north-east, south to the Burren in Co. Clare, and again eastwards to Clonmacnoise in Co. Offaly. It was

first found in Ireland at Castle Taylor in Galway in May 1864, by a
Miss More. Its present stronghold is centred on the Burren, where
it is occasional in open situations in short turf on calcareous drift
over exposed limestone pavement, and sometimes even on road
verges and in calcareous sand. Plants seem able to survive even in
the presence of quite heavy grazing. Rather surprisingly, there is
also a Burren locality in mixed ash and hazel woodland on the
limestones west of Mullaghmore. There are additional early records
to the north of the Burren which are off the limestone in more
acidic, even peaty habitats, but these appear to lack recent confirmation. In the Mediterranean region non-calcareous habitats
are also known for *N. maculata*; but a marked preference for calcareous soils is a propensity found in other orchid species at the
very edge of their range, that would normally tolerate a wider
range of substrates. *Neotinea maculata* also occurs on the Aran
Islands off the Irish west coast. In its limestone habitats, associates
include *Anacamptis pyramidalis, Epipactis atrorubens, Gentiana
verna* and *Ophrys apifera*, and, uniquely, *Dryas octopetala*. The

plants are winter-green, emerging the previous autumn, and are thus able to flower
comparatively early in the year. Plants with spotted leaves and pinkish-purple spotted perianth segments occur (the origin of the specific name *maculata*, 'spotted'),
but the majority in the Burren have unspotted leaves and green-white or yellowish
flowers. The isolated population at Little Island, Co. Cork is more than 140 km from
the nearest known locality. It was first reported there in 1974 by O'Mahony, when
14 fruiting spikes of *Neotinea maculata* were found in a small defunct limestone
quarry, growing with *Anacamptis pyramidalis, Anthyllis vulneraria, Leontodon hispidus, Linum bienne, Orchis mascula* and *Thymus polytrichus*. Despite much of
the surrounding area being apparently suitable for the plant, it is restricted to this
single, very small locality.

Plate 277. Clumps of
Neotinea maculata are
unusual, the plants more
often occurring as scattered
individuals in the turf. Limestone pavement, the Burren,
Co. Clare, 6 May 2003.

Plate 278. The Dense-flowered Orchid *Neotinea maculata* growing in sand dunes with *Ammophila arenaria*, an unusual habitat for this species. The Burren, Co. Clare, 7 May 2003.

The Dense-flowered Orchid was not known elsewhere in the British Isles until a small population of about 30 flowering plants was found on the Isle of Man by Miss M. Quilleash in 1966, growing on slightly calcareous fixed dunes on the Ayres at the northern end of the island. These were initially mistaken for *Dactylorhiza fuchsii* var. *okellyi*, and later for *Pseudorchis albida*, but were finally identified by V.S. Summerhayes, the Kew botanist, as *Neotinea*. The population occurred over an area of only a few square metres on the inland-facing slope of the outermost ridge of dunes, and within about 45 m of the high-water mark. In the year following its discovery there were at least 20 flowering plants but thereafter the population declined into single figures, with no plants at all in some years, and seems to have become extinct in about 1986. As it occurred on a dune ridge thought to be of relatively recent formation, within a general area considered to be geologically recent, and had also been previously undetected in what had been a quite well botanised area, this was probably a newly established population. It is very likely to have been the result of wind-borne seed from one of the Irish populations, the nearest of which is about 270 km distant in Co. Offaly and, significantly, is in the direction of the prevailing wind. Such occurrences are not unusual in members of this family, all of which have very fine, light seed capable of long-distance dispersal. On the other hand, the plant's early and limited flowering period and its inconspicuous appearance might have resulted in it remaining for some time undetected, there or elsewhere. Associates at the Ayres site included *Anacamptis pyramidalis, Galium verum, Jasione montana, Ononis repens, Thymus polytrichus* and *Trifolium repens*.

The only realistic opportunity to see the Dense-flowered Orchid in the British Isles is to visit the Burren in early to mid-May, although a few plants may be in flower in late April. A careful search of dry, calcareous turf should then yield a few

Plate 279. Self-pollination in *Neotinea maculata* results in a rapid transition from flowers to swelling capsules. The extraordinary limestone-pavement landscape of the Burren is made even more fascinating by the assemblage of plants that grow there: Mediterranean species such as *Neotinea* alongside arctic-alpines. Co. Clare, 13 May 1997.

of these insignificant plants, best identified by their dense inflorescence of dull green-ish white flowers. They cannot really be confused with any other plants of this habitat. Plants commence flowering asynchronously, and each plant lasts in flower for a relatively short time before fruiting capsules develop.

Little seems to be known regarding the pollinators of *N. maculata*, although the faintly scented flowers and nectar-containing spur no doubt attract small insects to the plants. The pollen masses that make up the pollinia are readily detached, and fall onto the stigmas below. This ready release is effected by the wind in the absence of insect activity, achieving self-pollination. This appears to be the norm in most Irish populations, although there will be some plants in which cross-pollination occurs. Resulting seed-set is known to be high. Delforge (1995) has even suggested that the plants may be cleistogamous. Vegetative reproduction is very unusual, but occasionally small clumps will develop. Varieties or hybrids are not recorded from the British Isles.

17.2. *Neotinea ustulata*

(L.) R.M. Bateman, Pridgeon & M.W. Chase

Syn. *Orchis ustulata* L.

Burnt Orchid

Plate 280. The Burnt Orchid *Neotinea ustulata* var. *ustulata*. Chalk downland, Wiltshire, 24 May 1997.

Perennial herb, glabrous throughout, with two rounded tubers; *stem* to 20 cm; *leaves* few, mainly basal, elliptic-oblong to lanceolate, deep green, unspotted, uppermost cauline leaf bract-like, the rosette winter-green; *inflorescence* a dense, many-flowered spike, ovoid, elongating later, the unopened upper buds red-brown; *bracts* lanceolate, veined, purple-red; *flowers* small, sweetly scented; *outer perianth segments* 3 mm long, ovate, purplish or reddish; *inner perianth segments* shorter, paler; *labellum* 4–8 mm long, trilobed, downpointing, white with a few bright red spots, the central lobe much the longer, divided at the tip; *spur* short, conical, lacking nectar; *column* very short; *anther* ovate, pale yellow; *pollinia* two; *stigma* partly concealed; *rostellum* three-lobed; *ovary* sessile, twisted, green; flowering (typical form) May to June, (later form) July (to August); 2n = 42.

Neotinea ustulata, the Burnt Orchid, occurs from the Mediterranean and Spain northwards to southern Scandinavia, and then eastwards throughout much of central Europe, the Urals and into central Russia. The earliest British record was in 1650 at 'Scosby-lease', near Doncaster, found by the Revd Walter Stonehouse (How 1650). That this should have been the first is surprising, since in those days the plant would presumably have been much more frequent in its larger populations on the southern downs (see below). Its rather curious common name and specific epithet are derived from the Latin *ustulare*, 'to burn', and are due to the scorched look of the darkly coloured unopened buds.

Plate 281 (below left). A particularly dark individual of *Neotinea ustulata* var. *aestivalis*: not only does this variant flower later than var. *ustulata*, but the flowers tend to retain their pigmentation, and the lobes of the labellum are shorter. Ramparts of Iron-Age fort, N. Hampshire, 12 July 2002.

Plate 282 (below right). The deep-red pigmentation of the sepals of the early-flowering *Neotinea ustulata* var. *ustulata* fades as the flowers age. The spots on the labellum are smaller than those of var. *aestivalis*. Chalk downland, Wiltshire, 24 May 1997.

The distribution and ecology of *N. ustulata* have been discussed in some detail by Foley (1990b) and Tali, Foley & Kull (2004). Confined to base-rich soils, this is a plant of short, well-grazed chalk and limestone grassland, the *Festuca ovina – Avenula pratensis* community (CG2) of the NVC classification, which has usually been free of physical disturbance or the application of fertiliser and herbicide. It shows a preference for a gentle slope with a warm, often south-facing aspect, as often found on the downs of southern England. Some of the largest British populations occur where there is a well-documented history of traditional grazing and farming over past centuries. The banks of ancient earthworks, undisturbed for long periods, are also favoured. Despite this, however, there is much apparently suitable habitat from which the plant is absent, perhaps because of a lack of a mycorrhizal associate, or some other ecological factor as yet unknown. Whilst ploughing and agricultural improvement are usually anathema to the plant, there are instances where it has quite quickly recolonised disturbed ground. One such instance is a population at Martin Down in Hampshire, which reappeared after about 30 years following the cessation of ploughing (D. Green, pers. comm. *c.*1990). The new colony presumably originated from a nearby seed source. Some populations in the south of England are exceptionally large. The nature reserve at Parsonage Down, Wiltshire can have in excess of 30,000 flowering plants in a good year, and must be one of the

strongest populations in north-west Europe. In northern England the plant is found in habitats similar to those it occupies in the south. These populations are much smaller, although at least one contains several hundred plants. The most northerly extant locality is on a golf course in Durham where mowing and trampling have kept the competing vegetation in check; others are in rabbit-grazed riverside pastures, especially near the River Ure in Yorkshire. A quite remarkable Lincolnshire site is set amidst extensive arable farmland, where the plant thrives amongst tall, competing meadowland vegetation.

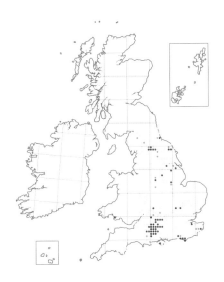

Anacamptis morio is often one of the close associates of *Neotinea ustulata*, as are other plants typical of well-grazed base-rich turf, such as *Anthyllis vulneraria, Hippocrepis comosa, Poterium sanguisorba, Primula veris, Rhinanthus minor,* and *Polygala* and *Gentianella* species. Other orchids present may include *Dactylorhiza fuchsii, D. viridis, Gymnadenia conopsea, Orchis mascula* and *Platanthera bifolia.* Many of the best sites for *Neotinea ustulata* are now protected as nature reserves or are on land owned by the Ministry of Defence, or have at least some conservation status. Others, unfortunately, have none, and especially where the populations are small, will come under considerable threat from human usage.

In Britain in the past the Burnt Orchid was very much more frequent but over the past hundred years or so there has been a drastic reduction in populations and contraction in its range. Its British stronghold is in Wiltshire, where there is the highest concentration of sites. It was formerly quite widespread in suitable habitats throughout England, reaching as far north as Northumberland, but has long been extinct there. It has also been lost, in quite recent times, from all of its several Cumbrian localities. It was recorded once from north Wales but has never been refound there, and although the reported locality does appear eminently suitable, this record may be erroneous. The plant does not occur in Scotland and Ireland. Changing agricultural techniques, increased ploughing during the Second World War, the reduction in grazing by rabbits following the onset of myxomatosis, and damage from man-made incursions seem to have been the main causes of loss.

The Burnt Orchid is readily recognised by its small stature, the dark red-brown of the upper part of the inflorescence, and its red-spotted whitish lip. It shows a superficial similarity to the much taller, more robust, and rarer Lady Orchid *Orchis purpurea.* Reproduction is usually by insect cross-pollination, although there is also evidence of occasional clonal propagation, observed in one Yorkshire population. The time from seed germination to flowering has often been stated to be in the region of 10–15 years, on the evidence of an elongated protocorm with constrictions that have been taken to be indicators of annual growth. Rasmussen (1995), however, believes this to be incorrect, and the studies of Möller (1985) showed that cultivated plants could flower in three years from seed. The best places to see the plant are at the large Wiltshire populations, where public access to the reserves is often available.

A later-flowering form also occurs, both in Britain and on the continent. Initially described as *Orchis ustulata* var. *aestivalis* Kümpel, and later 'upgraded' to *Orchis ustulata* subsp. *aestivalis* (Kümpel) Kümpel & Mrkvicka, this flowers in July, about a month after the normal form, and is taller with a more lax inflorescence. It also appears to exhibit small differences in flower colour and shape, but whether these are merely the result of slightly different ecological conditions present at the later flowering time is not known. Since it often, though not always, occurs in populations separate from the normal-flowering form, it is possibly an ecotype that has evolved through different habitat usage over a considerable period of time, and its recognition at subspecific level is debatable: treatment at varietal level in *Neotinea* is preferable. R. Bateman has informed us (pers. comm. 2004) that the necessary combination treating *aestivalis* as a variety of *Neotinea ustulata* will be published by Tali, Fay & Bateman in the near future. Bateman (2004) suggests that complete genetic isolation between the two populations has not yet been achieved. Several populations are known in Britain, especially in Hampshire, Wiltshire and Sussex, but not apparently in the north. A pale-flowered form of var. *ustulata*, f. *albiflora* Thielens, in which the labellum is unspotted and the hood almost white, occurs occasionally, as far north as Derbyshire.

Plate 283 (right). *Neotinea ustulata* var. *aestivalis*, ramparts of Iron-Age fort, N. Hampshire, 4 July 1999.

Plate 284 (opposite). The Burnt Orchid has declined dramatically in recent decades and is classified as Nationally Scarce. *Neotinea ustulata* var. *aestivalis*, ramparts of Iron-Age fort, North Hampshire, 12 July 2002.

18.1. *Himantoglossum hircinum* (L.) Spreng.

Lizard Orchid

Perennial herb, glabrous throughout, with two ovoid tubers; *stem* robust, erect, 20–65(–90) cm; *leaves* usually withering before flowering, basal leaves four to eight, dark green, ovate to broadly lanceolate, keeled, the cauline leaves smaller and clasping; *inflorescence* a lax to moderately dense spike; *bracts* linear, pale green; *flowers* large, smelling of goats, greenish with long, twisted labella, giving the inflorescence an untidy, straggling appearance; *outer perianth segments* 7–10 mm, greenish, violet-tinged, lined and spotted red within, arched forwards, connivent; *inner perianth segments* slightly shorter, narrow and linear; *labellum* to 50 mm long, greenish white at the base, purple-brown or pinkish distally, tri-lobed, with two short, narrow, greenish lateral lobes, and a very long, twisted, ribbon-like central lobe which is further divided into two short lobes at the apex; *spur* conical, short and broad, to 2.5 mm; *column* short, erect; anther greenish white; *pollinia* two; *stigma* ovate-cordate; *rostellum* projecting beyond the stigma; *ovary* pale green, ridged; *flowering* May to July; 2n = 24.

As recently redefined, the genus *Himantoglossum* now includes *Barlia* and *Comperia*, and encompasses ten species. All show some similarities to the Man Orchid *Orchis anthropophora*, and therefore to *Orchis*, but their robust stature and distinctive flower morphology appear to justify their placement in a separate genus. The overall distribution pattern of the genus is also rather similar to that of *O. anthropophora*. It is found from England (where it occurs as only one species, *H. hircinum*) southwards to North Africa and the Canary Islands, then eastwards through southern Europe, parts of the Mediterranean, Turkey and the Crimea, and on eastwards to Iran. *Himantoglossum hircinum* is by far the most widespread species, occurring throughout most of this range, as far east as Turkey. It is nowhere especially common apart from in France, where it is often met with, even in disturbed habitats.

Himantoglossum hircinum, the Lizard Orchid, is a plant which in Britain has shown a considerable fluctuation in its distribution pattern during its recorded history. It was an appreciable extension in its British range in the early-twentieth century that led Ronald Good to propose, in 1931, his 'Theory of Tolerance', linking the phenomenon to an amelioration of climate during that period. Recently, following the current interest in global warming, Good's theory has been re-examined by P.D. Carey (1999), who analysed a large number of historical records and concluded that Good's proposal was soundly based, but that the critical factor leading to the increased number of populations was a rise not in temperature but in rainfall. Data collected in southern England showed that two successive wet growing seasons, not followed by severe drought, were necessary to produce viable seed. When rainfall data were analysed for the hundred-year period post-1895 it was

Plate 285 (opposite).
On the edge of its range in southern England, the Lizard Orchid *Himantoglossum hircinum* is unmistakeable. The winter-green basal leaves wither as flowering commences. Coastal dunes, East Kent, 14 June 1998.

found that favourable conditions for population establishment occurred between 1910 and 1930, and after 1975, and that these periods coincided with the highest number of populations.

Until the end of the nineteenth century *H. hircinum* only occurred in Kent, but it subsequently spread, as very isolated populations, as far north as Yorkshire and west to Devon and Gloucestershire. By 1930 about 30 populations were known but a decline then set in, and by 1940 only about 10 were known. These were not the same each year, but the overall number was maintained as losses at one site were offset by gains elsewhere. More recently, additional populations have become established, and about 18 are known at present. Most of these are small but the largest, on the Kent coast, comprises 1000–3000 plants annually; the next largest, in Cambridgeshire, about 200.

The Lizard Orchid is a plant of tall grassland and light scrub, and is restricted to calcareous substrates. In the south these are mainly on chalk but occasionally also on limestone. One important site is on an ancient earthwork amongst quite tall, ungrazed vegetation; others are on coastal dune grassland on golf courses. Associates include *Astragalus danicus, Carex* spp., *Cirsium acaule, Dactylorhiza fuchsii, Gymnadenia conopsea, Helianthemum nummularium, Leontodon hispidus* and *Thymus polytrichus*. On dune grassland, species of *Allium, Anacamptis pyramidalis, Galium mollugo* and *G. verum* may be present. The NVC system lists *Himantoglossum hircinum* for the CG5 and CG7 subcommunities.

The first mention of the plant in the literature was for Kent in 1634, given by Thomas Johnson in his *Mercurius Botanicus*: 'Orchis saurodes sive Tragorchis Maximus, Nigh the highway between Crayford and Dartford ...' The plant continued to grow at this locality until it was suddenly lost at around the start of the nineteenth century. The name of the genus derives from the Greek words *himas*, 'strap', and *glossa*, 'tongue', obviously in reference to the shape of the labellum, and the species epithet is from the Latin *hircinus*, for the powerful goat-like smell emitted by the flowers. The common English name Lizard Orchid is thought to refer to the shape of the labellum, from its similarity to a long-tailed lizard, whilst the French name, *Orchis bouc*, is a further reference to goats.

Despite its size, in the field the plant is often difficult to detect from amongst the tall grasses with which it often grows, the long, twisted labella causing the flower spike to merge with the surrounding vegetation. Once found, however, the appearance of its flowers makes identification unmistakable. A well-known population in Cambridgeshire, or a much bigger one on the Kent coast, are the best places to see it with any certainty.

Although the odour of the flowers is repellent to humans, insects such as hoverflies, bees and moths are frequent visitors. Easy access to the broad spur ensures that a wide range of potential pollinators are able to visit the plants. The method of pollination is similar to that in *Orchis*, and the pollinia are removed in pairs to effect fertilisation, with about 30 per cent of capsules setting seed. Long-distance dispersal of seed, and the apparent relative ease of its germination, must account for the formation of remote new populations at times when the Lizard Orchid's range of distribution is expanding. The plants can be long-lived, with some individuals known to have survived for almost 20 years.

Hybrids, variants and two distinct subspecies have been described and recorded elsewhere in Europe, but not in Britain.

Plate 286 (opposite). A writhing mass of labella, the inflorescence of *Himantoglossum hircinum* has a strong goat-like scent. Coastal dunes, East Kent, 20 June 2002.

19. *Anacamptis* Rich.

Perennial herbs with ovoid tubers; *stem* bearing leaves, glabrous; *leaves* in basal rosette and on stem, not spotted; *inflorescence* dense or lax, few- to many-flowered; *bracts* membranous, shorter than to exceeding the ovary; *flowers* variable in size, usually pink to purple, sometimes with dark spots and markings; *lateral perianth segments* either free or the petals and dorsal sepal ± connivent to form a hood, when lateral sepals free; *labellum* occasionally ± entire, usually three-lobed, with central lobe sometimes weakly bilobed, glabrous, papillose or hirsute, sometimes with two calluses at base of labellum near entrance to spur; *spur* present, sometimes nectariferous but often lacking nectar, narrow and curved downwards or broad and horizontal or ascending; *column* short; anther at the top of the column; *pollinia* two, with separate viscidia or joined to a single viscidium; *stigmas* two, lateral, joined at base; *ovary* cylindrical, glabrous; 2n = 42.

Anacamptis, as currently defined, is an important genus in the Orchidinae, with about 12 species throughout Europe and North Africa, as far east as Iran, and south in Arabia to Yemen. The generic name originates from the Greek *ana-*, 'back', and *kamptein*, 'to bend', and appears to mean 'curved backwards'; the connotation seems obscure, but it may refer to either the relaxed tips of the floral bracts or the reflexed pollinia.

Long regarded as monospecific, with the familiar and distinctive *A. pyramidalis* as its only member, the genus *Anacamptis* now contains species formerly included in *Orchis*, that share a chromosome number of 2n = 32 or 36 (Bateman *et al.* 1997), but have little obvious similarity to *A. pyramidalis* or to each other. Within the *Anacamptis* clade there are five groups of somewhat disparate elements, and each of the three British species represents a separate group. The presence of cauline leaves and the absence of leaf spots are features of all members of the genus, and serve to distinguish it from *Orchis* (*sensu stricto*). The other character sometimes said to distinguish *Anacamptis* from *Orchis*, the galea or 'hood' formed by the petals and dorsal sepal (e.g. Pridgeon *et al.* 2001, Wood & Ramsay 2004) is not very helpful, as such a hood is also found in some *Orchis*.

The inclusion of the former '*Orchis*' *morio* in *Anacamptis* is perhaps one of the more surprising results of the research by Bateman and his colleagues into the phylogenetics of European orchids (Bateman *et al.* 1997). *Anacamptis morio* looks very similar to *Orchis mascula*, and very dissimilar to *A. pyramidalis*, but there is a wide disjunction in the ITS sequences of *O. mascula* and *A. morio*, and their chromosome numbers are different. The two species must therefore be seen as having evolutionarily convergent floral morphology, driven by pollinators. Within the expanded genus *Anacamptis*, *A. morio* forms a strong clade with *A. champagneuxii* and *A. boryi* (both formerly in *Orchis*), weakly linked to the group containing *A. pyramidalis* and *A.* (*Orchis*) *papilionacea*. The distinct floral morphology of *A. pyramidalis* is explained as being an adaptation to lepidopteran pollinators, the former *Orchis* species being pollinated mostly by bees and other insects (Bateman *et al.* 1997).

Pollination in *Anacamptis* is mainly through deceit, as the flowers usually lack nectar in the spur. Most species are visited by bees but *A. pyramidalis*, which flowers later than the others, is visited by Lepidoptera, which probe its long, curved spur.

Plate 287 (opposite).
The easily recognised
Pyramidal Orchid
Anacamptis pyramidalis,
growing here in coastal
sand dunes with
Eryngium maritimum,
East Kent, 21 June 2002.

19.1. *Anacamptis laxiflora*

(Lam.) R.M. Bateman, Pridgeon & M.W. Chase

Syn. *Orchis laxiflora* Lam.

Jersey Orchid or Loose-flowered Orchid

Perennial herb, glabrous throughout, with two rounded tubers; *stem* 20–80 cm, erect; leaves three to eight, 10–15 × 1(–2) cm, linear to lanceolate, acute at the apex, keeled, shining green, unspotted, the upper small and bract-like; *inflorescence* a lax, rather few-flowered (6–20) spike, ovoid to cylindrical; *bracts* linear-lanceolate, acute, tinged purple; *flowers* large, usually deep purple, occasionally much paler or rarely white; *outer perianth segments* 7–10 mm long, free, the lateral deep purple, ovate, somewhat veined, erect; *inner perianth segments* shorter than the outer, oblong, forming a helmet; *labellum* 6–10 mm long, trilobed, rather broader than long, with reflexed sides, deep purple, sometimes paler or rarely white, with a white, keeled central area, the middle lobe much shorter than the laterals, or occasionally absent altogether; *spur* 10–15 mm long, cylindrical, square or notched at the apex, dark purple; *column* c.4 mm, white; *anther* pyriform, violet, whitish at the base; *pollinia* two, greenish; *stigma* bilobed, with a violet edge; *rostellum* three-lobed; *ovary* sessile, tinged purple; *flowering* May to June; 2n = 36.

Formerly well known as *Orchis laxiflora*, the Jersey Orchid is another that has recently been placed by Bateman *et al.* (1997) in the genus *Anacamptis*; although they also indicate that there are sufficient distinctions in both ITS sequences and chromosome configurations to sup-

Plate 288. Not found as a native in mainland Britain, *Anacamptis laxiflora* appears in this book by virtue of its nationality rather than its biogeography; the Channel Islands are not considered to be part of the British Isles. Wet pasture, Guernsey, 10 May 2001.

port the formation of a separate genus for this species and its close relatives *Anacamptis* (*Orchis*) *palustris* and *A.* (*O.*) *robusta*, currently known as the 'laxiflora group' within *Anacamptis*. *Anacamptis laxiflora* has been known by several common or vernacular names, including 'des pentecôtes', from the Norman-French, referring to its time of flowering (Pentecost or Whitsuntide); others know it as the 'Jersey Orchid', or the 'Loose-flowered Orchid'. The Latin epithet *laxiflora* quite aptly describes the well-spaced arrangement of the flowers on the inflorescence. The plant was first found and identified in Jersey in 1838 by Charles Babington, who sent specimens to James Sowerby to illustrate his publication *English Botany*. In Guernsey its existence had been overlooked through Gosselin's misidentification of it (see below) as *A. morio*, a species that was not discovered on the island until much later.

In the British Isles this orchid is known only from the Channel Islands, where it is locally common on both Jersey and Guernsey but apparently unrecorded for Alderney and the smaller islands of the group. In the middle of the nineteenth century Babington stated that 'almost every wet meadow and bog' in Jersey and Guernsey contained a profusion of the plant, but more recent human impact has since changed that situation appreciably. The plant also occurs close by in northern France, and further extends throughout much of western and southern Europe, eastwards to Greece and Cyprus. In addition to the Channel Island populations there are old records of odd plants occurring, surprisingly, in north-eastern England, and a naturally reproducing population has been established at Wakehurst Place, West Sussex (Wood & Ramsay 2004).

In the Channel Islands *A. laxiflora* is a plant of water-meadows, damp pastures and boggy areas. In the past several commentators reported its former abundance and wide distribution on both islands. A report as recently as 1965 stated that a field near La Bequetterie, Jersey was purple with flowering plants and that it was almost impossible to walk there without stepping on them. Unfortunately this colony was badly damaged when a nearby stream was culverted, although other populations remain nearby. Another locality at St Peter's Marsh, considered to be one of the best on the island, where the plant had been recorded since the 1850s, was lost through building work in about 1940. Nowadays it is mainly restricted to the far west of Jersey, near St Ouen's Pond,

and to the east in the St Clement area. Drainage, changed farming methods and commercial development have been the main contributors to habitat loss, and such threats are likely to continue in the remaining areas where the plant is still found. To counteract this the National Trust purchased, in 1972, two fields near St Ouen's Pond where it was especially frequent, and there at least it should now be safe.

In Guernsey the plant was also formerly very abundant. The first recorded collection was made in the eighteenth century by Joshua Gosselin, who mistakenly identified it as *A. morio*. In 1890 Marquand reported it as being common in moist meadows all over the island, stating it to be especially abundant on the north-west side around Grand Mare and Vazon. There, in 1901, he found that '… at the beginning of June the fields are quite purple with these beautiful flowers'. Nowadays however the population is very much reduced there, and the area further west around St Peter Port, where *A. laxiflora* was first found in 1957, holds by far the largest number of plants. It was recorded there in thousands in 1972, and smaller populations occur also to the north-east as far as L'Ancresse. On Guernsey pressures on its habitat have been similar to those on Jersey and have similarly resulted in its decline.

Plate 289. Still abundant in a few places, *Anacamptis laxiflora* has greatly declined through loss of its meadow habitat. Wet pasture with *Ranunculus* spp., Guernsey, 13 May 2001.

Within the British Isles the natural restriction of *A. laxiflora* to Jersey and Guernsey is a close match to the distribution formerly observed for another British orchid, the once rare and now extinct Summer Lady's-tresses *Spiranthes aestivalis*. This also favoured dampish habitats and, apart from its former localities in the New Forest, Hampshire, was otherwise known only from St Ouen's Pond and Grand Mare; similarly, it also still occurs close by in Brittany.

Anacamptis laxiflora is quite easily recognised, possible confusion arising mainly from some slight similarity to *A. morio* and *Orchis mascula*, both now rather rare in the Channel Islands. It is distinguished from both by its more lax flower spike, and additionally from *A. morio* by the absence of prominent green veins on the lateral sepals; *O. mascula* has broader, usually quite heavily spotted leaves. To see *A. laxiflora* growing wild in the British Isles a visit must be made in mid-May to one of the remaining localities mentioned above, preferably a protected one.

Pollination is assumed to be mainly by bees, as for most other members of the genus. Seed-set is good, as evidenced by the density of populations and the abundance of the plant in favoured habitats, and vegetative reproduction may also take place to a minor extent. The great reduction in the plant's widespread distribution and local abundance from the late-nineteenth century to the present day is indicative of how human presence and developing technologies can impose a rapid decline on a species. Being a plant of damp, low-lying areas it is especially prone to the impact of drainage, and to the adverse effects of fertiliser run-off. The remaining populations therefore need to be adequately protected from these and similar threats if its British status is to be maintained.

In Guernsey the main variation appears to be in flower colour: alongside plants with flowers of the normal deep red-purple are found some with rose-coloured and even white flowers (McClintock 1975). Writing about Jersey plants, however, Lester-Garland (1903) found the colour to be 'remarkably uniform and constant'. The hybrid with *A. morio* ('*Orchis*' ×*alata*) has been recorded from both islands. It was first found in Jersey by T.W. Attenborough in 1914, at St Ouen's Pond, where it grew with both parents. It was found again by Attenborough in another locality somewhat later, and there have also been other occasional Jersey records since then. In Guernsey it was discovered at the Grand Mare by N.D. Simpson in 1949. This was a quarter of a century after the last *A. morio* record from there; but there have apparently been further records.

Plate 290. The comparatively sparse flowers give *Anacamptis laxiflora* both its specific name and its alternative English name of Loose-flowered Orchid. Guernsey, 13 May 2001.

19.2. *Anacamptis pyramidalis* (L.) Rich.

Pyramidal Orchid

Perennial herb with two globose tubers; *stem* to 60 cm, erect; *leaves* green, gradually decreasing in size up the stem, those below linear to lanceolate and keeled, the uppermost bract-like; *inflorescence* in the form of an initially ± pyramidal, densely flowered spike, which later elongates to some extent; *bracts* linear-lanceolate, green; *flowers* pink, sometimes deeper-coloured or occasionally white; *outer perianth segments* to 6 mm long, ± ovate-lanceolate; *inner perianth segments* slightly smaller, similar in shape and connivent; *labellum* 6–9 mm, broad, deeply three-lobed, the lobes oblong and ± equal in size, entire, diverging from each other; *spur* narrow, to 14 mm long; *column* short, obtuse at the apex; *anther* ovate; *pollinia* two; *stigmas* two, white; *rostellum* effectively separating the stigmas and partially obstructing the spur entrance; *ovary* sessile; *flowering* June to July; 2n = 36.

Anacamptis pyramidalis, the Pyramidal Orchid, is perhaps one of the best known and most distinctive grassland orchids of western Europe. Its overall range of distribution extends from southern Scandinavia southwards to northern Africa, and from the Iberian peninsula east to the Caucasus, Lebanon and Iran. It is found throughout the central and southern European mainland as well as on most of the Mediterranean islands. In the Alps it has been recorded at altitudes up to almost 2000 m.

Plate 291. As the spike of *Anacamptis pyramidalis* elongates it loses the 'pyramidal' shape and becomes more rounded. Colour variants are frequent in this species. Calcareous grassland, Barra, Outer Hebrides, 15 July 2003.

The specific name *pyramidalis* is readily recognisable as referring to the shape of the inflorescence, which is however strictly conical rather than pyramidal! Despite the plant's frequency in the southern part of the British Isles, the first reliable reference to it was not published until 1660. This was by John Ray in his Cambridge Catalogue, in which he states: '*Orchis sive Cynorchis purpurea spica congesta pyramidali* ... In a chalkie close at Hinton [presumably Cherry Hinton, Cambridge]'.

The Pyramidal Orchid is widespread throughout much of the southern half of the British Isles and is mainly a lowland plant. In England it is especially frequent in the south and east but becomes rarer in the west and north. It is absent from much of Devon and Cornwall, and whilst found in north and south Wales, is absent from much of the central area. In Scotland it is distinctly scarce, known only from a few localities in the Borders, Fife, Angus and the extreme south-west, with a few scattered records in the Hebrides and West Sutherland. In Ireland it has been found throughout much of the island other than the far south and the north. There are also records from the Channel Islands and the Isle of Man.

This is another orchid with a marked preference for base-rich soils. Its preferred habitat is rather dry, open, calcareous grassland where the competition is not too excessive. In the south of England it can be locally abundant in pastures and old

meadows over chalk or limestone. Another favoured habitat is coastal grassland, especially stabilised dune systems where there is a build-up of shell sand. The Pyramidal Orchid may also occur in old quarries, railway cuttings and on road verges, and sometimes in places where the alkalinity is much less marked. A more unusual record is from a fen in Dorset. Its occurrence in ruderal habitats suggests that an open, disturbed soil is advantageous for the establishment of new populations. In such cases the rapid increase in numbers can be quite spectacular. For example, a few plants were found in 1980 at a disused industrial site on the Cumbrian coast, where there had been no previous record of the species. The number of plants increased quickly thereafter. In the following three years counts totalled 47, 287 and 347 plants, respectively. By 1986 there were 902, and the population continued to increase until by 1991 there were thousands – far too many to count accurately (author's records). The population has since diminished somewhat, but is still large. Another interesting colonisation, in the same part of the country, occurred when just a few plants, known to be under threat from building development, were transplanted some distance along the coast. Shortly afterwards another very strong population developed in the new location, presumably originating from the transplanted individuals, whilst five other plants of the same origin, translocated to a different and apparently ecologically unsuitable habitat, persisted there for many years afterwards. Pyramidal Orchids often grow freely on roadsides and motorway banks, where they can be conspicuous in June. The rapid development of large populations can be attributed to the abundance of

Plate 292. The rich colour of *Anacamptis pyramidalis* makes it a conspicuous plant in summer. Calcareous grassland, Barra, Outer Hebrides, 16 July 2003.

seeds produced; Salisbury (1942) has estimated that a single inflorescence could produce 35,000 seeds.

Although showing a preference for the shorter calcareous turfs *A. pyramidalis* also has modest competitive abilities, and can sometimes be found partially hidden amongst taller grassland with species such as *Arrenatherum elatius, Bromus erectus, Dactylis glomerata* and *Helictotrichon pratensis*. It is often associated with other orchids of similar habitat such as *Dactylorhiza fuchsii, Gymnadenia conopsea* and *Ophrys apifera*, and occasionally also with rarer species, as well as with other calcareous grassland plants such as *Asperula cynanchica, Campanula glomerata, Carex humilis, Centaurea nigra, Cirsium acaule, Galium verum, Geranium sanguineum* and *Thymus polytrichus*. Its principal NVC groupings are the calcareous grassland communities (CG1–CG6) and, to a lesser extent, mesotrophic grasslands (MG1 and MG5) and sand dunes (SD7–SD9, SD15b and SD18). More rarely it has been recorded from woodland (W6d and W21d).

The species comes under threat wherever farmland improvement or disturbance occurs; populations occupying ruderal habitats such as road verges, disused areas and quarries are particularly at risk from human incursions. However its apparent readiness to recolonise suitable habitats will help to assist its survival.

Plate 293. The flowers of *Anacamptis pyramidalis* are adapted to butterfly pollination, with the long, nectar-containing spur inviting probing probosces. The pollinia become attached to the insect's proboscis. Barra, Outer Hebrides, 16 July 2003.

Plate 296 (opposite). Although increasing rapidly by seed in favourable conditions, the *Pyramidal Orchid* can also increase vegetatively, as demonstrated by this group on a roadside verge, North Hampshire, 6 July 1996.

Identification of the Pyramidal Orchid should not be a problem. Its rounded to conical, rather congested inflorescence of (usually) bright pink flowers, whose labella are equally trilobed, readily separates it from other species. Location of populations should not be too difficult either. The best place to search is on chalk and limestone grassland, but in the north and west of its range dune grassland might be more rewarding.

Anacamptis pyramidalis has a very interesting method of pollination. The flowers are sweetly scented and visited by day- and night-flying Lepidoptera attracted to the liquid in the spur. The column bears an erect stamen on which the two pollinia are attached to a single viscidium, so that they are removed together during pollination. The butterfly or moth alights on the labellum and inserts its proboscis into the spur. The proboscis is guided by the spur wall so that it enters immediately below the anther and pushes back the bursicle containing the viscidium. The viscidium is disc-shaped, and very sticky. On making contact with the proboscis the edge of the viscidium wraps around it and becomes firmly attached. One or more sets of pollinia, firmly attached by their viscidia, may then be carried away to another plant. The two pollinia quickly swing forward and diverge, and in doing so attain a configuration such that the pollen-bearing heads of the pollinia are ideally placed for contact with the two laterally placed stigmas of the next flower. Pollination is therefore very efficiently achieved, with a resulting comparatively high rate of seed-set. Neiland & Wilcock (1998) have recorded a mean fruit-set figure of 33.5 per cent in European populations. Seedlings emerge one to three years after germination, depending on conditions (Rasmussen 1995), with flowering occurring seven to eight years after germination, according to Wells (1981). Vegetative reproduction seems to be rare but there is evidence of it occurring in translocated plants (author's observations).

In the British Isles an attractive white-flowered form occurs in a low percentage amongst some populations. The flower colour is usually deep pink, but populations do occur in which it is much deeper. In one plant found in a Cumbrian population the labella of all the flowers were inverted. Plants with entire, rather than lobed, labella ('var. *emarginata*') have also been recorded. Hybrids are unlikely; records of those with the Chalk Fragrant-orchid *Gymnadenia conopsea* and the Common Spotted-orchid *Dactylorhiza fuchsii* have been discounted.

Colour variants of *Anacamptis pyramidalis*: an albino (Plate 294, near right), from chalk downland, West Sussex, 4 July 1999; and a pale pink individual (Plate 295, far right), growing on the ramparts of an ancient hill-fort on chalk, North Hampshire, 4 July 1999.

19.3. *Anacamptis morio*

(L.) R.M. Bateman, Pridgeon & M.W. Chase

Syn. *Orchis morio* L.

Green-winged Orchid

Perennial herb, glabrous throughout, with two rounded tubers; *stem* 10–30(–40) cm, erect; *leaves* elliptic-oblong to lanceolate, acute or obtuse at the apex, keeled, green to blue-green, unspotted, sheathing at their base, spreading to somewhat recurved below, smaller and bract-like above; *inflorescence* a rather lax and few-flowered spike, ovoid to cylindrical; *bracts* linear-lanceolate, acute, tinged purple; *flowers* large, usually deep purple, sometimes paler, rarely pink or even white, slightly scented; *outer perianth segments* 6–10 mm long, forming a rounded 'helmet', the lateral purplish, ovate-oblong, with very conspicuous greenish veins; *inner perianth segments* paler, shorter, and narrower than the outer, linear-oblong, forming a hood below the helmet; *labellum c.*10 mm long, broadly oblong, trilobed, broader than long, the lateral lobes folded back, deep purple, the centre paler and spotted, the middle lobe short, broad and truncate, equal to, or shorter than the laterals; *spur* 8–10 mm long, cylindrical, notched at the apex; *column* short, purplish; *anther* purplish; *pollinia* two, greenish or paler; *stigma* on the roof of the flower throat; *rostellum* three-lobed; *ovary* sessile, tinged purple; *flowering* April to June; 2n = 36.

Plate 297. Dark purple flowers are regarded as normal for the Green-winged Orchid *Anacamptis morio*, but it is very variable. It can occur in huge numbers in suitable sites. Disused gravel-pit, North Hampshire, 24 May 1996.

Although now transferred from the familiar *Orchis* to *Anacamptis*, the specific epithet *morio* has a long history. In Latin *morio* means 'fool' or 'jester', and in this case refers to the hooded appearance of the perianth segments, which resemble a fool's cap. This plant was known to Gerard and other sixteenth-century botanical authors as *Cynosorchis morio foemina*, the 'Female Foolstones', 'Fool-' deriving from the association described above and 'Female' from the fact that its tubers are smaller than those of the rather similar *Orchis mascula* ('Male Foolstones'), and consequently were accounted female. Gerard did not, however, give any specific localities for the plant. Another early though again unlocalised record was that of Thomas Johnson (Johnson 1634), as '*Orchis sive Cynorchis morio foemina … in pratis* [in meadows]', and it was definitely recorded a little later for Cambridgeshire by Ray (1660).

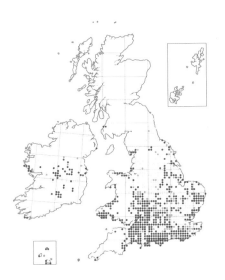

Anacamptis morio, the Green-winged Orchid, is quite widespread in continental Europe, ranging from the southern Baltic southwards to the Mediterranean, and eastwards into western Asia. In the south and east of its range, including parts of North Africa, *A. morio* is represented by other subspecies or closely related taxa.

At one time it was a frequent inhabitant of short, calcareous turf throughout much of southern and eastern England, but with the advent of more intensive farming practices it is now much more scarce. It can still be found in good numbers, however, on the chalk downs and limestones of the south, as well as parts of northern England and Wales, where it also occurs on limestone. There are only two isolated Scottish localities, one in Ayrshire, and another in East Lothian (not mapped), known to the landowners for over 70 years but confirmed only in 2002, by Sid Clarke. Possibly dubious records exist for one or two other former localities further north. In Ireland the plant is recorded as scattered in a wide band across the centre of the island but it is absent from most of the north and south. It is locally frequent in Jersey but in Guernsey, where it was not recorded until 1890, it seems not to have been seen since the 1920s.

The Green-winged Orchid is especially a plant of dry, short-grazed, unimproved calcareous turf, but can also favour marls and clays, and base-poor substrates, as well as damper conditions. It can also occur in meadowland, but there it is only a moderate competitor; occasionally it is a component of the fixed-dune flora. It is tolerant of moisture but an increase in the water-table may adversely affect its survival. In western Ireland it is surprisingly absent from the lime-rich Burren area, but occurs further north on heathy hillocks and granite knolls within blanket bog. In southern England, well-established populations growing in favourable conditions can be of considerable size, often numbering into tens of thousands, although the number of flowering plants may fluctuate wildly from year to year. It usually favours the lowlands and is very rarely found in shade, so tends to avoid woodland. The NVC system does, however, list it as a component of woodland, as well as of heaths, calcareous and mesotrophic grasslands and maritime cliffs. Typical grassland associates may include *Achillea millefolium, Asperula cynanchica, Cirsium acaule, Lathyrus pratensis, Neotinea ustulata, Ophioglossum vulgatum, Orchis mascula* and *Primula veris*, as well as the grasses and sedges typical of such habitats. To illustrate

Plate 298. Colour variants are common in *Anacamptis morio*, as seen here and in Plate 299 (opposite); the green veins in the lateral sepals are clearly visible in pale-flowered specimens. Disused gravel-pit, North Hampshire, 24 May 1996.

Plate 299 (opposite). Emerging in spring from an over-wintering rosette, the inflorescence of *Anacamptis morio* bears cauline leaves, a feature that distinguishes *Anacamptis* from *Orchis*. Disused gravel-pit, North Hampshire, 24 May 1996.

the plant's adaptability, an unusual habitat is recorded for islands off the Norwegian coast (Baugen 2003), where it occurs in soil-filled crevices of acid crystalline rock in situations exposed to and within 20 m of the sea.

Despite the existence of some large populations the plant is generally in decline, and has especially been so since the middle of the twentieth century. Ploughing and the effects on its favoured pastures of intensive farming practices, including heavy stocking and the application of artificial fertilisers, are probably the most important causes. The same threats also apply to other orchids of similar grazed-turf habitat such as the Burnt Orchid *Neotinea ustulata*. It is interesting to note that Gerard (1597/1633) commented, plants of *Anacamptis morio* grow 'naturally to their best liking in pastures and fields that seldome or never are dunged or manured'. Its decline in Ireland has been especially severe. Where previously it was known from 19 counties, since 1970 the Irish Red Data Book records it from only seven separate localities.

The plant is easily recognised in the field by the connivent attitude of the perianth segments, the lateral sepals of which are greenish-veined, contributing the descriptive name Green-winged Orchid, and by the broad labellum, the middle lobe of which is also broad and slightly longer than the laterals. Perhaps the most reliable area in which to find the plant is in the short, unimproved calcareous turf of southern England, during May and early June.

The flowers are sweetly scented and in consequence attract insects, and although lacking nectar they contain an accretion of sugar on the spur wall. Bumble-bees, especially queens that have recently emerged from hibernation, are a favoured pollinator and transport pollinia from flower to flower, so effecting cross-pollination, with good resultant seed-set. It is thought that the relative naivety of the bees leads them to these bright, showy but unrewarding orchid flowers (Nilsson 1984). Although there are relatively few flowers on each plant, each mature seed capsule contains 2000–4000 seeds (Salisbury 1942), and this adequately helps to ensure continued regeneration of the population. Wells (1981) estimates that, in the wild, first-flowering from seed occurs after four to five years, while Frosch (1980) records that seedlings grown initially *in vitro* flowered in 23 months. Later studies by Wells and colleagues have demonstrated that plants can flower for several years in succession, one individual blooming in 17 out of 18 years of the study (Wells *et al.* 1998).

Flower colour can vary from the typical reddish purple through a range of shades of pink to even white. Most large populations will contain at least a few plants of such differing colours. Other differences are usually related to labellum shape. Hybrids with *Orchis mascula* occur from time to time, and appear intermediate in form between the parents. Although *A. morio* does sometimes grow with, and flowers at the same time as *Neotinea ustulata*, the hybrid between these is not known in the British Isles, but it has been recorded in mainland Europe. It could well occur here, and should be watched for.

20.1. *Serapias parviflora* Parl.

Lesser Tongue-orchid

Perennial herb with two spherical, sessile tubers; *stem* 10–35 cm; *leaves* five to seven, 6–10 × 0.7–1.0 cm, linear-lanceolate, channelled, glaucous-green, the basal sheaths green, usually flecked with purple; *inflorescence* 3–5(–10)-flowered, elongated, racemose, lax; *bracts* shorter than to as long as the upwardly angled outer perianth segments, brown to purple, partially obscuring the small flowers; *flowers* mainly pinkish brown, 1.5–2.0 cm long; *perianth segments* connivent, the sepals red-green to grey-lilac, 14–18 × 3.5–4.5 mm, the lateral petals 13–15.5 × 3–4 mm, red-green; *labellum* pale red, veined, 14–19 mm long, with two red-purple calluses at the base; *hypochile* 8–10 × 9–11.5 mm, with a wedge-shaped base, the lateral lobes brown-red; *epichile* lanceolate, 7–11.5 × 2.5–4.5 mm, directed downwards or backwards, slightly hairy, dull red; *column* elongate, ending in pointed connective; *pollinia* two, with distinct caudicles; *ovary* erect, not twisted, sessile; *flowering* May to June; 2n = 36.

The name *Serapias* was applied to this genus by Linnaeus (1753), recycling a name used for an orchid by Dioscoridis. It is derived from the name of the deity Serapis, a Graeco-Egyptian god whose cult was established at Alexandria in the third century BC. Serapis was believed to be the human manifestation of the sacred bull Apis, also the god of the after-life and fertility. The cult was introduced into Rome in about 86 BC and, despite its licentious priestly rites, did not die out until the destruction of the temple of Serapis in Alexandria in AD 391. The connection appears to be the belief that certain orchids are reputed to have aphrodisiac properties.

A prominent lip and the absence of a spur are diagnostic characters of *Serapias*, the tongue-orchids, distinguishing all members of the genus. The number of species within *Serapias* is very much open to question, but there are considered here to be about a dozen. It is an essentially Mediterranean genus, distributed between the Canary Islands, southern Europe, North Africa and western Asia. *Serapias parviflora*, the Lesser Tongue-orchid, occupies much of this range, from the Canaries to Cyprus, and northwards to Brittany and Cornwall, although it is nowhere common. It is tolerant of a wide range of habitats and growing conditions, occuring in garrigue, damp meadows, coastal sands, olive groves and field margins, at altitudes of up to 1200 m, and on basic to weakly acidic substrates.

In Britain *S. parviflora* occurs as a single population, on rabbit-grazed, scrubby grassland on south-facing coastal cliffs in Cornwall. The population was first found in 1989, when it comprised just two flowering plants. Flowering has since occurred, intermittently, but the population has also been deliberately augmented with additional plants raised from seed originating from the same site; in 2002 three flowering spikes were recorded. It is possible that wind blown seed might have been the original source, as the nearest population is across the English Channel in Brittany

Plate 300 (opposite).
A recent arrival in the British Isles, the Lesser Tongue-orchid *Serapias parviflora*; the derivation of the English name is obvious. Rough grassland, East Cornwall, 16 May 1998.

Plate 303 (opposite). The possibly natural population of *Serapias parviflora* in Cornwall has been augmented with plants raised from seed. It remains to be seen whether the population will persist, and whether other sites will be colonised. Rough grassland, East Cornwall, 16 May 1998.

(Bournérias 1998). As is perhaps understandable, local botanists tend to consider it to be native, but Stace (1991) and Lang (1998) treat it as an alien and Dines (2002) also expresses doubts about its status. On balance it seems best to consider it as doubtfully native.

Serapias lingua L., the Greater Tongue-orchid, with larger flowers, was first recorded on the British mainland in 1998, in south Devon. The plant in question was considered to be *S. lingua* subsp. *duriuei* (Rchb. f.) Soó, a native of Algeria and Tunisia. Earlier, in 1992, *S. lingua* was also recorded at the Grand Mare, Guernsey by J.J. Finnie as a single plant growing amongst a population of the Loose-flowered Orchid *Anacamptis laxiflora*. It has not been recorded there subsequently. Its identification was confirmed by P. Cribb from a photograph taken at the time, but unfortunately its subspecies is not known (N. Jee, pers. comm. 2004). Both Devon and Guernsey are subject to 'red' rain, containing wind-blown sand originating from the Sahara, and it is tempting to believe that *S. lingua* may have arrived as seed in one such event (Lang 2004).

Three plants of *S. cordigera* L. were found in a chalk-pit in east Kent in 1996 and 1997 (Lang 2004). There is no definite evidence that these had been introduced, but *S. cordigera* was known to be present in a garden nearby. There is also a single British record for *S. neglecta* De Not., from a cornfield in the Isle of Wight in 1918. The origins of these plants remain mysterious, but Ettlinger (1997, 1998b) has suggested that some of these records are the result of deliberate introduction.

Pollination in *Serapias* is interesting. The hooded flowers of most species form a dark cavity that solitary bees find tempting as a sleeping place, as it remains a few degrees warmer than the ambient temperature. On occasion, they will push their head deep enough into the flower to pick up the pollinia. It has been suggested that this disturbs their rest and they move on to another flower, carrying the pollinia with them. Delforge (1995) reports, however, that *S. parviflora* is often cleistogamous, and that there is a form of pseudocopulation in *S. lingua*.

Plates 301 (near right) and 302 (far right). Individual plants of *Serapias lingua* have been recorded occasionally from both the British mainland and the Channel Islands, presumably colonists by long-distance seed dispersal. Widespread in Continental Europe, the species varies considerably in flower-colour. These well marked plants were growing at Garakari, Crete, 24 April 2000.

21. *Ophrys* L.

Bee Orchid, Fly Orchid, Spider-orchids

Perennial herbs with two ovoid to ± globose tubers; *leaves* rosette-forming, with cauline leaves sheathing the stem, decreasing in size upwards; *inflorescence* a lax, often few-flowered spike; *perianth segments* patent; *labellum* large, fleshy, entire to trilobed (if trilobed, the lateral lobes small), hairy or velvety and resembling an insect's abdomen, usually dark coloured but often conspicuously marked, and with a shiny, glabrous area (speculum), usually centrally placed on the mid-lobe; *spur* absent; *column* long, drawn out into a projection; *anther* placed close to the top of the column, with two pollinia which are attached to separate viscidia and enclosed in two distinct bursicles; *stigma* single, large.

Ophrys is restricted to Europe, North Africa and western Asia, but there is little agreement on the number of species. Considerable variation in the morphology of many taxa has led to the establishment of local races and populations, and this in turn to the description of a large number of subspecies and varieties, some justified, others probably not. A confused classification has been the outcome, with names and taxonomic statuses changing frequently. Opinions differ as to the number of species in Europe, with estimates varying between 20 and 200! The centre of distribution for the genus is the Mediterranean area; in the British Isles only four species are native, two of which are rare, the others local. The British species are the subject of a fascinating short book by Stephen Blackmore (1985).

Plate 305 (above). *Ophrys* flowers are adapted to pollination through pseudocopulation: here *Ophrys insectifera* is visited by a Two-girdled Digger Wasp *Gorytes mystaceus*. Derbyshire, 3 June 1993.

The generic name *Ophrys* derives from the Greek word for 'eyebrow', referring to the hairy appearance of the labellum. The resemblance of the labellum to the body of an insect has led to a range of fanciful, colloquial names for the plants, but it is only relatively recently that the importance of this mimicry for pollination has been elucidated. Male insects, deceived by the appearance of the flowers and by their scent, which is chemically mimetic of sex hormones similar to the pheromones secreted by bees and wasps, visit the flowers and attempt to copulate with what they perceive to be a female of their species. In the process the pollinia are removed, and pollen is transferred to the next flower visited. It is significant that the male insects involved usually emerge ahead of the females; the temporary shortage of mates results in increased competition, which favours pollination by this means. The method is known as 'pseudocopulation', a term coined by Pouyanne (1917), from observations made in Algeria. Many others, including Godfery (1933), Kullenberg (1961), and Proctor and Yeo (1973) have also studied the pollination of *Ophrys* in great detail. A large number of hybrids have been recorded within the genus.

Plate 304 (opposite). The pollinia of the Late Spider-orchid *Ophrys fuciflora* remain attached to the column until they are removed by an insect, unlike those of the Bee Orchid *O. apifera* which dangle on long caudicles (see Plate 14, p. 8). Chalk downland, East Kent, 14 June 2003.

21.1. *Ophrys insectifera* L.

Fly Orchid

Plate 306. The slender plant and inflorescence of the Fly Orchid *Ophrys insectifera* can be hard to spot, especially amongst taller plants. Old chalk-pit, North Hampshire, 4 June 1996.

Plate 307 (opposite). Although not very spectacular, the flower of *Ophrys insectifera* is well adapted to pollination by pseudocopulation. This is the normal colour and pattern. Old chalk-pit, N. Hampshire, 5 June 1996.

Perennial herb with two ± globose tubers; *stem* 20–40(–60) cm, erect; *leaves* few, not as a basal rosette but borne on the stem, those below oblong to broadly lanceolate, those above narrower, clasping; *inflorescence* a lax, rather few-flowered spike; *bracts* lanceolate, conduplicate; *flowers* small, greenish with a brown labellum, scentless; *outer perianth segments* 6–8 mm, broadly lanceolate, yellow-green; *inner perianth segments* 4–6 mm, deep violet to purplish brown, the edges rolled back and appearing filiform, similar to an insect's antennae; *labellum* to 10 mm long, rich velvety brown, trilobed, the lateral lobes patent, the central lobe elongated, indented at the base, with a ± rectangular violet speculum; *spur* absent; column with a short blunt beak; *anther* adjacent to the top of the column; *pollinia* two; *viscidia* in two orange bursicles; *stigma* placed at the base of the column; *rostellum* very small; *ovary* sessile, pale green; *flowering* May to July; 2n = 36.

The Fly Orchid *Ophrys insectifera* is restricted to Europe, where it is widespread. It is absent from the far north and much of the south, including a large part of the Mediterranean region. Its northern limit is in central Sweden (also the northern limit for the genus as a whole); southwards it occurs to north-eastern Spain. In mainland Europe it is a plant of grassland, woodland, woodland margins and scrubby areas, to an altitude of 1850 m. In the British Isles it is largely a southern plant, with its main area of distribution in south and south-east England, but it also occurs in more scattered populations as far north as Cumbria and Yorkshire. It is generally absent from Wales, but is present in Anglesey and in central and western Ireland. The earliest record traced is that given by John Gerard in his *Herball* of 1597, where he reported it to grow with *Ophrys apifera* and *Platanthera* species 'upon barren chalky hils ... adjoining to a village in Kent named Greenhithe, upon Longfield downs by Southfleet ...', and also '... half a mile from S. Albons'.

The Fly Orchid is essentially a plant of calcareous substrates, and in southern England is frequently found in partial, or even deep shade along woodland margins and in openings in beech woods. Here it may grow with *Cephalanthera damasonium, C. longifolia, Neottia ovata, Orchis mascula, Platanthera chlorantha*, and more rarely in Kent with *Orchis purpurea*. More open scrub is also favoured, especially in the north, as well as rocky ground including quarries, chalk-pits, limestone pavement, open grassland, and even roadside verges and track borders. Populations on steep limestone slopes in the upper Eden valley in Cumbria represent the northern British limit of the plant. It can also occupy a distinctly contrasting habitat in western Ireland and Anglesey, where it occurs in damp fens, growing in association with species usually considered more typical of such habitats such as *Dactylorhiza incarnata, D. traunsteinerioides* and *Epipactis palustris*. If one knows the plant mainly from its typical dry scrub and woodland locations it can come as quite a surprise to find it in such an association. Rarely, it can also occur amongst heather

where there is a rather more acidic covering of an essentially calcareous substrate. Classified in the NVC system as being of calcareous grassland (CG) and woodland (W12) communities, it is also listed as a component of *Schoenus nigricans – Juncus subnodulosus* mires (M13) and the associated *Briza media – Pinguicula vulgaris* (M13b) subcommunity.

Although sometimes quite happily occupying man-made habitats such as quarries and road verges, the Fly Orchid is liable to elimination from these by subsequent disturbance. A similar fate may await woodland populations if felling operations are imminent. Owing to the unobtrusive appearance of the plants, their collection for decoration or garden use is not likely to pose much of a threat. One infamous nineteenth-century case, however, was reported by S.L. Petty in the *Naturalist* of 1898, collectors having raided what is now a National Nature Reserve in northern England. The locality had to be strictly guarded since 'Dozens of people with baskets (and sometimes trowels too) invaded the woods, and, of course, asked no permission to take roots away, but did so. The owner objected, and rightly.' The plant is often very local and occurs sporadically, usually in small numbers; it is believed to be decreasing rapidly. The 2005 Red List regards it as Vulnerable (Cheffings & Farrell 2005).

The origin of the Latin name *insectifera* clearly derives from the flowers' insect-like appearance, and the same may be said for the common name, Fly Orchid. *Ophrys insectifera* is readily distinguished from other British species of the genus by its relatively long, narrow labellum and shiny speculum, reminiscent of an insect's body with folded wings. The very life-like appearance of the narrow inner perianth segments, suggesting an insect's antennae, adds to this impression. To find the plant in the wild searches should be made in late May or early June in known localities, details of which are best obtained from local or county naturalist societies and Wildlife Trusts. Even then, much patience will be required.

Although a relatively tall plant, the Fly Orchid is one of the most difficult British orchids to detect in the field when growing in scrub or grassy places, as it tends not to stand out from the surrounding vegetation. The widely spaced flowers on relatively bare stems quite realistically imitate insects resting on grass stalks, and it is not until one has located a few plants and 'got one's eye in' that others come more readily into view. This makes censusing of populations difficult and may lead to substantial under-recording.

The flowers are visited by small male wasps of the genus *Gorytes*. These appear to mistake the flowers for females of the species, and pseudocopulation occurs; but only for a limited period until the emergence of the female wasps, after which the males lose interest in the flowers. In consequence, successful pollination may be haphazard. When seed-set is estimated it is frequently

Plate 308. A pale, yellow-edged variant of *Ophrys insectifera*. Deciduous woodland, North Hampshire, 22 May 2002.

found that only 20 per cent of flowers bear mature seed, and the percentage can be much lower. This no doubt contributes to the fluctuating occurrence of the plant at many sites.

Hybrids and variants are occasionally recorded, the hybrid with the Early Spider-orchid *O. sphegodes* having been found in Kent on several occasions. A rarer hybrid is that with the Bee Orchid *O. apifera* (*O. ×pietzschii*). Four plants were discovered in 1968 at Leigh Woods in the Avon Gorge, near Bristol, on the floor of a long-disused quarry, and persisted there for many years. It was also found in 1998–2000 as a single plant near Arundel, Sussex, and in 2004 five plants were seen on a roadside verge in Somerset. Aside from hybrids, colour variations to the labellum are occasional, usually involving the lack of a speculum, or of the dark base colour of the labellum. Flowers with more than one labellum may sometimes also be found.

Plate 309 (top left). *Ophrys insectifera*, colour form, old chalk-workings, N. Hampshire, 6 June 2003.

Plate 310 (top right). A pale *Ophrys insectifera* with normal flower shape and pattern. Old chalk-workings, North Hampshire, 6 June 2003.

Plate 311 (bottom left). A dark-coloured *Ophrys insectifera* variant with a broader lip than normal. Deciduous woodland, North Hampshire, 15 May 2002.

Plate 312 (bottom right). *Ophrys insectifera* – a yellow-edged, brighter-flowered form. 15 May 2002. Variation within a species is the foundation for evolution: usually a very uniform species, this population of Fly Orchids in a wood in North Hampshire is exceptionally variable. See also Plate 311 (left), Plate 308 (opposite).

21.2. *Ophrys apifera* Huds.

Bee Orchid

Perennial herb with two ± globose tubers; *stem* 15–50 cm, erect; *leaves* three to six, the lower as a rosette produced in autumn and overwintering, narrowly elliptical, yellowish green, the upper smaller, clasping the stem; *inflorescence* a lax, few-flowered spike; *bracts* lanceolate, to 4 cm long; *flowers* relatively large; *outer perianth segments* 10–15 mm, narrowly ovate to elongate-triangular, patent, pinkish or paler coloured; *inner perianth segments* linear, much shorter, 5–8 mm, ± linear, greenish, hairy; *labellum* 10–15 mm, bee-like, semi-globose, convex, trilobed, the lateral lobes small, hairy, the central lobe broad above, velvety, long-pointed at the tip, the tip being recurved beneath the labellum and so not apparent from the front, deep red-brown, typically marked with a distinctive, yellowish, ± horseshoe-shaped pattern and two yellowish spots below, though the pattern can vary appreciably; *spur* absent; *column* long, the base forming a chamber; *anther* beaked; *pollinia* two, yellow; *viscidia* in bursicles; *stigma* within the column chamber; *rostellum* very small; *ovary* sessile, curved; *flowering* May to July; 2n = 36.

Plate 313. Two stems with identical flowers suggest that, unusually, this is a clonal group of *Ophrys apifera*. The markings around the speculum are incomplete, and the sepals are deep pink. Coastal chalk grassland, Dorset, 8 June 2002.

Of all British orchids the Bee Orchid is perhaps the one that excites most interest in the casual observer. This is partly due to the fact that whilst it is widespread though local in England (elsewhere in the British Isles it is scarce), its unpredictable annual appearance and unusual flower shape impart to it a degree of mystery and attractiveness.

Ophrys apifera occurs throughout south, west and central Europe, northwards to northern England and Ireland, and south to North Africa. It also extends eastwards into Turkey, the Middle East and parts of south-west Asia. In continental Europe it is a plant of scrub, phrygana, disused vineyards and olive groves, and other similar habitats. Based on floral characters, several distinct varieties are recognised, some of which occur, if only rarely, in the British Isles. Here it is most frequent in the eastern half of England, especially in the south, becoming much less common in the west. There are also good populations as far north as Durham and Cumbria, and in Wales, particularly along the northern coast (including Anglesey), and also occasionally in the south. It has always been very rare in Scotland, with a few old records in the south, and had been thought to be extinct there until in August 2003 two fruiting plants were found at an old industrial site in eastern Ayrshire (Laney & Stanley 2004) (not mapped). These two plants did not reappear in 2004 but six others made their first

appearance at the same site. The Bee Orchid also occurs in the Channel Islands, whilst in Ireland it is local in suitable habitats throughout most of the island. In Northern Ireland it is rare, however, being known only from 11 sites.

The plant shows a marked preference for a dry, base-rich habitat. Short turf pasture and downland over chalk and limestone, earthworks, disused quarry floors, chalk-pits, and other anthropogenic calcareous habitats, including scrub and railway embankments, are the ones most favoured. It is also frequently found in the

Plate 314. Old quarries, such as this one on the Dorset coast, are often good sites to search for orchids, as they are not subject to agricultural disturbance. Bee Orchids grow in the short turf here. 8 June 2002.

drier margins of dune slacks and dune grassland, on calcareous shell sand. More rarely it is recorded from woodland margins or even deeper into the woodland itself, and from heavier clays and marls; also, in one instance in the Isle of Wight, in a wet, alkaline flush. In Ireland it occupies a similar habitat, although in the Burren it is also known from the drier parts of fens, and from the crevices of limestone pavement. As expected, its associates are species typical of such habitats, including other orchids such as *Anacamptis morio, A. pyramidalis, Dactylorhiza fuchsii, Epipactis atrorubens* and *Neottia ovata.* In the NVC system *Ophrys apifera* is classified especially as a component of certain calcareous grassland communities (CG1–CG3, and CG5), and to a lesser extent of the mesotrophic grassland community (MG1). Threats to populations are the same as for other species of these habitats (see *Chapter 6. Approaches to the Conservation of British and Irish Orchids*); because of their attractiveness, however, Bee Orchid plants are also sometimes dug up for transplantation to gardens, where they are unlikely to survive without care.

The plant's common name in English and the specific epithet *apifera* both refer to the bee-like appearance of the labellum (Latin *apis,* 'bee'), and this similarity is also noted in its names in French (*Ophrys abeille*), German (*Bienen Ragwurz*) and Italian (*Vesparia*). Other local names include Bee-flower, Bumble Bee and Honey-flower, and an unusual colloquial name in Surrey is Dumble Dor. The first published record seems to be that in John Gerard's *Herball* (Gerard 1597), where he refers to it growing with Fly and Butterfly-orchids in bare chalk hills 'adjoining to a village in Kent named Greenhithe, upon Longfield downs by Southfleet', as well as near St Albans. Gerard's name for it was the Humble Bee Orchis.

Within the genus this is the species most likely to be encountered in the British Isles. It might be confused with the very rare Late Spider-orchid *O. fuciflora,* but this has a larger, more square-shaped and more intricately marked labellum. The Bee Orchid is not an especially rare plant in the south and east, and should be relatively easily found there if appropriate habitats are searched. In northern England there are many good colonies on the floors of disused chalk and limestone quarries. As with most orchids, a sympathetic local conservation group or Wildlife Trust will be able to suggest possible localities where it can be seen.

Plate 315. Inconspicuous in the grass, the leaf rosette of the Bee Orchid *Ophrys apifera* emerges in autumn and is photosynthetically active through the winter. Oxfordshire, March 1991.

Although the plant is adapted to cross-pollination through pseudocopulation, it appears that in the British Isles self-pollination is the norm. The caudicles of the pollinia are longer and narrower than in other British species of *Ophrys*, and shrink when the flower opens, drawing the pollinia out of the stamen so that they hang above the stigma below. Any movement then allows the pollinia to contact the stigma and effect fertilisation. Even so, an element of cross-fertilisation must also occur, as evidenced by the occasional occurrence of hybrids. Seed-set is efficient and the abundant, very fine, dust-like seed is readily dispersed on the wind, enabling the establishment of new populations a considerable distance away. *Ophrys apifera* may take up to eight years to come into flowering condition, and although it was once thought to be monocarpic (dying after flowering), studies on marked plants have indicated that this is not always the case (Anon 1978). In the autumn, a

Plate 316. Bee Orchid variants, such as this var. *chlorantha*, can grow scattered amongst populations of the normal var. *apifera*, or they may form local sub-populations derived from self-fertilised plants. Chalk grassland, Essex, 15 June 1997.

careful examination of localities where the plant normally occurs will reveal the early formation of the basal rosettes. Another character that is especially noticeable in this species is the enormous fluctuation in numbers that often occurs from year to year at individual sites (Summerhayes 1968). There are well-documented cases where in one year there have been thousands of flowering plants to be found but in the following year only a very few (Lang 1989).

The tendency towards self-fertilisation can in some ways be disadvantageous to the species, since any genetic abnormality within an individual will be passed on to its subsequent offspring. This no doubt accounts for the number of well-defined varieties within *O. apifera*, described below. Less clear-cut variants also occur in some populations, such as plants with almost pure white sepals, or with differing patterns on their labella. In one large Cumbrian population, amongst typical plants, many individuals were found in which the labellum markings differed from plant to plant, and in labellum shape some also approached var. *trollii* (see below), although well outside the normal geographical range of that variety. Other than these, the hybrid with *O. insectifera* (*O.* ×*pietzschii*) has also been found (discussed in more detail in the account for *O. insectifera* above, p. 297).

Plate 317. A normal Bee Orchid *Ophrys apifera*, with pale pink sepals and a complete set of markings around the speculum. Coastal chalk grassland, Dorset, 8 June 2002.

Infraspecific taxa

(a) var. *trollii* (Hegetschw.) Rchb. f.

Named to commemorate the Swiss painter and copperplate-engraver Johann Heinrich Troll (1756–1824) (Reinhardt *et al.* 1991), this variety is quite distinct in having flowers in which the labella are long and pointed, with the appendage not recurved beneath the labellum as in the normal form. The labella also lack the characteristic markings of the typical plant, being dull brown or barred. Colloquially known as the Wasp Orchid owing to the appearance of the labellum, it is mainly restricted to southern and western England, especially to Gloucestershire, Somerset and Dorset, where its persistence is no doubt a result of inbreeding due to self-pollination. However, similar plants occur elsewhere, such as those mentioned previously in the Cumbrian population, and although occasionally treated at species level as *O. trollii*, any claim for this to be other than an infraspecific taxon is misguided. Otherwise

Plate 318. A group of 'Wasp Orchids', *Ophrys apifera* var. *trollii*, a variation found especially in south-west England. Coastal chalk grassland, Dorset, 8 June 2002.

normal plants in which the labellum apices protrude rather than recurve have sometimes been referred to by the illegitimate name '*pseudotrollii*'.

(b) var. *chlorantha* (Hegetschw.) K. Richter

This is a most attractive plant, occurring locally and sometimes in association with individuals of the normal flower colour. Otherwise typical, it is a leucistic variant in which the labellum lacks its usual deep brown base colour, appearing instead in a pale greenish yellow (hence *chlorantha*, from the Latin), and the sepals are not pink but white. Within large populations of var. *apifera* it often occurs in small groups, which is further evidence for almost total self-pollination within the species. It occurs locally throughout much of the British range of *O. apifera*. In 1990 one population of the latter in South Yorkshire was estimated to comprise upwards of 10,000 plants, of which approximately 20 per cent were of var. *chlorantha* (M. Foley, unpublished). It is widespread in the south, including Dorset, East Suffolk, East Sussex and Essex, and also in South Yorkshire.

(c) var. *flavescens* Rosbach

A small population of Bee Orchids from Beachy Head, Sussex is thought to be of this taxon, which is also known from north-west Europe. It is similar to var. *chlorantha* but has flowers with dull green-brown labella. The epithet *flavescens* indicates its slightly yellowish colour. These plants are of rather uncertain taxonomic status. Other populations are known at Hayshott Down, West Sussex, and Greenham Common, Berkshire.

(d) var. *bicolor* (O. Nägeli) E. Nelson

This is much rarer than most of the other varieties of *O. apifera*. The labellum colour is pale or greenish at the position where the speculum and yellowish pattern should be, whilst the rest of the labellum is dark brown and especially so towards the apex. The plant is known from only four populations, in Essex, Dorset, Warwickshire and Anglesey, although it now appears to be extinct in Anglesey.

(e) var. *friburgensis* Freyhold

Syn. *O. apifera* subsp. *jurana* Ruppert; *O. botteroni* (Chodat) Asch. & Gräb.

This plant was first found in the British Isles in Wiltshire in 1984 (Lang 1989). The inner perianth segments are pink with hairy margins, and are similar in size and shape to the outer segments; the labellum also has a more diffuse pattern. Recorded nearby on the Continent, it has also been found in Hampshire, Somerset, Suffolk, Sussex and Derry. The name refers to its discovery near Fribourg, in Switzerland. Intermediates are also known to occur.

Plate 319 (opposite). In *Ophrys apifera* var. *bicolor* the markings around the speculum are blurred and lighter than in the apical half of the labellum. Young conifer plantation on clay, Essex, 15 June 1997.

(f) var. *belgarum* Turner Ettl.

In var. *belgarum* the labellum is rounded, chestnut-brown and marked with yellow bands, the upper edges are very hairy and the side lobes are absent. This is one of the rarer varieties of *O. apifera* and, at present, is known only from Cumbria, Essex, Hampshire, Hertfordshire, Kent and Somerset. The epithet *belgarum* derives from the Roman name for Winchester (*Venta Belgarum*), once the capital of the tribe of the Belgae; plants seen near Winchester in 1993 were later described as this variety by Ettlinger (1998a). The plant is also apparently rare in continental Europe, where it has been recorded only occasionally in France and Switzerland (Ettlinger 1998a).

Plate 320 (top left). In *Ophrys apifera* var. *trollii* the apex of the labellum is not recurved and forms an acute point below the narrower central portion with its irregular markings. Coastal chalk grassland, Dorset, 7 June 2002.

Plate 321 (top right). The flowers of *Ophrys apifera* var. *chlorantha* lack anthocyanin pigments, resulting in a white, green and yellow coloration. Chalk grassland, Dorset, 6 July 1996.

Plate 322 (centre left). *Ophrys apifera* var. *friburgensis* has enlarged petals that approach the sepals in size. Old lead-mine spoil-heap, Mendip Hills, North Somerset, 7 July 1996.

Plate 323 (centre right). The labellum of *Ophrys apifera* var. *belgarum* lacks side-lobes, appearing more rounded than normal, and has boldly defined markings. Roadside verge on chalk, N. Hampshire, 27 June 2002.

Plate 324 (bottom left). Reduced anthocyanin pigments define *Ophrys apifera* var. *flavescens*, which has some brown and pink coloration. Coastal chalk grassland, E. Sussex, 17 June 1999.

Plate 325 (bottom right). A dark-flowered variant of *Ophrys apifera*. East Kent, 13 June 2004.

21.3. *Ophrys fuciflora* (Crantz) Moench

Syn. *Ophrys holoserica* auctt. non (Burm. f.) Greuter

Late Spider-orchid

Perennial herb with two ovoid to globose tubers; *stem* 15–50 cm, erect; *leaves* three to five, the lower as a rosette, narrowly elliptical, grey-green, shiny above, the upper clasping the stem; *inflorescence* a few-flowered, lax spike; *bracts* lanceolate, green; *flowers* relatively large; *outer perianth segments* 10–12 mm, ovate, obtuse, pinkish; *inner perianth segments* much shorter, ± triangular, pale pink, velvety; *labellum* large, ± square, obscurely trilobed, the laterals reduced to bosses or sometimes absent, the central lobe broad, deep red-brown, velvety, conspicuously marked with a distinctive, symmetrical pattern; *spur* absent; *column* curved to form a chamber; *anther* on top of the column; *pollinia* two; *viscidia* colourless; *stigma* positioned within the column chamber; *rostellum* very small; *ovary* sessile, curved; *flowering* June to July; $2n = 36$.

Plate 326. The Late Spider-orchid *Ophrys fuciflora* only occurs at a few sites on the downland of East Kent. 28 May 1997.

The main area of distribution of the Late Spider-orchid *Ophrys fuciflora* is in central and southern Europe. It also penetrates eastwards into Turkey and the Middle East, and attains a northern limit in south-east England. Like the Early Spider-orchid *O. sphegodes*, it is represented in continental Europe by a range of subspecies showing appreciable variation, especially in respect to markings on the labellum. In Europe it is mainly a plant of dry scrub and garrigue, recorded in the Alps at altitudes of up to about 1300 m. In some European countries it is considered an endangered plant.

In the British Isles its range is extremely limited, being restricted to a small area of south-east Kent where it is now known from only four 10 km squares, with one additional old, presumed extinct, record in the north of the county. Records other than these are thought to be errors for other *Ophrys* species, in particular atypical forms of *O. apifera*. *Ophrys fuciflora* has been recorded from about 20 separate localities but now only occurs regularly at five of these, with occasional appearances elsewhere. All these populations are on the chalk escarpment and plateau of the North Downs situated between Wye and Folkestone, where some have been known for a considerable time. The largest population is at Wye Downs and has been estimated to comprise up to half the total British population of around 500 plants. A survey in 2004, however, of all known *O. fuciflora* sites in Kent, yielded a count of only 220 flowering plants (R. Bateman & B. Tattersall, pers. comm. 2004).

The plant is found on well-drained, short, herb-rich *Festuca* grassland over chalk. A favoured habitat is on the small ledges formed on steep downland slopes, but it also occurs occasionally in grazed turf on the sides of earthworks. Associated

species include *Achillea millefolium, Bromopsis erecta, Centaurea nigra, Linum catharticum, Polygala vulgaris* and, occasionally, *Gymnadenia conopsea* and other grassland orchids. Some populations are found where grassland has formed over previously disturbed areas but these are always limited and discrete, with the plant showing no tendency to colonise other adjacent, almost identical habitats. Within the NVC system it is classified as being mainly a component of the *Festuca – Avenula pratensis* grassland community (CG2). In the past populations have been lost through ploughing or changes in grazing patterns, but all the main colonies now have a degree of protection within SSSIs or protected reserves. Consequently, the habitat is managed for the benefit of the plant, especially through controlled grazing to maintain an ideal sward and prevent the dominance of coarse grasses. A plant of attractive and somewhat exotic appearance, it was often, in the past, picked or even dug up, but nowadays this is largely prevented by strict wardening of the sites (see Plate 368, p. 336).

The English name, Late Spider-orchid, is a direct reference to its relatively late flowering time of mid-June to early July. The Latinised specific epithet *fuciflora* is derived from *fucus*, 'deceit' or 'pretence', and presumably relates to the insect-like appearance of the flowers. The alternative epithet *holoserica* describes the overall velvety appearance of the labellum (Greek, *holo-*, 'everywhere', Latin, *sericeus*, 'silky'), but this name does not have nomenclatural priority. Sir Edward Smith, in his *English Flora* of 1828, seems to have been the first to publish a record of the plant in England (as *Ophrys arachnites*) on 'Chalky downs near Folkestone, Kent, Mr Gerard E Smith'. Owing perhaps to the great rarity of the plant, associated colloquial names and attributed folklore appear to be unknown. Within the genus it is unlikely to be confused with any other species, except perhaps unusual forms of *O. apifera*. The large, squarish, velvety labellum of *O. fuciflora*, however, with its rather more elaborate pattern, should be sufficient to distinguish it. To see the plant

Plate 327 (near right). In this individual of *Ophrys fuciflora* the labellum is edged with yellow along its whole apical margin. Chalk downland, East Kent, 11 June 2002.

Plate 328 (far right). Superficially resembling the common Bee Orchid *Ophrys apifera*, the Late Spider-orchid can be recognised by its wider, flatter labellum with a conspicuous yellow apex. Chalk downland, East Kent, 11 June 2002.

in the wild it ought to be possible, after obtaining permission, to visit one of the sites controlled by the Kent Wildlife Trust.

Pollination in British populations is thought most likely to be by pseudocopulation. Hybrids with the Bee Orchid *O. apifera* are certainly known in Britain, and must have resulted by this method. In mainland Europe plants are known to be pollinated by bees of the genus *Eucera*, which have been observed there with pollinia attached to their abdomens. Self-pollination is thought to be rare, although whilst in bud the position of the pollinia can alter so that they come into contact with the stigma below. Vegetative reproduction also appears to be unrecorded.

As remarked above, there have been several records in Britain of the hybrid with *O. apifera*, this being the only other British *Ophrys* with a similar flowering time. However, there are also records for the hybrid with the early-flowering *O. sphegodes* which, if correct, must have originated in an exceptional year when the flowering periods of the parents overlapped. Considerable variation in labellum marking and flower colour can also occur, even within a single population, and has sometimes led to difficulties in correct identification. Plants have also been known to possess double labella, or to have other atypical floral parts.

Plate 329. *Ophrys fuciflora* has a population in England of only a few hundred plants, but the labellum markings are extremely diverse, suggesting active outbreeding. Chalk downland, East Kent, 14 June 2003.

21.4. *Ophrys sphegodes* Mill.

Early Spider-orchid

Perennial herb with two ± globose tubers; *stem* 10–20(–35) cm, erect; lower *leaves* oblong-elliptical to ± ovate, those above narrower and more acute; *inflorescence* a short, lax, few-flowered spike; *bracts* lanceolate; *flowers* yellowish brown, scentless; *outer perianth segments* 6–10 mm, ovate-lanceolate, yellow-green, the laterals patent; *inner perianth segments* slightly smaller, narrowly oblong with a wavy edge, obtuse at the apex, yellowish green; *labellum* to 12 mm long, convex, ± round to broadly ovate, ± entire, or with two small lateral lobes, velvety brown, usually with a horseshoe-shaped, bluish marking; *spur* absent; *column* curved forwards; *anther* resembling a bird's head; *pollinia* two; *viscidia* enclosed in two bursicles; *stigma* placed at the base of the column; *rostellum* very small; *ovary* ridged; *flowering* April to June; 2n = 36.

The geographical range of the Early Spider-orchid *Ophrys sphegodes* covers much of western, central and southern Europe, eastwards to Turkey, the Crimea and western Asia, and south to the Mediterranean islands and North Africa. Being absent from northern central Europe and Scandinavia, it attains its northern limit in southern England and Holland. Throughout its range the flowers occur in a large number of colour forms, at least 14 of which have been described as separate subspecies; the British plant is the nominate subsp. *sphegodes*. In continental Europe the Early Spider-orchid is a plant of dry grassland, woodland clearings and maquis and, especially in the south, of stony ground, garrigue and phrygana, where it sometimes

Plate 330. The suggestion of a plump spider can be found in the flowers of *Ophrys sphegodes*, the Early Spider-orchid. Coastal chalk grassland, Dorset, 9 May 1996.

occurs under light cover of *Pinus* or shrubs. It is mainly a lowland plant and is absent from the high ground of the central Alps.

In the British Isles it is now restricted to southern and south-eastern England, where it is rare. With the exception of a now extinct, isolated record from north Wales, all known localities lie to the south-east of a line drawn from the Bristol Channel to the Wash. It is now classified as a British Red Data Book plant, and although described as being at low risk, is largely restricted to Dorset, East Sussex and Kent. It has always been a local plant but formerly had a much wider range, occurring in England as far north as Northamptonshire, and west to Cornwall.

Its favoured habitat is short, species-rich calcareous turf, often close to the coast. Correct management of this appears to be vital for the plant's survival, winter-grazing by cattle affecting it adversely but grazing by sheep, except near its flowering time, being beneficial. Associates in such habitats include herbs typical of short, calcareous turf such as *Asperula cynanchica, Gentian-ella amarella, Hippocrepis comosa, Ononis repens, Polygala vulgaris* and *Thymus polytrichus. Ophrys sphegodes* can also colonise disturbed ground such as disused quarried areas or track borders, and – most spectacularly – the great spoil-heap of chalk marl excavated from the Channel Tunnel near Folke-stone, Kent. It has also been found on coastal shingle in Kent. NVC classified habitats include various calcareous grassland subcommunities (CG2b, CG5a). The population on the Dorset coast to the west of Swanage is the most important in Britain, with over 15,000 flowering plants recorded in a good year. This has been

Plate 331. The Dorset coastline west of Swanage is the *locus classicus* in England for the Early Spider-orchid, which is usually in flower there in April. Coastal chalk grassland, Dorset, 18 April 2002.

Plate 333 (opposite). Although morphologically unmistakeable, *Ophrys sphegodes* is a short plant and can be difficult to see at first. Coastal chalk grassland, Dorset, 9 April 2002.

Plate 332. The pale form of *Ophrys sphegodes* has been named var. *flavescens* Schultze. It grows among normal plants. Chalk grassland, E. Sussex, 6 May 2002.

estimated to comprise more than 60 per cent of the total British population, but in 2004 about 9000 plants were recorded on the Channel Tunnel chalk-marl spoil site. Aside from these, the other main populations are also in Kent, and in Sussex. Most are now in SSSIs and so protected to some extent from damage by harmful farming methods. It is very likely, however, that such methods have contributed to the demise of the plant in counties further north and west, in most of which it no longer survives.

The current specific name *sphegodes* (Greek, 'wasp-like'), as well as epithets applied by other authorities such as *arachnitis* and *aranifera* (both derived from the Greek *arachne*, 'spider'), all relate to the appearance of the labellum, which somewhat suggests the abdomen of an arthropod. The first British record is that made by a Dr Bowle from an old stone-pit at Barnack in Northamptonshire, quoted in 1650 by William How in his *Phytologia Britannica* as 'Orchis Arachnitis, Spider Orchis … hard by Walcot a mile from Barneck …'; John Ray recorded it in Cambridgeshire from near Shelford in 1663. In the field, as well as being notable for its early flowering and usually low stature, it is readily distinguished from other members of the genus by its yellow-green sepals and velvety brown labellum with prominent, contrasting H- or horseshoe-shaped marking. In April (or sometimes earlier) to early May, a careful search of short, calcareous turf on the Dorset coast will give the best chance of finding the plant. However, it is very local, and as when searching for many orchids, a degree of patience will be required.

Pollination appears not to have been studied in detail. Insects, probably Hymenoptera, are attracted to the flowers for the nectar secreted in two small, bright patches at the base of the column. Cross-pollination probably occurs (natural hybrids with other species are known, so insects must be transferring some pollen from plant to plant), but only to a limited extent, and fertilisation is likely to be achieved largely through self-pollination. Recorded seed-set is low, less than 20 per cent being normal. A detailed study of the life cycle of *Ophrys sphegodes*, carried out by Hutchings (1987), has indicated that 70 per cent of plants flower within the first year of leaf development, and that within a further three years almost all non-dormant plants are in flower. It was also found that no more than half of the population is above ground during any given flowering period, and that only a few individuals will flower for more than three years in succession.

The labellum of *O. sphegodes* can occur in quite a wide range of shapes and colours, and the sepals can also show variation in colour. Plants may sometimes occur with double labella, and also with inverted flowers. Hybridisation with the Fly Orchid *O. insectifera* has been recorded on several occasions in Kent, giving plants with dark, narrow, inner perianth segments similar to those of *O. insectifera*, together with a long, narrow, brown labellum lacking lateral lobes.

Orchid Hybrids in the British Isles

While there are many undoubted cases of hybridisation in the British orchid flora, all putative hybrids should be considered very carefully indeed to rule out the possibility of plants being merely morphological variants, or true teratological mutations. Hybridisation is almost always confined to closely related taxa; the more distantly related a pair of putative parents, the less likely is the hybrid between them. The only really frequent hybrids to be found in the British Isles are between species of *Dactylorhiza*, and to a lesser extent between *Dactylorhiza* and *Gymnadenia*. Most others are very infrequent and quite unlikely to be found. Some highly improbable crosses have been recorded, and even described with nothogeneric names, as in the case of the putative *Platanthera chlorantha* × *Pseudorchis albida* (×*Pseudanthera breadalbanensis* McKean) from Scotland. In this case the plants were later shown to be an aberrant form of *Platanthera chlorantha*. Other dubious records are those for hybrids between *Anacamptis pyramidalis* and *Gymnadenia conopsea*, and *Anacamptis morio* and *Dactylorhiza maculata*.

In examining a putative hybrid it is never easy to determine which species was the seed-bearing (female) parent, and which the pollinating (male) parent. Maternal

Plate 334 (opposite). Hybrids are recognised by their possession of features of both parents, as in this individual of *Gymnadenia borealis* × *Pseudorchis albida* (×*Pseudadenia schweinfurthii*). Such intermediate plants in a mixed population of orchids should immediately arouse suspicions of hybridity. Edge of native Caledonian pinewood, east Inverness-shire, 30 June 2003.

Hybrid progeny from the same parentage may look quite different. Here the parents were the same, but it is assumed that the directionality of the cross was different in the two cases. Describing the variation possible in such hybrids is difficult. Plate 335 (far left): *Dactylorhiza fuchsii* subsp. *fuchsii* × *D. purpurella* var. *purpurella*, damp neutral grassland, West Ross, 26 June 2003; Plate 336 (near left): *D. purpurella* var. *purpurella* × *D. fuchsii* subsp. *fuchsii*, disused limestone quarry, Co. Durham, 6 June 1998. Both are nothosubsp. *venusta*.

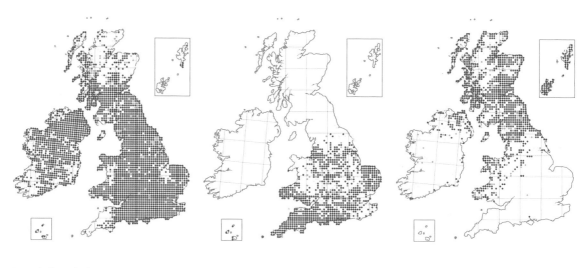

Dactylorhiza fuchsii   Dactylorhiza praetermissa   Dactylorhiza purpurella

Dactylorhiza fuchsii × D. praetermissa   Dactylorhiza fuchsii × D. purpurella
(D. ×grandis)   (D. ×venusta)

Hybrid orchids can be expected to be found only where the two parents overlap. This sequence of maps demonstrates this for the progeny of the widespread *Dactylorhiza fuchsii* and the two common marsh-orchids, *D. praetermissa* in southern Britain and *D. purpurella* in northern areas. The progeny (*D. ×grandis* and *D. ×venusta*, respectively) are recorded only from the areas occupied by their marsh-orchid parent. Isolation is not complete, and identification problems can be expected in the transition zone in north-central England.
(*D. ×grandis* is illustrated in Plate 201, p. 202; *D. ×venusta* in Plates 335 and 336 overleaf, p. 315; and, as nothosubsp. *hebridella*, in Plate 342, p. 320.)

features are often said to be the most strongly inherited, but this is not always the case. In indicating hybrid parentage it is conventional to give the name of the female parent first: so in the parentage formula *Dactylorhiza fuchsii × D. purpurella*, *D. fuchsii* would be expected to be the seed-bearing plant. This convention works well for artificial crosses, but is less useful in the case of wild populations in which hybrids appear spontaneously. In such cases one parent's name must, inevitably, appear first, but the directionality of the parentage cannot be assumed to be known.

The desirability of coining binomials for hybrids is often debated by taxonomists. When such names are created the taxonomic rank in question is prefixed by 'notho-', to indicate a hybrid origin: hence **nothogenus**, **nothospecies**. A nothogeneric name is preceded by a multiplication sign (e.g. *×Pseudadenia*), while a nothospecies is indicated in the form *Dactylorhiza ×grandis*. Such naming can be seen as a rather futile exercise – both if the hybrid is rare, and also if it is more common and fertile, when a range of morphological characters may appear in the hybrid plants and succeeding generations. On the other hand, it provides a 'handle' for otherwise nameless plants and may prevent circumlocution in discussing them. In this book we have included names of hybrids in cases where they have been validly published, but have not attempted to supply names for the remaining plethora of innominate crosses. In some cases, reclassification of certain species into different genera has rendered a nothogeneric name superfluous – the parents in the case of ×*Dactyloglossum* (*Dactylorhiza* and *Coeloglossum*), for example, now being regarded as belonging to the same genus, and similarly ×*Orchiaceras* (*Orchis* and *Aceras*). A major review of the taxa involved would be required before attempting the taxonomic changes necessary to regularise the position, so in the list that follows we have given the anachronistic names, indicating them in quotation marks.

Other names applied to hybrids between recently redefined allotetraploid species of *Dactylorhiza* may not be strictly relevant to that particular genetic origin: such names are prefaced by a question mark. Again, answering such questions will require considerable research.

The nothogeneric name ×*Dactyloglossum* was given to hybrids between the Frog Orchid ('*Coeloglossum viride*') and members of *Dactylorhiza* but *Coeloglossum* is now regarded as a primitive member of *Dactylorhiza*, so the nothogeneric name is no longer relevant. Here we see progeny of crosses between *D. viridis* and two subspecies of *D. fuchsii*: Plate 337 (left), *D. viridis* × *D. fuchsii* subsp. *fuchsii*, Hampshire, 4 July 1999; Plate 338 (right), *D. viridis* × *D. fuchsii* subsp. *hebridensis*, Outer Hebrides, 12 July 1991.

Orchid hybrids recorded in the British Isles

This list of primary hybrids is arranged according to the taxonomic sequence adopted in this book. Each pairing of parents is listed only once, although the cross might occur with parenthood in either direction. Original records do not always identify parents to infraspecific rank; in most cases the commonest subspecies is the probable parent. All hybrids involving *Dactylorhiza* are listed under that genus.

Cephalanthera

Cephalanthera damasonium × *C. longifolia*
   (*C.* ×*schulzei* Camus, Bergon & A. Camus) (Plate 42, p. 35)

Epipactis

Epipactis atrorubens × *E. helleborine* (*E.* ×*schmalhausenii* K. Richt.)
   (Plate 86, p. 83; Plate 87, p. 84)

Epipactis helleborine × *E. purpurata* (*E.* ×*schulzei* P. Fourn.)

Epipactis dunensis × *E. helleborine* var. *youngiana*

Epipactis helleborine × *E. leptochila*

Plates 339 (near right) and 340 (far right). The overall appearance of this plant and the unusual colour of its flowers immediately suggest a hybrid origin. Seen close-up the flower has features (the flattened hood of sepals and lateral petals, and the narrow lip) identifying the cross as that between *Dactylorhiza purpurella* var. *purpurella* and *D. viridis* ('×*Dactyloglossum*' *viridella*). Dry machair grassland, West Sutherland, 25 June 2003.

Orchis

Orchis anthropophora × *O. purpurea* ('×*Orchiaceras*' *melsheimeri* Rouy)

Orchis anthropophora × *O. simia* ('×*Orchiaceras*' *bergonii* (Nanteuil) A. Camus)

Orchis militaris × *O. simia* (*Orchis* ×*beyrichii* A. Kern.)

Orchis mascula × *Anacamptis morio* ('*Orchis*' ×*morioides* Brand)

Platanthera

Platanthera bifolia × *P. chlorantha* (*P.* ×*hybrida* Brügger)

Gymnadenia

Gymnadenia borealis × *Platanthera bifolia*

Gymnadenia borealis × *Pseudorchis albida*
(×*Pseudadenia schweinfurthii* (Hegelm. ex A. Kern.) P.F. Hunt)
(Plate 334, p. 314)

Dactylorhiza

Dactylorhiza × Dactylorhiza

Dactylorhiza incarnata × *D. occidentalis*
(? *D.* ×*aschersoniana* (Hausskn.) Soó)

Dactylorhiza incarnata × *D. praetermissa*
(*D.* ×*wintonii* (A. Camus) P.F. Hunt)

Dactylorhiza incarnata × *D. traunsteinerioides*
(? *D.* ×*dufftii* (Hausskn.) Peitz) (Plate 57, p. 49)

Dactylorhiza incarnata subsp. *incarnata* × *D. purpurella*
(*D.* ×*latirella* (P.M. Hall) Soó) (Plates 267, p. 253; 343, p. 320)

Dactylorhiza incarnata subsp. *coccinea* × *D. purpurella*

Dactylorhiza incarnata subsp. *pulchella* × *D. maculata*
(*D.* ×*carnea* (A. Camus) Soó) (Plate 341, right)

Dactylorhiza viridis × *D. fuchsii* subsp. *fuchsii*
('×*Dactyloglossum*' *mixtum* (Asch. & Graebn.) Rauschert)
(Plate 337, p. 317)

Dactylorhiza viridis × *D. fuchsii* subsp. *hebridensis*
(Plates 224 and 225, p. 222; Plate 338, p. 317)

Dactylorhiza viridis × *D. maculata*
('×*Dactyloglossum*' *drucei* (A. Camus) Soó)

Plate 341. A putative hybrid between *Dactylorhiza incarnata* subsp. *pulchella* and *D. maculata* (*D.* ×*carnea*). The possibility of the plant being an extreme variant of one of the parents should always be borne in mind, but this is a true intermediate. New Forest, South Hampshire, 10 June 1999.

Plate 342 (below left). *Dactylorhiza* hybrids usually show some features from their assumed parents. In this *Dactylorhiza pur-purella* var. *purpurella* × *D. fuchsii* subsp. *hebridensis* the overall appearance suggests subsp. *hebridensis*, but the labellum is the wrong shape. Machair, West Sutherland, 25 June 2003.

Plate 343 (below right). Marsh-orchid hybrids are particularly difficult to identify with certainty, but this *Dactylorhiza purpurella* var. *purpurella* × *D. incarnata* subsp. *incarnata* (*D.* ×*latirella*) clearly has features of both parents. Coastal dunes, Co. Durham, 6 June 2003.

Dactylorhiza viridis × *D. purpurella*
    ('×*Dactyloglossum*' *viridella* (Hesl.-Harr.) Soó) (Plates 339 and 340, p.318)

Dactylorhiza viridis × *D. incarnata* subsp. *coccinea*

Dactylorhiza fuchsii subsp. *fuchsii* × *D. incarnata* subsp. *incarnata*
    (*D.* ×*kerneriorum* (Soó) Soó nothosubsp. *kerneriorum*) (Plate 372, p.340)

Dactylorhiza fuchsii subsp. *hebridensis* × *D. incarnata* subsp. *incarnata*
    (*D.* ×*kerneriorum* nothosubsp. *variabilis* (Hesl.-Harr.) P.D.Sell)

Dactylorhiza fuchsii subsp. *hebridensis* × *D. incarnata* subsp. *coccinea*
    (Plate 238, p.232)

Dactylorhiza fuchsii subsp. *fuchsii* × *D. maculata*
    (*D.* ×*transiens* (Druce) Soó nothosubsp. *transiens*)

Dactylorhiza fuchsii subsp. *hebridensis* × *D. maculata*
    (*D.* ×*transiens* nothosubsp. *corylensis* (Hesl.-Harr.) P.D. Sell

Dactylorhiza fuchsii × *D. praetermissa* (*D.* ×*grandis* (Druce) P.F. Hunt)
    (Plate 201, p.202; Plate 376, p.344)

Dactylorhiza fuchsii subsp. *fuchsii* × *D. purpurella* var. *purpurella*
    (*D.* ×*venusta* (T. & T.A. Stephenson) Soó nothosubsp. *venusta*)
    (Plates 335 and 336, p.315)

Dactylorhiza fuchsii subsp. *hebridensis* × *D. purpurella* var. *purpurella*
  (*D.* ×*venusta* (T. & T.A. Stephenson) Soó nothosubsp. *hebridella*
  (Wilmott) P.D. Sell) (Plate 342, opposite)

Dactylorhiza fuchsii × *D. traunsteinerioides*

Dactylorhiza maculata × *D. occidentalis* (? *D.* ×*dinglensis* (Wilmott) Soó)
  (Plate 243, p. 237)

Dactylorhiza maculata × *D. praetermissa* (*D.* ×*hallii* (Druce) Soó)

Dactylorhiza maculata × *D. purpurella* (*D.* ×*formosa* (T. & T.A. Stephenson) Soó)

Dactylorhiza maculata × *D. traunsteinerioides* (? *D.* ×*jenensis* (Brand) Soó)

Dactylorhiza praetermissa × *D. purpurella*
  (*D.* ×*insignis* (T. & T.A. Stephenson) Soó)

Dactylorhiza praetermissa × *D. traunsteinerioides*

Dactylorhiza purpurella × *D. ebudensis*

Dactylorhiza × *Gymnadenia*

Dactylorhiza incarnata × *Gymnadenia conopsea*
  (×*Dactylodenia vollmannii* (M. Schulze) Peitz)

Intergeneric hybrids are most frequent between closely related genera, and especially between *Gymnadenia* and *Dactylorhiza*: it is worth searching for intermediates in any area containing members of both these genera. Current records do not always differentiate between the progeny of the newly segregated fragrant-orchids, and more information is needed. Two similar hybrids are compared here. Plate 344 (below left): *G. borealis* × *D. fuchsii* subsp. *fuchsii*, rough grassland, Fife, 2 July 2003; Plate 345 (below right): *G. conopsea* × *D. fuchsii* subsp. *fuchsii*, chalk downland, Salisbury Plain, Wiltshire, 20 June 2003.

Dactylorhiza incarnata × *Gymnadenia borealis*

Dactylorhiza incarnata subsp. *pulchella* × *Gymnadenia borealis*
  (Plates 217 and 218, p. 216)

Dactylorhiza viridis × *Gymnadenia conopsea*
  ('×*Gymnaglossum*' *jacksonii* (Quirk) Rolfe)

Dactylorhiza fuchsii subsp. *fuchsii* × *Gymnadenia borealis*
  (Plate 344, p. 321; Plate 402, p. 370)

Dactylorhiza fuchsii subsp. *fuchsii* × *Gymnadenia conopsea*
  (×*Dactylodenia st-quintinii* (Godfery) J. Duvign.) (Plate 345, p. 321)

Dactylorhiza maculata × *Gymnadenia borealis*
  (×*Dactylodenia legrandiana* (A. Camus) Peitz)
  (Plates 244 and 245, p. 237)

Dactylorhiza praetermissa × *Gymnadenia conopsea*
  (×*Dactylodenia wintonii* (Druce) Peitz)

Dactylorhiza praetermissa × *Gymnadenia densiflora*

Dactylorhiza purpurella × *Gymnadenia borealis*

Dactylorhiza purpurella × *Gymnadenia conopsea*
  (×*Dactylodenia varia* (T. & T.A. Stephenson) Druce)

Dactylorhiza × *Platanthera*

Dactylorhiza viridis × *Platanthera bifolia*

Dactylorhiza × *Pseudorchis*

Dactylorhiza maculata × *Pseudorchis albida*
  (×*Pseudorhiza bruniana* (Brügger) P.F. Hunt)

Anacamptis

Anacamptis laxiflora × *Anacamptis morio* ('*Orchis*' ×*alata* Fleury)

Plate 346 (opposite).
Ophrys ×*pietzschii* –
the extremely rare hybrid
between *O. insectifera*
and *O. apifera*, showing
indisputable intermediate
characters. A major find for
the orchid enthusiast. Edge
of deciduous woodland,
W. Sussex, 24 June 2000.

Ophrys

Ophrys apifera × *O. fuciflora* (*O.* ×*albertiana* A. Camus)

Ophrys apifera × *O. insectifera*
  (*O.* ×*pietzschii* Kümpel ex Rauschert nom. inval.) (Plate 346, opposite)

Ophrys fuciflora × *O. sphegodes* (*O.* ×*aschersonii* Nanteuil)

Ophrys insectifera × *O. sphegodes* (*O.* ×*hybrida* Pokorny ap. Rchb. f.)

Chapter 6

Approaches to the Conservation of British and Irish Orchids

Ian Taylor

The pressure of a large human population with a high material standard of living crammed onto the comparatively small islands of Britain and Ireland has had, and continues to have, a devastating impact on their flora.

Prior to industrialisation in the nineteenth century human activity was already having an effect through large-scale changes in land use, particularly reduction in woodland cover. Many plants of open habitats would, however, have benefited from these changes, and large populations of woodland species did also survive; some indeed benefited from intensive woodland management techniques such as coppicing. Some orchids would have been collected, for medicinal or forage use, but whilst this may have been locally significant it probably had relatively little impact on most plant populations at the national level.

Then came the industrialised Victorian age, with its rapid expansion of human populations and increased leisure time (for some at least), and many of our native plant species went into a period of continuing decline. The causes of this decline can be summarised under four categories of threat: persecution, habitat degradation, habitat destruction and the negative impacts of non-native species. The relative importance of these factors has changed significantly through time.

Persecution, habitat degradation and habitat destruction

The enthusiasm of nineteenth-century naturalists for making collections of natural objects, particularly the unusual and beautiful, was perhaps the most remarkable phenomenon as, within the total flora, orchids (alongside ferns and high alpines) became for the first time especially vulnerable. The legacy of the Victorian passion for plant collection – for herbaria as much as for horticulture – is still evident today in the plight of the Lady's-slipper Orchid *Cypripedium calceolus*, which remains critically endangered following nineteenth-century depredations.

Also in the nineteenth century, some plant species suffered from the impact of early aspects of habitat degradation, including improved seed-cleaning techniques and increasing pollution of water courses, but as orchids are very poorly represented in the arable and aquatic floras they were relatively little affected by these factors.

The next major impact probably began in earnest during and after the Second World War, although signs of trouble ahead had already been seen during the 1920s

Plate 347 (opposite). The rediscovery of *Orchis militaris* in 1947 by J.E. Lousley, after 25 years without a record, caused great excitement. Active conservation management has greatly assisted this still very rare plant. *O. militaris* var. *tenuifrons*, grassy valley on chalk, Buckinghamshire, 25 May 1996.

Plate 348. Unimproved lowland meadows are among the most threatened habitats in the British Isles, most having been lost to intensive agriculture in the second half of the twentieth century; they are an important habitat for some orchids, in this case *Dactylorhiza incarnata* subsp. *incarnata*. Water meadow, W. Suffolk, 20 May 2002.

Plate 349. The Burnt Orchid has declined dramatically and is the subject of much conservation concern. It survives in undisturbed grassland. *Neotinea ustulata* var. *aestivalis*, on ramparts of an Iron-Age fort, North Hampshire, 12 July 2002.

and 1930s. Increasingly intensive agriculture, employing heavy applications of fertilisers, the widespread use of effective herbicides, and the conversion of permanent pasture to short-term lays and arable use, had a devastating impact on floral biodiversity. This time it was grassland habitats that were most severely affected, and orchids – many of which occur in grassland and are particularly vulnerable to increasing levels of soil nutrients – began a dramatic decline that continues today. The meadow-growing Green-winged Orchid *Anacamptis morio* and the Burnt Orchid *Neotinea ustulata* are perhaps the most obvious victims. There can be little doubt that the introduction of higher-yielding milking cattle and the concomitant switch from hay-making to silage production lies behind much of this loss. Add to this the effects of other changes in land management – the abandonment of traditional coppicing, for example, and the increased extent to which agriculturally marginal land is planted with conifers – and it is easy to understand why through the second half of the twentieth century and into the twenty-first it is habitat degradation that is primarily to blame for the perilous state of many British orchids.

To make matters worse, the same period has seen the outright destruction of many sites, through urban and infrastructural development, and locally this has had a serious impact. Increasing urbanisation, particularly in southern England, and the expansion of the road network throughout the country have destroyed many orchid populations. This has been visible to the majority of the public who live and work in our larger settlements. It has affected familiar and highly valued plant populations, orchids amongst them, and the damage is often immediate and permanent. The visible nature of this threat has led, however, to its importance being over-emphasised in the minds of many, and it is perhaps worth stating clearly that agricultural intensification has been and continues to be the greater problem.

Fortunately the situation may now be on the turn, although whether the improvements under way are too little, too late for some species remains to be seen. Current changes in agricultural support mechanisms are giving much more attention to biodiversity and may alleviate, at least locally, some of the problems associated with nutrient over-enrichment, extensive herbicide applications and orchid-unfriendly management systems like silage production. Improvements in the conservation context should also help (see below), and public attitudes to the collection of wild plants have changed dramatically, although orchids remain the most vulnerable group in this respect. Habitat destruction as a result of urban and infrastructural development does continue, but improved integration of biodiversity protection into the planning system is reducing its negative effects.

Non-native species

One of the major impacts on the environment in the late-twentieth and early twenty-first centuries comes from the spread of non-native species – widely believed to be a major threat to wildlife throughout the world, particularly in aquatic habitats. Fortunately, orchids in the British Isles appear to be relatively unaffected, although some populations of woodland, moorland and bog species have undoubtedly been harmed by expanding *Rhododendron ponticum* populations, and *Fallopia japonica* is a problem in many lowland areas, particularly on the urban fringes.

The legal framework

That nature might be worthy of active protection rather than simple exploitation would have been a strange concept to most people until comparatively recently. The hardships of life, coupled with the sheer abundance and familiarity of many species, would have rendered such notions not only unthinkable but unnecessary. The realisation did, however, finally dawn that some species were under threat and in need of positive action to protect them, and the first steps of the conservation movement were taken. From the late-nineteenth to the mid-twentieth century nature conservation was a small-scale, marginal and voluntary activity, but in the years following the Second World War the idea gradually took root more widely and a legal framework for both species and habitat protection came into being.

Plate 350. The Lizard Orchid *Himantoglossum hircinum* is afforded the special protection of Schedule 8 of the Wildlife and Countryside Act (1981), and is an indicator species for Special Areas of Conservation under an EU Directive. Coastal dunes, East Kent, 20 June 2002.

In Great Britain the National Parks and Access to the Countryside Act (1949) enabled the establishment and appropriate management of National and Local Nature Reserves. It also set out the concept of Sites of Special Scientific Interest (SSSIs), in recognition of natural and semi-natural habitats and other locations that support important plant or other wildlife populations. Sadly, SSSIs established under the 1949 Act proved largely ineffectual, and losses continued apace. The Conservation of Wild Creatures and Wild Plants Act (1975) gave protection for all wild plants against uprooting. Five orchids (*Cephalanthera rubra, Cypripedium calceolus, Epipogium aphyllum, Orchis militaris* and *O. simia*) were afforded special protection by this Act, but it was another 32 years before the Wildlife and Countryside Act (1981) secured much improved protection for orchids and significant orchid habitats. Section 13 of this Act made it illegal to uproot any wild plant without the permission of an authorised person, and gave special protection to any species listed on Schedule 8 of the Act. Schedule 8 is reviewed every five years and currently includes 11 orchid species throughout Britain: nine of these are fully discrete sexual species (*Cephalanthera rubra, Cypripedium calceolus, Epipogium aphyllum, Himantoglossum hircinum, Liparis loeselii, Ophrys fuciflora, O. sphegodes, Orchis militaris* and *O. simia*), whilst the other two ('*Dactylorhiza lapponica*' and '*Epipactis youngiana*') lie within taxonomically complex genera (see p. 339) and are not recognised as full species in this book.

In addition to Section 13, which focuses on the relatively limited threat of direct persecution to particular plant species, the Act included significant improvements for the practical protection of SSSIs; nineteen years later, in the Countryside and Rights of Way Act (2000), the effectiveness of SSSIs in England and Wales was strengthened further. The selection of SSSIs and their subsequent management is currently overseen in England by the statutory body English Nature, in Scotland by Scottish Natural Heritage and in Wales by the Countryside Council for Wales. Additional emphasis has been placed on orchid-rich dry calcareous grassland sites of European importance through their designation as Special Areas of Conservation under the European Union (EU) Habitats and Species Directive (1992). In the UK this habitat has been interpreted as including key sites for *Herminium monorchis, Himantoglossum hircinum, Neotinea ustulata, Ophrys fuciflora, O. sphegodes, Orchis anthropophora, O. militaris, O. purpurea* and *O. simia.* Such sites often have other orchids present in addition to these rare or scarce species, that benefit from the same protection measures. The directive also recognises the Europe-wide threat to both *Cypripedium calceolus* and *Liparis loeselii* by listing them in Annexes II and IV, requiring action including the designation of Special Areas of Conservation expressly for their protection.

Plate 351. Irish Lady's-tresses *Spiranthes romanzoffiana* is one of four orchids protected by statute in the Republic of Ireland, and is the subject of a Biodiversity Action Plan in the UK. Wet peaty grassland by loch, Island of Barra, Outer Hebrides, 16 August 2000.

National Nature Reserves may be managed directly by the same three statutory bodies for England, Scotland and Wales or, with their agreement, by other approved bodies such as Wildlife Trusts and the National Trust. The management of Local Nature Reserves is overseen by Local Authorities. Wildlife Trusts, the conservation charity Plantlife and other organisations throughout the country also manage significant areas as nature reserves without the benefit of statutory designations. These non-governmental organisations, together with private individuals and societies such as the Botanical Society of the British Isles and the Hardy Orchid Society, organise many other activities of relevance to orchid conservation – monitoring populations, raising awareness, and when necessary undertaking management or even plant rescues in the face of legal development.

In Northern Ireland Section 14 of the Wildlife (NI) Order (1985) works in a similar way to Section 13 of the Wildlife and Countryside Act (1981) in Great Britain, and its Schedule 8 gives special protection to nine species: *Anacamptis (Orchis) morio, Dactylorhiza 'traunsteineri', Epipactis palustris, E. phyllanthes, Hammarbya paludosa, Neottia nidus-avis, Ophrys apifera, Pseudorchis albida* and *Spiranthes romanzoffiana.* Areas of Special Scientific Interest (ASSIs) in Northern Ireland (equivalent to SSSIs) are the responsibility of the Environment and Heritage Service.

The Government of the Republic of Ireland can also confer special protection on plant species of conservation concern, and this is done from time to time by issuing orders through Section 21 of the Wildlife Act (1976). The Flora (Protection) Order (1999) lists four orchid species: *Cephalanthera longifolia, Hammarbya paludosa, Pseudorchis albida* and *Spiranthes romanzoffiana*. The previous order (1987) additionally listed *Anacamptis (Orchis) morio*.

Site protection is also enabled in the Republic of Ireland through the Wildlife Act (1976), as amended in 2000, allowing the establishment of Natural Heritage Areas (similar to the British SSSIs). However, it is probably fair to say that much more conservation effort in the Irish Republic has gone to the state-owned National Parks and Statutory Nature Reserves. As in the UK, areas of European importance are recognised through the designation of Special Areas of Conservation under the EU Habitats and Species Directive (1992).

One of the main delivery mechanisms for conservation action in the UK in recent years has been through Biodiversity Action Planning (BAP) – a process designed to identify and set recovery targets for those species for which Britain has particular global responsibility, or which are most likely to move towards extinction unless positive conservation action is taken. The latter are identified primarily by their rate of decline over a recent 25-year period. Priority species identified in this way have Action Plans drawn up for them, with explicit targets for recovery. The Countryside and Rights of Way Act (2000) supports the BAP process in England by placing on landowners and occupiers a legal duty to safeguard BAP Priority species, among which there are currently three orchids: *Cypripedium calceolus, Liparis loeselii* and *Spiranthes romanzoffiana*. Similar provision is made in Wales, although the list there is tailored to the needs of the Welsh flora and the only orchid included is *Liparis loeselii*.

Essential though they are, statutory conservation measures have no effect without practical application. The bodies responsible for delivering conservation on the ground are involved in activities as diverse as habitat management through stock-grazing, reed-cutting and coppicing of woodland, care of seedlings reintroduced under recovery programmes, and of course that all-important element, continuing education of the public.

Assessing threat and rarity status

Threats to wildlife are generally assessed in the UK in the following way. The Joint Nature Conservation Committee (JNCC) maintains a list of species considered to be threatened in the UK, classifying them according to the current criteria of the World Conservation Union (IUCN) under the categories Extinct, Extinct in the Wild, Critically Endangered, Endangered, Vulnerable or Near Threatened (IUCN 2001). These are known as the Red List species and now include 25 of the principal native orchid taxa, an exceptionally high proportion for a single family. The criteria employed in the analysis reflect the various constituent attributes of threat such as rates of population decline, contractions in range or area occupied, presence in small numbers, in limited numbers of localities or as isolated disjunct occurrences. *Cephalanthera rubra* and *Cypripedium calceolus*, for example, are considered Critically Endangered in the UK because they each have total population sizes numbering fewer than 50 individuals. *Ophrys fuciflora*, by contrast, is considered Vulnerable because it has a total population size of between 250 and 1000 mature individuals

TABLE 3. RED LIST CATEGORIES OF ORCHIDS IN GREAT BRITAIN

Extinct

Epipogium aphyllum
Spiranthes aestivalis

Extinct in the Wild

None

Plate 352. Not all development is a conservation disaster: the spoil-heap from the Channel Tunnel, now called Samphire Hoe, has been spectacularly colonised by thousands of Early Spider-orchids *Ophrys sphegodes*. Samphire Hoe, East Kent, 22 April 2002.

Critically Endangered

Cephalanthera rubra
Cypripedium calceolus

Endangered

Epipactis sancta
Liparis loeselii
Neotinea ustulata
Orchis anthropophora
Orchis purpurea

Vulnerable

Cephalanthera damasonium
Cephalanthera longifolia
Corallorhiza trifida
Dactylorhiza ebudensis
Dactylorhiza viridis
Herminium monorchis
Ophrys fuciflora
Ophrys insectifera
Orchis militaris
Orchis simia
Platanthera bifolia
Pseudorchis albida

Near Threatened

Anacamptis morio
Himantoglossum hircinum
Platanthera chlorantha
Spiranthes spiralis

In addition, several scarce or rare orchid taxa are listed as Data Deficient and have not been placed into a threat category: *Epipactis leptochila*, *E. dunensis*, *Gymnadenia densiflora*, *Dactylorhiza incarnata* subsp. *ochroleuca*, *D. incarnata* subsp. *cruenta* and *D. purpurella* var. *cambrensis*.

The Red Data List and JNCC lists of Nationally Rare and Nationally Scarce taxa have not yet adopted some of the taxonomic changes reflected in this book, but a review is in progress.

and that population is restricted to a very small area of south-east England, which means that it is vulnerable to localised random events. IUCN threat assessments can be very complex, involving combinations of criteria and threshold levels for attributes such as area of occupancy, extent of occurrence and decline that are difficult to measure. Unfortunately the criteria used to determine which taxa qualify as threatened are often overlooked once the threat assessment has been completed but they are critical, considered alongside autecological attributes, when deciding on the most appropriate conservation strategy.

The new *Vascular Plant Red Data List* for Great Britain by Christine Cheffings and Lynne Farrell (2005), published just as we go to press, has taken a long hard look at the British flora and presents an alarming picture of declining populations of many species. Among the orchids the situation is particularly serious, with 25 species now being listed in the top categories of the assessment (see Table 3, which shows the currently accepted threat statuses of orchids in Great Britain). Most worrying is the inclusion of species often thought to be reasonably common or abundant, as sometimes indicated elsewhere in this book: the elevation of *Orchis anthropophora* to the Endangered category, alongside *Liparis loeselii*, for example, and the assessment of *Platanthera bifolia* as Vulnerable together with such 'rarities' as *Ophrys fuciflora*, *Orchis militaris* and *O. simia*. In such cases it is not so much the number of individuals that gives rise to concern, but the rate of their decline in occurrence. Although foreshadowed in the distribution maps in the *New Atlas of the British and Irish Flora* (2002), which show how ranges have frequently diminished in the past few decades, this survey (available online at www.jncc.gov.uk) is the first to acknowledge the decline of 'common' species and is likely to become a landmark in the history of British conservation, awakening us to the vulnerability of all our native plants. Red List species do not occur in isolation: they are part of the plant communities in which they occur. If increased attention is given to their conservation, other, less threatened species will also benefit through the maintenance of the habitat.

To many field botanists the presence of orchids adds that degree of excitement that comes from experiencing rare plants in the wild. In addition they can be considered to add value to special sites by contributing to the overall botanical diversity. Rare orchids may also be useful indicators of high-quality habitats, given that their rarity often reflects demanding habitat requirements.

In what follows of this chapter, threatened orchid taxa will be discussed on a case-by-case basis. In an attempt to reflect the complications outlined above they will be considered to fall into three categories according to general approaches to their conservation, responding to the types of threat they face: these are the highly restricted (and indeed extinct) species, the rapidly declining, and the taxonomically complex. Obviously these groupings are not mutually exclusive, and for the purposes of this discussion taxa have been placed in the category that most closely reflects their conservation context.

Plate 353. Woodland and scrub clearance, coupled with hand-pollination, have enabled the main Buckinghamshire population of *Orchis militaris* var. *tenuifrons* to increase significantly in recent years. The plants show considerable genetic diversity. Clearing in mixed woodland, Buckinghamshire, 21 May 1997.

Case studies

The response of the conservation community to a threatened taxon tends to vary. The cause of the threat may dictate an obvious solution or pathway to follow, but the philosophical approach taken by different bodies may also have an influence. Some conservation techniques involving direct intervention, for example, such as population re-enforcement or full reintroduction, remain somewhat controversial.

The case studies given below illustrate how conservation organisations have approached some of the threats faced by orchids of the British Isles.

Highly restricted (and extinct) species

Anacamptis laxiflora, Cephalanthera rubra, Corallorhiza trifida, Cypripedium calceolus, Epipogium aphyllum, Himantoglossum hircinum, Liparis loeselii, Neotinea maculata, Ophrys fuciflora, Ophrys sphegodes, Orchis militaris, Orchis simia, Serapias lingua, Serapias parviflora, Spiranthes aestivalis, Spiranthes romanzoffiana

In this as in our other two categories the taxa included range widely in the degree of threat that they face, from the extinct (*Spiranthes aestivalis*) to the reasonably widespread (*Corallorhiza trifida*) and from the historically persecuted (*Cypripedium calceolus*) to some recent arrivals (*Serapias* spp.). Other taxa that are restricted but are also declining rapidly, or are members of the two complex genera *Dactylorhiza* and *Epipactis*, are included in the next two categories, discussed below. What the species listed above have in common (if to very varying degrees) is the need for concerted conservation action focused on generally small populations at a limited number of localities. They may be subject to what is sometimes unkindly referred to as 'gardening' – highly species-centred and interventionist activity, perhaps better thought of as short- to medium-term emergency care whilst the groundwork is done to establish larger and more sustainable populations. Such species have traditionally and understandably received much attention from both statutory and voluntary conservation bodies.

This is also the category that, precisely because of the rarity of the species within it, has received most attention from orchid collectors, and they remain vulnerable to this activity despite the shift in attitude of most people towards collecting (and its decline almost to insignificance for other vascular plant groups in the UK).

Cephalanthera rubra

As described above, Biodiversity Action Planning has in recent years been one of the main delivery mechanisms for conservation action in the UK: Action Plans, including hard targets for recovery, are drawn up for species that are identified as priorities. This mechanism has served and continues to serve many species well, but some others that have suffered major historical declines nonetheless failed to meet the criteria for Priority status and as such have received relatively little attention (from the national perspective) over the last 10 years. The Red Helleborine

Cephalanthera rubra is one of these species. In the course of reassessing priorities within the English vascular flora it has become increasingly apparent that the existing BAP criteria have failed to highlight some historically declining species that remain under serious threat of extinction; some of these, furthermore, are species for which the English conservation community has a very high level of international responsibility. *Cephalanthera rubra* is considered, by the IUCN assessment criteria, to be Critically Endangered in England (Cheffings & Farrell 2005), and Vulnerable across Europe as a whole (Red Data Book, third edition, ed. Wigginton 1999).

Plate 354. The Red Helleborine *Cephalanthera rubra* is subject to intense conservation activity, but so far it has not been possible to propagate it artificially. Deciduous woodland on chalk, Buckinghamshire, 16 June 1997.

Fortunately, local action (by English Nature in the Cotswolds, Hampshire County Council in Hampshire and the local Wildlife Trust in the Chilterns) has maintained small populations throughout this period, ensuring the survival of the plants present today. All of these sites lie within SSSIs, and recent genetic analyses have revealed a surprisingly high level of genetic diversity in the English population – equivalent, in fact, to that which might be expected in a typical Continental population. The total UK population almost certainly now numbers fewer than 30 plants, and possibly fewer than 20 (some seedlings at the sites are currently too small to attribute to the species with any certainty). These are in three tiny populations, all of which are receiving that desperate level of care afforded to species believed by all concerned to be on the brink of extinction. Although enough plants still persist with sufficient genetic diversity that potentially sustainable populations might be restored, the species is proving very difficult to propagate *ex situ*. It therefore appears currently to have very limited potential for reintroduction, highlighting the primary importance of careful, well-informed and intensive site protection and management. Ultimately, however, positive conservation action is likely to be the only way out of the danger zone for this species, and to this end seed was collected in 2004 from one of the few ripe pods produced. Some of this is banked at the Millennium Seed Bank at Wakehurst Place, some will enter the micropropagation and genetics research programme, funded by English Nature, being undertaken in conjunction with partners at the Royal Botanic Gardens, Kew, and some has been scattered on site in the hope that management actions undertaken recently or in progress will enhance the conditions for germination.

Cypripedium calceolus

Prior to the Victorian enthusiasm for collecting orchids from the wild for cultivation and herbaria, the Lady's-slipper Orchid was to be found across the limestones of northern England. By 1888, however, it was very rare and by 1917, thanks to the avarice of the age, it had been declared extinct. Then in 1930 a single plant was discovered at a remote site in North Yorkshire. Surprisingly, perhaps, there were enough conservation-minded people around at that time to safeguard the plant, and its location was kept a closely guarded secret. In the years leading up to the Second World War there were usually between eight and fourteen shoots on the plant and a flower was produced maybe one year in two. Between 1939 and 1959, however, only two to five shoots were produced annually and the plant could only muster two flowers. In the 1960s it was once more the target of plant collectors and part of the plant was stolen. At this point a decision was taken to adopt a more active conservation strategy and the Cypripedium Committee was born – a partnership between the Nature Conservancy (predecessor of the present statutory conservation agencies in Great Britain), the Yorkshire Wildlife Trust and the Yorkshire Naturalists' Union.

Initially the Committee's strategy was confined to managing the site and guarding the plant during the spring and summer months, but by 1985 it was obvious that a more dynamic approach would be needed to achieve any meaningful restoration of the species' former range. Under English Nature's Species Recovery Programme a scientific project was instigated, in conjunction with the Sainsbury Threatened Orchid Project at the Royal Botanic Gardens, Kew. Seed was collected from the wild plant and the two cultivated plants of known wild origin and, after a frustrating series of false starts, young *in vitro* ('test-tube') plants were eventually produced. Persuading these young plants to re-establish in the wild continues, however, to be a challenge for the Committee, and it is slowly becoming apparent that if the aim of establishing 12 large, self-perpetuating colonies of the species across its former range is to be realised, our understanding of its ecological requirements must be refined. Reintroductions have been attempted at 23 sites to date, and some degree of success has been achieved at 11 of these. Of the 2000 or so plants drafted into the programme 76 have survived, over 20 of these at a single location. This is not perhaps at first glance a high survival rate, but it is probably higher than a stable wild population of *Cypripedium* would achieve, despite the considerable longevity of individual plants (perhaps over 100 years) and their phenomenal potential seed output. Happily, one of the reintroduced plants flowered for the first time in 2000, a further plant flowered in 2004, and a number of others look set to do so shortly.

On a less optimistic note, the wilful damage to the well-known and venerable Lady's-slipper Orchid (of continental European origin) at Silverdale in Lancashire in 2004 serves to remind us that the threat of direct persecution has not yet entirely gone away.

Plate 355. Young plants of *Cypripedium calceolus* being grown in pots prior to transplantation into the wild, as part of the reintroduction programme for this species.

Liparis loeselii

The Fen Orchid is one of Britain's most highly threatened species. In addition, genetic analyses have indicated that the UK population may be of international significance in terms of its genetic diversity, particularly at the smaller and most vulnerable East Anglian localities. The species is one of only three orchids listed as Priorities in the Biodiversity Action Plan and one of only two requiring special protection under the EU Habitats and Species Directive. In the dune slacks of south Wales, where populations are reasonably strong, appropriate habitat management to keep on top of encroaching competitors seems to be the key to recovery. Work towards the recovery of the smaller English fen populations is also under way through the Species Action Plan, led jointly by the Royal Botanic Gardens, Kew and the Norfolk Wildlife Trust, in collaboration with English Nature. Here, however, it is proving particularly difficult to identify the precise ecological requirements of the species, and experimental translocations with micropropagated plants are being used in an attempt to pin down its niche. Initial experimental introductions in both Norfolk and Suffolk have failed to establish populations but the exercise has contributed to our understanding of the autecology of the species, which has been the primary objective of the work to date.

Plates 366 (below left) and 367 (below right). The Fen Orchid *Liparis loeselii* var. *loeselii* is endangered and has special protection under the EU Habitats and Species Directive. Appropriate management of its reed-bed habitat is critical. Norfolk Broads, East Norfolk, 10 June 2002.

Ophrys fuciflora

The Late Spider-orchid is the rarest member of the genus *Ophrys* in the UK and its population is highly concentrated on the chalk downlands of Kent. The species has suffered from loss of habitat through agricultural improvement, absence of livestock-grazing and reduced grazing by rabbits as a result of myxomatosis. A 12-year monitoring programme studying its requirements in minute detail has, however, uncovered

some fundamental autecological factors that will be essential in securing its future in England. Analysis of the data (Stone & Russell 2000) has shown that the plant relies primarily on seed for reproduction, that it produces overwintering rosettes, that it prefers a broken sward within chalk grassland on soils of particularly low fertility, that it is able to behave opportunistically when regeneration niches present themselves, and that it prefers soils that drain well and situations where there is ample movement of air. Such information is critical in determining appropriate and sustainable management regimes and is all too often unavailable, even in what is probably the best understood flora in the world.

Plate 368. Active conservation measures may include protection from grazing animals for individual plants. Here the Late Spider-orchid *Ophrys fuciflora* flowers under protection cages on chalk downland. East Kent, 28 May 1997.

Ophrys sphegodes

An interesting and very encouraging case has been the remarkable development recently of what is now perhaps the second largest population of Early Spider-orchids in the UK. During construction of the Channel Tunnel large quantities of spoil were produced, consisting primarily of chalk marl, and the decision was taken to place approximately 5 million cubic metres of this material at the foot of the chalk cliffs near the entrance to the tunnel. About 30 hectares of land were added to Kent in this exercise and the site – now known as Samphire Hoe – was landscaped in 1994, managed sensitively without adding excessive nutrients or nutrient-rich topsoil, and opened in 1997 as a reserve and public access area. In 1998, 61 plants of *Ophrys sphegodes* were discovered at this location, demonstrating the opportunistic establishment strategy so typical of this genus under the right circumstances. It is

Plate 369. Their light, wind-dispersed seeds mean that orchids can colonise appropriate habitats; the challenge is to ensure that such places continue to exist. The success of *Ophrys sphegodes* on Samphire Hoe was unexpected. East Kent, 11 May 2001.

believed that the population arrived as seed, produced by plants living in the short wind-blown turf of the cliff-top grasslands above. By 2004 there were about 9000 plants on the site – a spectacular demonstration of the ability of orchids to succeed in appropriate habitats.

Orchis militaris and *Orchis simia*

A fine account of the dramatic improvement in the fortunes of the Military and Monkey Orchids in their Chilterns localities is given in a recent paper by Sumpter *et al.* (2004). Populations of both species had persisted at well-known sites in the Chilterns for many years but flowering and recruitment had been relatively poor. In recent years, and in line with the understanding that many orchids are better able to tolerate disturbance than the competition faced under succession to scrub, an increasingly interventionist approach has been adopted in the management of these localities. Whilst a number of factors (including climate change) may be contributing to the recently improved fortunes of these Continental species, the element most likely to be making the difference is a very active management programme, including hand-pollination to improve seed-set and vigorous habitat management to reduce shading and increase open ground for colonisation.

Considering these practical examples of conservation on the ground, it is interesting to note how priorities may need to be altered significantly when the results of genetic investigations contradict previous assumptions. In *Orchis militaris*, for example, and also in *Liparis loeselii,* it had previously been assumed that the largest populations would be the most important for safeguarding the future of the species. Studies have shown, however, that the genetic diversity in some of the smaller populations is actually greater than in some much larger ones – with obvious implications in terms of priorities for conservation action.

Plate 370. Strict protection and active management have transformed the Oxfordshire site for the Monkey Orchid *Orchis simia*, from the refuge of a few survivors to the home of a thriving population. Here it grows with the Cowslip *Primula veris*. Grassy hillside overlooking the River Thames, Oxfordshire, 20 May 1994.

Rapidly declining species

Anacamptis morio, Cephalanthera damasonium, Cephalanthera longifolia,
Herminium monorchis, Neotinea ustulata, Neottia nidus-avis,
Ophrys insectifera, Orchis anthropophora, Orchis purpurea, Platanthera bifolia,
Pseudorchis albida, Spiranthes spiralis

In common with many of the species already discussed, these taxa are character-ised by their sensitivity to changing practices of land use in the British and Irish landscapes. They have not yet, however, reached the parlous state of many of the species described in the first category (although some, such as *Cephalanthera longi-folia*, may not be far behind). They remain relatively frequent in the British Isles – probably by virtue of having been more widespread to begin with – and in common with many orchid species they are believed to be capable of responding positively under appropriate management. Two examples will serve to illustrate the general principles for landscape-scale recovery advocated for the plants in this category, one from a wooded landscape (*Cephalanthera longifolia*) and the other from low-land meadows and pastures (*Anacamptis morio*).

Cephalanthera longifolia

The Narrow-leaved Helleborine is widespread in the British Isles but populations are generally very small, isolated and declining. Bold experimental management in Hampshire undertaken by the Wildlife Trust and the County Council, again founded upon the understanding that many orchids benefit from active habitat management, has resulted in quite spectacular increases in both flowering and population size. Although this species favours wooded areas it actually thrives best under quite high levels of light, perhaps indicating a natural adaptation to exploiting gaps in the wild wood created either by tree-fall or localised grazing by large herbivores. The man-agement adopted by conservationists in Hampshire mimics both these types of per-turbation, employing selective thinning of trees and scrub and the introduction of sheep-grazing for limited periods each year. At a second site the selective tree-felling phase has been followed up not by grazing but by mowing for hay. This latter site now holds the largest population of *Cephalanthera longifolia* in the British Isles, and the former has seen a 500 per cent increase in numbers in just 10 years.

Anacamptis morio

The decline suffered by the Green-winged Orchid has been one of the most dra-matic seen for any plant in Britain. The species has been reduced from being a widespread, often abundant, constituent of hay meadows throughout lowland Eng-land to occurring only in small isolated populations, often just hanging on outside the functioning agricultural landscape. *Anacamptis morio* was particularly well suited to the traditional low-input – low-output management regimes that used to be prac-tised on many neutral, relatively nutrient-poor soils. Today, however, such soils are readily improved, in particular for dairying, using chemical fertilisers, pesticide sprays and silaging techniques. Given our understanding of the requirements of this plant

and the fact that its populations remain widespread, even if heavily depleted, it should lend itself well to landscape-scale action for recovery through incentive schemes aimed at helping farmers adopt less aggressive (and less productive) land-management techniques. This case could test the effectiveness of the Government's recently introduced Higher Level Environmental Stewardship Scheme – although the plant's response may be disappointingly slow given the ability of many of the soils involved to hold on to applied nutrients (particularly phosphates) for many years. If we are to avoid a situation in which all sensitive species are confined to nature reserves we need to protect the health of the wider landscape, and the fortunes of widespread but declining species such as *A. morio* could be significant indicators of recovery on that scale.

Plate 371. One of the most rapidly declining plants in the British Isles, *Anacamptis morio* has lost much of its habitat to agricultural improvement. Where it is found, however, it is often present in huge numbers. Disused gravel-pit, North Hampshire, 23 May 1996.

Taxonomically complex genera

Dactylorhiza and *Epipactis*

The majority of the foregoing discussion has focused on the conservation of discrete, identifiable taxa that can be defined as species. Within the genera *Epipactis* and *Dactylorhiza*, however, as explained elsewhere in this book, speciation is still

Plate 373 (opposite). Our most recently recognised orchid, *Epipactis sancta*. Conservation policies must be flexible enough to accommodate evolving populations and emerging species. Dune slack, Holy Island, Northumberland, 5 July 2003.

Plate 372. The diploid hybrid *Dactylorhiza fuchsii* subsp. *fuchsii* × *D. incarnata* subsp. *incarnata* (*D.* ×*kerneriorum*). Several marsh-orchids are allotetraploid derivatives from this parentage. Habitats must be protected to allow the evolutionary process to continue. W. Ross, 26 June 2003.

occurring relatively rapidly, either through the formation of self-pollinating (autogamous) lines (*Epipactis*) or through repeated hybridisation and changes in ploidy level (*Dactylorhiza*). Recent advances in genetic investigation techniques are helping us to appreciate better how these taxa relate to each other, and how the processes driving evolution itself are operating. In these genera the delimitation of species is difficult and can indeed be a barrier to the most rational consideration of which plants actually merit conservation attention.

For example, the taxonomic entity previously described as the full species *Epipactis youngiana* (treated in this book as a variety) has absorbed considerable time and effort on the part of conservationists, when perhaps it was the sheer diversity of *Epipactis* in places like the Tyne valley that should have grabbed our attention. Nevertheless, in trying to evaluate correctly the significance of variants of this kind a much clearer view has emerged of the level of segregation within the genus and we can now identify with greater confidence autogamous species such as the Dune Helleborine *Epipactis dunensis* and the Lindisfarne Helleborine *E. sancta*, which do appear to be justifiable endemic British species. In addition, the expression of variation in the Broad-leaved Helleborine *E. helleborine* under certain circumstances (usually associated with a degree of soil toxicity) that led to the recognition of '*E. youngiana*' is itself fascinating to ecologists.

In *Dactylorhiza* the presence of hybrids is of considerable interest, to taxonomists and amateur naturalists alike, but has always presented difficulties to conservationists trying to fix upon entities to conserve. The excellent work carried out in recent years by Richard Bateman and his co-workers has clearly elucidated the importance of repeated hybridisation within the genus and serves to remind conservationists that in very dynamic genera such as this it might be more appropriate to make space for the evolutionary process to happen, rather than attempting to 'fossilise' the products of earlier phases of that process through an overly rigid species-centric approach. By leading conservationists into the territory of conserving evolutionarily significant units rather than morphologically defined taxa, and by encouraging conservationists to allow those units the freedom to change, it may be geneticists who are taking us into the next phase of conservation activity in Britain and Ireland – a phase that could take us out of the reserves and back into the wider dynamic landscape.

Chapter 7

Native Orchids in the Garden

Barry Tattersall

Many orchid enthusiasts are also keen gardeners and the question is often asked, 'Can I grow wild orchids in the garden?' The answer is 'Yes – with care', and as well as being an attractive addition to the garden, a carefully tended stand of native orchids growing under horticultural protection may form a valuable genetic reservoir in a countryside so greatly depleted of suitable natural habitats.

Orchids from the tropical areas of the world have been cultivated since the mid-eighteenth century. Most were epiphytes with magnificent flowers, ruthlessly collected from the wild and transported to northern Europe and North America. Upon arrival many were already dead, and the remainder were likely to suffer a lingering demise. The few plants that did survive were cultivated in hot, steamy greenhouses or 'stove houses'. It was discovered, however, that such high temperatures were not necessarily needed and that much cooler conditions suited most species. The craze of orchid cultivation had begun. From the mid-nineteenth century onwards enthusiasts began to attempt to raise orchids from seed, though with only limited success until the development in the twentieth century of methods of *in vitro* cultivation.

In contrast, the cultivation of European and North American terrestrial orchids has only recently become truly and legally viable, as seed-raised plants have become available from specialist nurseries. Although these orchids were cultivated previously, most of the plants involved were taken from wild populations and very few survived for more than a couple of years.

Plate 374 (opposite). The Common Spotted-orchid *Dactylorhiza fuchsii* is easy to grow and can be a spectacular garden plant. It is ideal for novices to orchid cultivation. Private garden, Berkshire, June 1997.

Plate 375. Advances in cultivation techniques have made it possible for hardy orchids to be raised from seed with comparative ease, making them available to gardeners legally. A pan of two-year old *Ophrys apifera* seedlings in an orchid nursery, March 2005.

Raising orchids from seed

As discussed earlier (see *Chapter 1. The Orchid Plant*), to develop beyond the immediate germination phase orchid seeds require a fungal partner. This mycorrhizal fungus provides the developing plant with carbohydrates and nutrients, enabling it to grow until it can develop normal photosynthetic leaves and produce its own carbohydrates. Thereafter, in most orchids, the plant's dependence on the fungus diminishes and it assumes the normal cycle of annual growth, resulting eventually in the production of flowers and seeds.

Plate 376. The robust hybrid *Dactylorhiza fuchsii* subsp. *fuchsii* × *D. praetermissa* (*D. ×grandis*) is suitable for moist places in the garden. It varies in the degree of leaf-spotting. Private garden, Berkshire, June 1997.

In laboratory conditions it is possible to replicate the supply of nutrients from a fungus by sowing the orchid seed on a sterile, nutrient-rich medium, usually an agar jelly containing a selection of nutrients and plant hormones. The process is carried out under aseptic conditions, starting with surface-sterilised seed to ensure that fungal or bacterial contaminants do not invade and destroy the culture. Most orchids will germinate and develop well in these conditions, growing from protocorms to small plants with tubers, that can be carefully weaned into a potting mix and grown in normal greenhouse conditions. A few species, however, seem still to benefit from the presence of a fungal associate, and in such cases the appropriate fungal strain can be isolated from tubers of a mature orchid plant and cultured for use in this way. Species of *Ophrys* and *Anacamptis* particularly benefit from this technique and grow much more rapidly than in cultures without a fungal associate. In recent years great advances in technology, together with the dedication, skill and perseverance of interested growers and staff at the Royal Botanic Gardens at Kew and Edinburgh, have made possible the cultivation at will of native and other temperate terrestrial orchids from both hemispheres. Skilful growers can raise thousands of seedlings, producing from seed capsules yields that are many hundreds of times above the natural survival rate of orchid seedlings in the wild. Raising orchids from seed does, however, remain a technical process, requiring laboratory conditions, and is therefore beyond the capabilities of most gardeners.

The technique of *in vitro* germination of orchid seed is not only of benefit to those wishing to grow orchids, enabling them to acquire plants legally at a reasonable cost, but is also seen as a good tool for conservation, supplying plants of known provenance for reintroduction into new areas, or to bolster existing populations that have become depleted. This has clearly been demonstrated by the joint efforts and funding of English Nature together with a number of Wildlife Trusts, the Sainsbury Threatened Orchid Project and the staff of the Micropropagation Unit at the Royal Botanic Gardens, Kew, over the reintroduction of the Lady's-slipper Orchid *Cypripedium calceolus*. Other introductions have also been undertaken, with mixed results, and certainly more are planned.

Now that these fascinating and beautiful plants are easy and inexpensive to acquire, and relatively easy to grow, I would urge anyone interested to 'have a go'. Orchids are immensely rewarding subjects, and the knowledge that can be gained from their cultivation can assist in many aspects of the conservation of our native orchid flora.

Growing orchids in the open garden

The key to success in growing native orchids in the garden is to get the conditions right. Manicured and manured gardens are unlikely to see the establishment of orchids; for lasting success conditions must be close to those of a natural habitat. In most cases this means relatively low fertility of the soil, limited disturbance and appropriate growing companions. Conditions of high fertility will lead to vigorous growth of other plants that will outcompete young orchids so that they fail to become established. This is particularly the case with vigorous lawn grasses.

Sites chosen for deliberate planting of orchids should match wild habitats as closely as possible: warm and dry for downland species, more moist for spotted- and marsh-orchids, shaded for some helleborines. In almost all cases where a good population of native orchids occurs in a garden the plants arrived spontaneously through the dispersal of seed from wild populations. In such cases the fortunate gardener can best proceed by continuing the same maintenance regime and ensuring that the plants are able to develop and shed their seed. When conditions are right orchid seedlings will appear naturally, maintaining and extending the population. In some cases seedlings may appear in apparently unsuitable conditions – in the herbaceous border, for example, or on an alpine trough. A carpet of low-growing plants, such as *Cotula*, is often found to be a good natural nursery site, producing surprising numbers of orchid seedlings. Such situations provide conditions of constant humidity and remain undisturbed during the critical early stages of the orchids' germination and establishment.

Growing orchids successfully in a lawn or meadow is a challenge that requires the right combination of relatively low-nutrient soil, a diverse and not too vigorous sward, and an appropriate mowing schedule. Several recent books have described the surprisingly difficult task of creating a species-rich turf; Christopher Lloyd's *Meadows* (2004), in particular, contains some useful comments on growing orchids in lawns. High fertility of the soil is the biggest problem, resulting in excessively vigorous grass-growth; regular hard cutting and raking-off of the hay helps, as does introduction of the hemiparasitic plant Yellow Rattle *Rhinanthus minor*, which reduces the vigour of grasses. A lawn originally sown with tough grasses can be very recalcitrant, however, and in such cases the best option may be to remove the turf altogether, replace the upper part of the soil with a sandy or gravelly mix, and resow with seed from a native meadow, available from specialist suppliers. (Ideally, choose seed of local provenance.) Once suitable conditions have been established orchids can be introduced, by sowing seed or by careful transplantation.

Plate 377. Integrating wild plants with the garden: a managed lawn area at Forest Edge, Hampshire. Several species of orchids follow the buttercups. May 2000.

Relatively few of our native orchids can be considered to be good subjects to grow in normal garden conditions. The taxa most likely to succeed are the various species of *Dactylorhiza*. These will often establish, and seedlings can appear in very improbable places. About ten years ago I planted several tubers of the Common Spotted-orchid *Dactylorhiza fuchsii* (kindly donated by a friend) into a border adjacent to my lawn. Although the plants only lasted for one season, their passing gift was hundreds of seedlings in my lawn the following year. The only downside to this was the meticulous care that had to be taken in cutting the grass around them. Several of their progeny are still present, and these have been joined spontaneously by plants of the Southern Marsh-orchid *D. praetermissa*. Where more than one species is present hybrids are likely to appear. Fine displays of hybrid swarms of *Dactylorhiza* may be seen, for example, at the Royal Horticultural Society's Garden at Wisley.

I would recommend starting with any (or all) of *Dactylorhiza fuchsii, D. praetermissa*, the Heath Spotted-orchid *D. maculata* and the Northern Marsh-orchid *D. purpurella*, all of which are capable of becoming naturalised. Soil pH is not really important with these species, so long as it is not too extreme. The *Dactylorhiza incarnata* group (the Early Marsh-orchids) are somewhat trickier, as they require more specific moisture conditions and are more pH-sensitive. In favoured places some species of *Dactylorhiza* will form clumps that can be divided to increase stock; this can be done in late summer or as growth begins in spring.

Plate 378. *Anacamptis morio* and other orchids have been successfully naturalised in the turf of the lawns at Christopher Lloyd's garden at Great Dixter, East Sussex, where the management regime of late mowing and raking-off of the hay has been followed for decades. Great Dixter, May 2004.

The Green-winged Orchid *Anacamptis morio* is certainly worth the effort to naturalise, and likes conditions similar to those enjoyed by the *Dactylorhiza* species, in short turf or well-drained soil on a rock garden. The Pyramidal Orchid *Anacamptis pyramidalis* will also flourish in these conditions, especially on warm banks where the soil dries out somewhat in summer. It often appears spontaneously. Mowing in this case must be delayed until the seed is ripe, in late summer. Another species that appears spontaneously and is fairly tolerant in its requirements is the Common Twayblade *Neottia ovata*, which will make a quiet contribution to the garden.

In areas that dry out in the summer and are relatively sparsely covered, both the Bee Orchid *Ophrys apifera* and Autumn Lady's-tresses *Spiranthes spiralis* could be tried. *Spiranthes spiralis* is somewhat different to all of the above, owing to its flowering time in August or September. Its rosette of leaves, which appears as soon as the flowers die back, remains green and active right through the winter, spring and early summer but the leaves lie flat against the soil surface, thus avoiding the blades of the mower. In fact, mowing is a positive advantage to the plant as it allows light to reach the leaves. The classic situation here is the 'sudden' appearance of *S. spiralis*, flowering on a lawn or tennis court that has not been mown during the absence of its owners on an August holiday.

Ophrys apifera can also sometimes appear unexpectedly on lawns that have not been cut too closely between late autumn (when the winter-green rosette appears) and early summer. It can also be grown successfully in gritty soil in a rock-garden situation, where the rosette can expand unimpeded by other plants. If the garden has an open area or pondside that remains moist to wet throughout the summer period, the Marsh Helleborine *Epipactis palustris* is a superb addition to any patch of grass, and will increase rapidly by vegetative reproduction. The only slight problem with this plant is that it is reluctant to grow from seed; but it is available commercially, and is easy to establish.

In areas that are partially or even quite densely wooded, the Broad-leaved Helleborine *Epipactis helleborine* could quite easily be naturalised by broadcasting seed. It can grow in all sorts of rough places, and even seems to have some resistance to glyphosate herbicides!

With all orchids, as for other wild plants naturalised in the garden, the mowing regime is very important, and the best choice will vary depending on the species in question. Needless to say, the area should not be mown at any time when the orchids are above ground. Winter-growing species need short turf all year round, while meadow species can tolerate longer grasses throughout the summer until they have shed their seeds, after which the grass should be cut and removed. Probably the last to die back would be *Epipactis palustris*, in September or early October. All plants will have shed their seed by then, and a couple of mowings should be undertaken before the onset of winter, to prevent a thatch of grass developing and impeding the emergence of new shoots.

The Lady's-slipper Orchid *Cypripedium calceolus* is a somewhat different proposition. Growing this beautiful plant in the open garden is possible, and on very

Plate 379. Autumn Lady's-tresses *Spiranthes spiralis* quite frequently appears on garden lawns if conditions are right: velvety turf with perfect stripes is counter-indicated. Tadley, North Hampshire, 2 September 1996.

Plate 380. The Broad-leaved Helleborine *Epipactis helleborine* is an opportunist, readily colonising gardens. The garden habitat is important in otherwise built-up areas. Suburban garden, Edinburgh, Midlothian, 23 July 1992.

rare occasions – in favourable situations – self-sown seedlings may occur. Young plants, raised *in vitro* from seed, are now quite freely available from nurseries. If *C. calceolus* is to be tried in the open garden I would suggest finding an area of semi-shade, preferably fairly moist, and digging a hole at least twice the size of the root ball. Make up a very free-draining mix of limestone chippings, coarse pumice, calcareous loam and finely chopped or sieved broad-leaved leaf mould, preferably beech. Place the plant in the hole so that the growth tip is about an inch below the surface and then very carefully work the mixed soil into the root ball and around the roots. The first growing season will be very critical; the soil must never be allowed to dry out completely, and will almost certainly require regular manual watering (with rain water). After the first growing season the roots should have grown into the surrounding soil and the plant should be capable of sustaining itself through periods of little rain. One additional word of warning: molluscs adore the young, new growth tips of all *Cypripedium* species.

Although somewhat out of the realm of this book, plenty of other terrestrial orchids from the northern hemisphere could be tried in various positions in the open garden, including a normal flower border. Many hardy terrestrial orchids are commercially available as flask-raised seedlings. There have been huge advances in the breeding of garden-worthy species and hybrids of the genus *Cypripedium*. Some of the named hybrids really are disease-resistant and vigorous, and will thrive in the garden. Other commercially available orchids include *Bletilla striata*, for a sunny south-facing position; *Spiranthes cernua* var. *odorata* 'Chadds Ford', for any moist position; and various named *Dactylorhiza* forms and hybrids. The list becomes longer as more advanced germinating and breeding techniques are tried.

Growing orchids in containers

Growing orchids in containers makes it possible to try a much greater range of plants. In fact, subject to it being possible to acquire them legally, most British natives can be grown with reasonable rates of success. Container-growing enables the gardener to control environmental conditions much more, even tailoring them to the requirements of a particular species, and this is the key to success.

The exceptions are the few mycoheterotrophic (saprophytic) species, that do not produce green leaves and are unable to gain nourishment through photosynthesis. Most often found growing in moderate to deep shade, these plants gain all or part of their nutrients through fungal activity from the decay of fallen leaves. Although these taxa could probably be germinated it would be very difficult to create and maintain the conditions needed actually to grow them. It is also worth mentioning that the species that produce pseudobulbs – the Bog Orchid *Hammarbya paludosa* and the Fen Orchid *Liparis loeselii* – are almost impossible to maintain for any length of time.

Containers

I would recommend using clay (terracotta) pots for the summer-dormant species and plastic pots or containers for the summer-growing (winter-dormant) species. To improve drainage, clay pots should be crocked with shards of broken pots; for plastic pots, Hydroleca™ – a lightweight clay aggregate, easily obtained from most garden centres – is easy and very clean to use.

Plate 381. With care, native orchids can be grown in pots. A superb clump of *Orchis anthropophora* on an Alpine Garden Society show bench, April 1997.

Composts

The best growing medium to use varies depending on what is to be grown. For the summer-dormant, round-tuber taxa, including *Anacamptis*, *Himantoglossum*, *Ophrys* and *Orchis*, a very free-draining mix should be used. Ingredients can vary slightly but should roughly consist of, say, equal parts of calcareous loam (possibly collected from fresh mole-hills), alpine grit, pumice (2 mm), well-sieved beech leaf mould and John Innes No. 2 compost. The pumice (which is used as a moisture-retainer, as it absorbs moisture when available and then releases it during dry periods) could be substituted by an extra part of alpine grit. As a concession to the plants' possible need for a fungal symbiont the ingredients should not be sterilised, in the hope that beneficial fungal spores might be introduced with one of the organic ingredients. The species belonging to these genera are normally winter- or spring-growers, with a summer rest period, although the British members of true *Orchis* do tend to remain green and active for part of the summer.

For all the others the mix should also be very free-draining, but generally more water-

Plate 382. Terrestrial orchids being grown in a dedicated greenhouse. Note the open windows for ventilation. Private garden, Oxfordshire, January 1998.

Plate 383. The Heath Spotted-orchid *Dactylorhiza maculata*, growing with dwarf rhododendrons in a trough containing acidic compost. Private garden, Berkshire, June 1997.

retentive. The mix I would recommend should consist of: one part loam (neutral or calcareous, depending on the plant's requirements), two parts alpine grit, two parts fairly coarse pumice (5 mm), one part composted bark, and either one part beech leaf mould (for calcareous species) or one part rotted pine needles (for acid-loving species). Once again, none of the ingredients should be sterilised. This mix suits all the palmate-tuber genera – *Dactylorhiza, Gymnadenia, Platanthera*, etc. – and also the rhizomatous genera – *Epipactis, Cephalanthera* (very difficult) and *Cypripedium calceolus*. Creeping Lady's-tresses *Goodyera repens* responds well to a mix of coarse, part-rotted pine needles, but this must be kept moist at all times.

Although the compost mentioned above does suit *C. calceolus*, many growers of this plant find it very beneficial to use an extremely fast-draining compost: pumice or Seramis™ (an inert water-retaining substance made from 5 mm clay granules with similar qualities to pumice) and fairly course grit forms 80 per cent of the mix, the remaining 20 per cent being equal parts loam and leaf mould or composted bark. With this mix, however, artificial feeding is usually needed, using fertiliser at about 25 per cent recommended strength. Proprietary orchid-fertiliser compounds are best and are readily available from garden centres and orchid nurseries. With the other compost mixes described above I find that additional feeding is unnecessary.

Positions and treatment

Growing position is very important. The winter-growing species prefer an area where they can enjoy warmth and as much light from the winter sun as possible, and are best grown on a greenhouse bench where their pots can be plunged in moist sand or gravel. This ensures even temperatures and moisture at the roots. No extra heat is needed, but good ventilation is vital: still, stagnant air spells disaster, so leave all the doors and vents open. Even an electric fan is beneficial. The only time the doors and vents need closing is when the weather is going to be excessively cold. Although the leaves can freeze and recover, it is highly inadvisable to allow the roots to freeze.

From about mid-February it is usually necessary to add some sort of shading to the greenhouse; a sunny day in February can push up the temperature behind glass excessively, and could easily force plants into early dormancy. Once they have finished flowering, the seed has matured and the leaves are starting to yellow and decay, water should be withheld and summer dormancy allowed to commence.

To avoid desiccation in the summer heat inside the greenhouse it is wise to remove pots from their growing position to a cooler spot. Some growers remove the tubers from their pots and store them during the summer in brown paper bags. Equally they could be placed, in their pots, in a shady spot under the greenhouse bench. Small amounts of water could be given occasionally to prevent the tubers from shrivelling. Re-potting should begin in August or early September, as growth usually begins from mid-September. Water should be given at this stage, and plants should not be allowed to become desiccated during their period in growth; in winter, however, care must be taken not to allow the soil to become too damp.

My summer-growers I house in Access™-type garden frames, all in plastic pots, and plunged to the rim in sharp builders' sand. The advantage of this type of garden frame is that all the glass can be very easily removed in hot weather, and shading, in the form of shade cloth, can be applied at short notice. My frames stand on two courses of bricks, in two different situations. One provides full sun in the morning and dappled shade in the afternoon. The other, with a north-facing aspect, receives no direct sunshine in winter, keeping the plants consistently cold and dormant. This second frame does receive direct sunshine during the summer months, but only from midday to late afternoon. The orchids that thrive in the 'full-sun frame' are: all the *Dactylorhiza* species, the Marsh Fragrant-orchid *Gymnadenia densiflora*, the Marsh Helleborine *Epipactis palustris*, and several non-native *Cypripedium* species; the 'shade frame' houses other *Epipactis* and many other *Cypripedium* species.

The growth cycle of all the summer-growing taxa is similar. All start to appear from about early March, flower through the summer, at various times, and go dormant in October or November. They should never be allowed to dry out, and should be re-potted every other year.

Plate 384. A garden in which orchids thrive will be well suited to all sorts of wildlife. Emerging dragonfly on *Dactylorhiza praetermissa*, Forest Edge, Hampshire, May 1999.

Obtaining plants

Unfortunately, wild-collected orchids are still being imported into the UK, mainly from the Far East. This makes it all the more important that we acquire our plants from reputable sources. Guaranteed seed-grown orchids can now be obtained from many nurseries in the UK and elsewhere in Europe. A search through the various horticultural publications, or on the internet, should help you to locate such nurseries. Ask for confirmation that the orchids they offer are raised from seed.

Seed for naturalising is best obtained from other local garden populations, but sparing collections could be made from large wild populations of common species growing on private land, with the permission of the landowner.

Although orchids, and indeed other species, should never be collected from the wild, situations do occasionally arise where plants need to be rescued from an impending disaster such as road-building. In every such case, however, permission from the landowner or site manager must be sought, and it is also advisable to inform local wildlife organisations of your intentions. Permission having been acquired, the plants should be removed together with a generous quantity of surrounding soil and transplanted to a well-prepared garden site. As they may not survive this trauma it is also worth collecting seed and ensuring that it is scattered in suitable conditions close to the original site. Once the plants have gone dormant it may be advisable to extricate them carefully from the original sod and pot or transplant them into media as recommended above, incorporating a small quantity of the original soil.

Chapter 8

Photographing Orchids

Sidney Clarke

This chapter describes equipment and techniques for photographing orchids in the wild. These are personal recommendations based on my experience of over thirty years practising as a professional plant photographer – seeking the utmost quality and sparing no effort to achieve superior results. Not every reader will wish to commit the same amount of time and resources to achieving their orchid photographs. For example, many plant photographers refuse to carry a tripod, and rely solely on flash for each and every exposure. Personally, as I will explain later, I would not be satisfied with the results of such an approach.

Suggested field kit for plant photography

Camera body

To photograph plants and their habitats it is not necessary to have the latest high-tech equipment. What is required is a robust and reliable camera body that allows the photographer full manual control of both shutter speed and lens aperture, and thus total command of exposure. The body you choose should be by a manufacturer offering a range of quality lenses in focal lengths from 20 mm up to 400 mm. To photograph wild orchids you may never need more than two or three lenses but interests do develop and change, and it is good to know that you have options should your photography take a new direction. Ensure that the manufacturer you decide on includes a choice of focal lengths for the macro lenses in their range. Most nature photographers use equipment from either Canon or Nikon, both of whom offer a choice of three focal lengths of macro lenses: 55 mm or 60 mm, 100 mm or 105 mm, and 180 mm or 200 mm.

If you are selecting a camera body specifically for plant photography, choose a model that offers the following functions.

A full range of shutter speeds

Shutter speeds of longer than a second are occasionally required and should be available. The camera I use most frequently (a Nikon F3) has shutter speeds extending to 8 seconds, which is usually long enough for photographing orchids. There

Plate 385 (opposite). A portrait of *Orchis anthropophora* on limestone scrubland to the south of Coimbra in north-central Portugal (19 March 2003). Here I deliberately chose a large aperture, coupled with a long-focus lens, to help isolate the plant from the background. A Nikon F4 was used, with a 200 mm Micro-Nikkor lens, at an exposure of 1/250 second at full aperture (f/4), on Fujichrome Velvia 50 ISO film. Strong sunlight from behind the subject was diffused through a screen of white taffeta. The side of the plant towards the camera was then illuminated by two silver reflectors. As a consequence of using such a large aperture, the front two leaves are out of focus.

have, however, been occasions when I have had to use the camera on the 'B' (bulb) setting and time the length of the exposure using the second-hand on my watch. At the other end of the scale, one rarely requires a shutter speed of shorter duration than 1/250 second. Many of the newer electronic cameras greatly extend this range of available shutter speeds, in both directions.

Manual metering

Full control of exposure is vital, and can be achieved using a totally manual camera or one where any automation can be conveniently overridden. If an auto-exposure function is available it should be used in 'aperture priority' (A_V) mode, where the photographer makes a conscious choice of aperture and the camera automatically sets the correspondingly correct shutter speed. The camera-selected exposure can then be varied as necessary using the exposure-compensation control.

Depth-of-field preview

With single-lens reflex (SLR) cameras the potential photograph is viewed as an image projected onto the focusing screen by the same lens as will be used to create the actual photograph. Focusing and selection of composition are always carried out with the lens at its widest aperture (for the brightest possible viewing of the image). The moment the camera is fired the aperture closes down to the f-stop previously selected. Many cameras have a 'depth-of-field preview' button, that you can use to close down the aperture manually and thus view the subject at whichever f-stop you have chosen. This allows you to see the extent of the zone of sharp focus (depth of field), and also the degree of blur in the areas that are out of focus. You can then

Plate 386. Sidney Clarke photographing *Orchis mascula* (Lammermoor Hills, East Lothian, 15 May 2004), using a Nikon F3T with 105 mm macro lens, camera mounted on Manfrotto 190D tripod and Linhof Profi 2 ball-head with RRS quick-release plate. This photograph illustrates the positioning of silver reflectors, supported by knitting needles. Plates 393 and 394 (p. 365) and Plates 395 and 396 (p. 366) were taken on this occasion.

observe the changing depth of field offered by different aperture settings. To reduce costs some camera-makers have omitted the depth-of-field preview function, but for plant photography and other close-up work it is vital to choose a camera model that incorporates this device.

Mirror lock-up

Most SLR cameras have a hinged mirror, that raises up just before the shutter fires; as the mirror flips up a slight vibration may result. This is not usually a problem with very short or very long exposures. In close-up, macro and long-lens photography, however, it can be discernible at shutter speeds of 1/15 second, 1/8 second and 1/4 second. With 'mirror lock-up' control you can raise the mirror manually in advance of releasing the shutter. As with the depth-of-field preview button this is a useful function that many manufacturers have dropped from their specifications, and only a few camera models now feature it.

If your camera does not have mirror lock-up it may be best to avoid using the vulnerable shutter speeds when working with long lenses or close up. It might also be worthwhile to conduct a simple test, by photographing a close-up of a subject that contains plenty of fine detail, deliberately using these vulnerable shutter speeds. Upon the return of the processed film, critically appraise your results on a light box using a quality 4× loupe (magnifier). In some camera models (the Nikon FM2, for instance) the mirror can be raised in advance using the self-timer. This can be useful, as long as neither the light nor the wind changes during the 10 seconds or so between the release button being pressed and the shutter firing. Nikon's F3, F4 and F5 models all have mirror lock-up, as do Contax RTS, Pentax KR and LX, Leica R6, Canon EOS 3 and EOS 5, plus some older models of Olympus OM cameras.

Many of the newer camera models have very efficient dampening to help eliminate vibration produced by the rising mirror. In recent tests that I have conducted using a Nikon F100 – a camera without mirror-lock – and lenses up to the Nikon 200 mm f/4 ED A/F Micro, I have been unable to detect any lack of sharpness owing to mirror-bounce at the vulnerable shutter speeds. I ran a parallel test of the same subjects, with the same lenses, using a Nikon F4 body with mirror-lock, and the resulting transparencies from the two cameras were indistinguishable as far as sharpness was concerned.

Interchangeable focusing screens

For many years the standard focusing screen supplied by most manufacturers incorporated a microprism ring, or split-image wedges, in the centre of the field. These are not suitable for critical focus when photographing a tight close-up with lens extension. The best all-round screen for plant photography has as its centre field an area of fine ground glass. I also prefer such a screen to have horizontal and vertical lines etched on its surface. These help to keep the horizon truly horizontal in habitat photographs, and upright plants vertical. One such screen made by Beattie also gives a useful increase in focusing brilliance. Many of the newer auto-focus cameras are supplied with a plain ground-glass screen, and these will be adequate for close-up photography, though lacking grid lines.

Spot-metering

This highly desirable function is offered by many newer cameras. It allows the photographer to make his exposure assessment from an area of the image as small as 1°. It is very convenient to meter from a small area of the subject, such as a mid-toned leaf, rather than taking the reading from the much larger area assessed by an averaging or centrally weighted metering system. One of the main reasons for adding a Nikon F4 to my photo kit was to allow me the facility of spot-metering.

Lenses

If I were to restrict myself to only two lenses, my choice would be a 105 mm macro (or similar) and either a 28 mm or 35 mm wide-angle, or a suitable close-focusing wide-angle zoom lens (see below). The macro lens should be capable of focusing down to life size, either on its own or with a dedicated extension tube. This would be used for plant portraits and detailed close-ups, the wide-angle lens being used for scenics, habitats and plant-in-habitat shots. In general, fixed focal-length wide-angle lenses will usually focus closer than a zoom lens of equivalent focal length. Some of the newer zooms, however, such as Nikon's AFS f/2.8 17~35 mm and A/F f/3.5–f/4.5 18~35 mm, along with Nikon's fixed focal-length lenses of 24 mm, 28 mm and 35 mm, will all focus down to distances from the subject of about 30 cm or less.

Auto-focus

For plant photography there is no obvious advantage in using auto-focus, as one normally has plenty of time to achieve accurate focus manually. Indeed, I can think of many instances where auto-focus would be a real handicap to achieving accurate focus speedily, especially when the principal subject is off-centre.

Accessories

Right-angle finder

This periscope-like attachment slides or screws onto the eyepiece of the camera viewfinder and allows the photographer to view the image comfortably when working close to the ground: using it one avoids the necessity of lying on possibly soggy terrain to focus and compose a shot. These devices swivel through 90° for use with the camera in either horizontal or vertical orientation. Most right-angle finders incorporate a variable correction lens that can be adjusted for the eyesight or spectacles of the photographer.

Lens hoods

I recommend using a dedicated lens hood for each of your lenses to avoid image degradation due to extraneous light hitting the front lens glass and causing flare.

Use a lens hood for every photograph you take, regardless of lighting conditions. As well as preventing flare they also offer a measure of protection from rain. To avoid 'vignetting' (cutting off the corners of your shot through inclusion of part of the lens hood), it is important to have a lens hood suitable for the focal length of the lens in use. Obviously, lens hoods for zoom objectives are something of a compromise.

Filters

I normally use only two types of filter, a circular polariser and a warming filter. The polariser is used to reduce surface reflections from foliage, thereby increasing colour saturation. It can also be used to reduce reflections from water and to darken skies.

On a sunny day, when working in the shade your results will inevitably have a blue colour cast that may not have been perceptible at the time of shooting. A warming filter – either an 81A or 81B – will reduce this 'cold' effect. Normally, depending on which film you are using, the 81A will suffice, but I usually also carry an 81B to cope with more extreme conditions. When choosing your camera lenses it is worth checking the size of filters each will require. It is convenient if all your lenses have the same diameter filter thread, reducing the number of filters required.

Tripods

The most important piece of equipment, after the camera body and macro lens, is the tripod. In fact, I consider it to be a waste of time and film to attempt any form of

Plate 387. This habitat photograph is of *Anacamptis morio* growing in a disused gravel quarry in North Hampshire (25 May 1996). A Nikon F3 was used with a 24 mm Nikkor wide-angle lens stopped down to f/16 for maximum depth of field. It was exposed for 1/8 second in soft sunlight, on Fuji Velvia 50 ISO film. This scene is a typical mid-toned subject.

plant photography without using a suitable tripod! It is well worthwhile taking the time and effort to choose your tripod wisely. For plant photography a well-designed tripod is a joy to use, while a model that is unsuitable for the task will only lead to frustration. The essential feature in choosing a tripod for photographing plants is its allowing you to place the camera, when required, within a few inches of the ground. Currently the most suitable models will be found in the ranges from Gitzo, Manfrotto, Benbo and Unilock. Most useful to the plant photographer are those that have no centre column, or where the centre column can be discarded. Probably the best tripods – taking into account weight, rigidity and value for money – are those in the Manfrotto 190 series, such as the 190D. Choose a model from this range that comes with a removable centre column and a low-level plate. Remove the centre column and replace it with the supplied plate. This will allow you to position the camera from almost ground-level to a height of about 125 cm *without* using that centre column. This tripod will be tall enough to tackle most terrestrial orchids, and

Two photographs of *Dactylorhiza fuchsii* subsp. *hebridensis* (Island of Barra, Outer Hebrides, 17 July 2003). Plate 388 (left) was taken with direct sunlight coming from the left side and a silver reflector used on the right side to lighten the shadow area caused by the harsh sunlight. In Plate 389 (right), the sunlight has been softened by 'tenting' the plant using a white taffeta diffuser. Both photographs were taken on Fuji 50 ISO Velvia film with a Nikon F100 camera and 200 mm macro lens. A medium aperture of f/8 was selected, to ensure that the background was reproduced as a pleasing soft wash of colour. The taffeta diffuser absorbs just over one stop of light: the direct-sunlight photograph was exposed at 1/125 second while the diffused shot required 1/50 second.

indeed most other ground-dwelling plants, but will be too short for general photography. With a suitable ball-head (see below) it can be used with lenses up to an 80 ~ 200 mm f/2.8 zoom. The relatively light Manfrotto 190D excels for low-level plant photography and for backpacking. However, my heavier Gitzo 340 (now the G-1340) is unsurpassed for stability when using lenses longer and heavier than the 80 ~ 200 mm f/2.8, or when a higher viewpoint is required.

To either tripod I would recommend adding a professional-quality ball-and-socket head such as the Linhof Profi 2, with an Arca Swiss-type quick-release clamp. Purchase this head without the dedicated Linhof quick-release plate, and substitute the more versatile RRS B2-Pro clamp plus the 1/4–20 stainless-steel stud for attaching this clamp to the Linhof head. The Manfrotto tripods (sold under the name Bogen in North America) and the Linhof head are readily obtainable, but the recommended quick-release clamp is at present available only direct from the manufacturer, Really Right Stuff. Details of this and the matching attachment plates for your particular camera model can be found in their current catalogue (request one from Really Right Stuff, PO Box 6531, Los Osos, CA 93412, USA).

A final word about tripods: a lightweight tripod is almost invariably an unstable tripod, especially when the conditions are windy or when using a lens of longer than normal focal length. The tripod I have recommended above is about the lightest that I am prepared to use, and if faced with having to shed weight (on long treks in the mountains, for instance), I would rather compromise with lenses and other equipment than be without a decent tripod.

Remote release

To prevent the transmission of possible vibrations from the photographer's person to the camera mounted on its tripod, always use a wire cable or electric release to fire the shutter. Unfortunately, a remote-release socket is yet another feature that several manufacturers are now omitting from some of their camera models. My preference is for a simple wire cable or air release over the newer electric types; there is less to malfunction and they are cheaper to replace should one be lost in dense vegetation. After losing one many years ago, when I had no spare with me, I now tie a piece of brightly coloured tape to mine so that I can find it easily should I inadvertently drop it. Some of the newer electronic cameras will only accept the more expensive types of cable release, making it even more important that they can be easily found.

Reflectors and diffusers

These are used mainly under sunny conditions to reduce visible contrast in close-up photography. A diffuser is a piece of colourless, translucent material held between the light source (usually the sun) and your subject. I carry a small sheet of 'Correx' – a very lightweight plastic material – that I prop in position using knitting needles pushed into the ground (get them from a charity shop). Many other materials can be utilised as diffusers: butter-muslin stretched taut, opal plastic, tracing paper, etc. As long as the material you choose has no inherent colour it should be usable. The effects of a diffuser are immediately seen and can be adjusted until you achieve the lighting that you like best.

Reflectors are pieces of white or silver card held (knitting needles again!) in such a way as to reflect extra light into shadow areas of your shots; they are often used on bright days in conjunction with a diffuser. Commercially available folding reflectors and diffusers are available from manufacturers such as Lastolite and Photoflex.

Films

Generally speaking, the most versatile film for nature photography will be one with a speed rating of 100 ISO. Many nature photographers (including myself) opt, however, for Fujichrome Velvia, which has an ISO rating of 50, half the speed of a 100 ISO emulsion. Velvia 50 is arguably capable of recording a wider range of subtle tones than any other film currently available and is extremely fine-grained, but its colour rendition and high saturation may not be to every photographer's liking. In terms of choice of quality films available the wildlife photographer has never been better served than at the present time, and it would be wise to try out a few different brands of 50–100 ISO types before selecting your personal favourite. When using a tripod you are unlikely to require film much faster than 100 ISO. Some of the newer 200 ISO emulsions are capable of yielding a quality that only a few years ago would have been impossible, but even so, they cannot compete with the exceptionally fine results of the slower materials.

Digital photography

At present few nature photographers prefer digital cameras to using film. Digital cameras are useful in the field for run-of-the-mill recording, but to achieve film-quality results only the very best digital equipment will suffice. Top-of-the-range digital SLR cameras currently are capable of producing a quality comparable with 100 ISO film, but they involve a high initial outlay, and their residual value declines at an alarming rate even if well cared for. At least for the present, most photographers will settle for using the best film that is available, and scan the resulting transparencies should a digital image be required. This is a rapidly changing scene, however, and these comments may not hold good for very long!

Technique

Setting up

First, take great care in choosing your subject. Is it in peak condition? Have any of its leaves been eaten at the tip? These and other blemishes can mar a particular specimen. If the subject is not rare there may well be others to choose from. It is worthwhile being discerning in your choice of specimen, rather than being disappointed when viewing the processed films. Of course if the subject is as rare as is, say, the Ghost Orchid in the Chilterns, then the criteria are different! When

Plate 390 (opposite). A three-quarter length portrait of the Lady's-slipper Orchid *Cypripedium calceolus* growing in a clearing in mixed woodland (6 June 1999). The site is an alpine river-valley in the Austrian province of Vorarlberg. The yellow slipper-shaped labellum is considerably lighter in tone than the rather dark wine-coloured sepals. The dull drizzly conditions were ideal in that they compressed the tonal range to a contrast ratio that the film could accommodate without loss of detail. The camera used was a Nikon F3, with a 105 mm Micro-Nikkor lens; the exposure was 2 seconds at f/22, on Fuji Velvia 50 ISO film. Few brands of colour-transparency film can compete with the quality of Fuji Velvia 50 when shooting in dull light.

selecting your plant do also consider the background; it is all too easy to spoil an otherwise fine subject by portraying it against a poor or distracting setting. The camera should then be set up on its tripod, the image composed and the lens focused on the principal part of the plant that must be tack sharp.

One reason for favouring a long-focus macro such as a 105 mm or 200 mm lens over the more normal 55 mm or 60 mm focal length is that you can be more selective about how the background will be represented on film. The narrower acceptance angle of the longer lenses makes it easier to exclude unwanted objects appearing as distractions in the background. Indeed, I look on my 105 mm macro lens as my standard optic, regarding my 55 mm macro as a 'long' wide-angle. A further advantage of using a long-focus macro lens is that it allows a greater working distance between lens and subject, and therefore more scope for the positioning of reflectors and diffusers.

It is impossible to show every aspect of an orchid species in a single photograph, and I usually take three differing views: the habitat, the portrait and the close-up. **The habitat** is normally shot with a wide-angle lens, and may or may not show the actual plant. The principal purpose is to show the terrain in which the orchid is found, and if possible, associated plant species. **The portrait** normally shows the entire plant from ground level to the top of the inflorescence, with no leaf tips cut off. The purpose here is to show the plant's typical habit. I usually shoot this with one or other of my long-focus macro lenses. **The close-up** shows detail in the flowers or seed capsule, or some other aspect of interest such as leaf-spotting, if relevant. This is conveniently shot using a lens that can reach 1:1 (life-size). I currently use my 200 mm macro, but the shot is also possible (if less convenient) with my 105 mm macro.

When setting up the camera for either a portrait or a close-up it is important to get down to the plant's level and ensure that the camera is positioned so that the film-plane (essentially the camera back) is parallel to the upright stance of the subject. For most orchids this will necessitate orientating the camera to the vertical (upright) format. Aligning the camera parallel to the subject is important if you want to gain the utmost from the limited depth of field encountered in any close-up photography. Even when using a smallish aperture such as f/16, depth of field can be measured in millimetres.

Lighting

Without any doubt whatsoever, the best lighting for quality plant photography is cloudy-bright daylight. With this sort of lighting you will have a choice of where to set up your tripod. In other words, you can photograph the plant from any aspect and still have pleasing illumination. This gives you freedom to choose a camera position that portrays the plant to best advantage, while also allowing a greater choice of background.

Conditions are not always ideal, however, and the photographer has to cope with everything that our fickle climate offers. Bright sunshine can lead to excessive contrast in colour photography, the highlights being washed out and the shadows lacking detail. This is especially problematic with white or pastel-coloured flowers, such as pale pink or yellow, where the brightness range (from sunlit white to darkest

Plate 391. A few wild orchids, especially mycoheterotrophic (saprophytic) species, can grow in really dark places, and to photograph these you will have to use flash as the sole illumination. One such species is the Ghost Orchid *Epipogium aphyllum*. This photograph was taken in dense Norway Spruce *Picea abies* woodland in the southern Black Forest, Germany (29 July 1998). To light the shot I used two Lumedyne flash units fired through large sheets of 'Correx' to give a soft, even illumination. The camera was a Nikon F3, with a 55 mm Micro-Nikkor lens; exposure 1/60 second at f/16–f/22, on Fuji Velvia 50 ISO film.

shadow) exceeds the exposure range that colour-transparency film is capable of recording. The difficulty can be overcome by the combined use of light diffusers and reflectors, as mentioned earlier. The diffuser should be positioned so that it softens the illumination falling on the plant, and if necessary a reflector can be placed to introduce additional light to the areas of shadow. Often a very pleasing quality of light can be achieved by this method.

Very dull, 'flat' lighting can often be improved by the use of reflectors or fill-in flash. 'Fill flash' is the term for adding a small burst of flash to supplement – but not overpower – the available daylight. It is most easily employed when using one of the latest generation of camera bodies and dedicated 'smart' flash units. Using both camera and flash in manual 'through-the-lens' (TTL) mode, the photographer can pre-programme his preferred amount of 'fill' and achieve repeatable results.

Great care must be taken in using flash as the sole illumination for plant photography. Unless you are prepared to use a multiple-light set-up, which requires considerable skill, it is difficult to achieve a natural-looking photograph. Also, because of the spectral output from electronic flash it is virtually impossible to get a faithful colour rendering from species that have pinkish purple flowers. Many of the *Dactylorhiza* species, for example, are reproduced as much too red in colour when photographed using flash. If you *must* use direct flash from a small electronic flash

Plate 392. Although where possible I favour utilising natural light, there are times when one must resort to using flash. This photograph of *Epipactis helleborine* was taken under a canopy of deciduous woodland (Chilterns, Oxfordshire, 4 August 1996). A breeze was blowing and this, combined with the poor light, necessitated the use of flash. Rather than using straightforward direct flash, however, I decided to make the shot more interesting by trying to create the effect of sunlight filtering down through the overhead branches. I used two heavyweight Lumedyne units fitted with 20″ × 16″ softboxes to create an overall soft frontal illumination. To achieve the effect of dappled sunlight I then held a small Nikon SB 26 flashgun above and behind the subject. All three flash units were fired simultaneously by synchronising to the camera with photo-electric cells. A Nikon F3 was used, with a 105 mm Micro-Nikkor lens, and the exposure was 1/60 second at f/16, on Fuji Velvia 50 ISO film.

gun, it may be useful to tape a Kodak 'Wratten' Filter No. 2B over the flash-head to help reduce this 'red effect'.

Exposure

Having selected your composition, ensured that the camera is completely stable (use a tripod!) and checked that your lens is critically focused on the most important part of the subject, usually the flower, the next thing to consider is the exposure. Achieving the correct exposure – consistently – is probably the greatest problem the plant photographer faces. The two variables to be considered are the speed of the film and the amount of light reaching the film.

As far as film speed is concerned, many modern cameras automatically set the ISO speed rating by reading the bar-code on the film cassette. I would recommend, however, that you set this manually so that you can fine-tune your camera's exposure meter to the film in use. Slightly different manufacturing tolerances in the film, camera or lens may make a difference to your actual exposure. For instance, when using Fujichrome Velvia I set my camera for 50 ISO, which is the speed recommended by Fuji. However I know a good number of professional nature photographers who always expose Velvia at 40 ISO, as they prefer the result that they get using that speed rating. When trying any film for the first time I would advise that you use part of the first roll to fine-tune your camera system. On a day with consistently cloudy or cloudy-bright conditions this can easily be done by aiming your camera, with your most-used lens, at a mid-toned subject such as an expanse of fresh green lawn. With the camera in manual exposure mode, set the ISO speed as indicated on the film box, adjust the shutter speed and aperture for correct exposure and take a shot. Move the ISO dial by one indent (a third of a stop) towards a faster ISO speed and make a further exposure; then make two more, each time advancing the ISO dial by one indent. Then repeat the exercise, this time moving the ISO dial towards slower film-speed settings, each exposure differing again by a third of a stop. During this procedure take a careful note of the exact sequence of the shots you take. You will end up with a series of exposures ranging from one stop under to one stop over the film's recommended speed rating. After processing you should have a strip of film on which the first exposure is the one that was recommended, followed by three shots getting progressively darker, then three getting lighter. Appraise this strip of seven transparencies carefully and choose the one that you think looks best, noting the ISO rating for that particular shot. This is the ISO rating you should use in future when working with that particular film with that camera body. For example, using Velvia your first exposure would be made at 50 ISO as recommended by Fuji. If your preference is for shot number two, then in future you should set your camera at 64 ISO (i.e. one third of a stop faster); if your preferred exposure is number five, you should in future set it at 40 ISO (one third of a stop slower).

When considering exposure it is fundamental to understand that objects of different tonality reflect differing amounts of light. It is also important to appreciate that all exposure meters built in to SLR cameras have one thing in common, in that they are all calibrated to a universal standard set to give the correct exposure for a mid-toned subject. A mid-toned subject is one that is mid-way between black and white: in other words, medium grey.

Many subjects in nature are also mid-toned: brown rabbits and tree trunks, green grass, red geranium flowers, medium blue sky. These subjects will also be correctly exposed without any deviation from the exposure recommended by your camera's meter. But what if your subject is not mid-toned, but lighter or darker than mid-tone? Your camera will still expose for a mid-toned exposure, resulting in a light

Plates 393 (left) and 394 (right). Two photographs of *Orchis mascula*, taken using a Nikon F3T camera with 55 mm macro lens, showing the difference between high and low viewpoints (Lammermoor Hills, East Lothian, 15 May 2004). In nearly every case the lower viewpoint gives a more natural perspective. A greater amount of 'gardening' may, however, be required, owing to the low viewpoint showing more background area.

subject being recorded too dark on your colour-transparency film, and a dark subject being rendered too light. To obtain correct exposure when photographing subjects that are lighter or darker than mid-tone you must override the camera's exposure meter. This is most easily accomplished using a camera with a spot meter, in manual mode. In the camera viewfinder, the area covered by the spot meter will be marked by a small circle in the centre of the focusing screen. For a light subject, such as a yellow dandelion, take a reading with your spot meter from only the flower (so that the area of the sensor of the exposure meter is filled by the image of the yellow flower) and then give one extra stop of light. For example, if your camera indicates an exposure of 1/8 second at f/11, you could either *increase the exposure time* and take your shot at 1/4 second, f/11; or *increase the aperture* and expose for 1/8 second at f/8. Either way, you will have achieved the correct exposure for the dandelion. For a very light flower such as, say, a white-flowered *Dactylorhiza*, you should repeat the above procedure but this time add even more light, as the white flower is brighter than the yellow one. It is notoriously difficult to expose correctly for white and I would suggest that you take a couple of shots, first adding one and a half stops of light and then, for your second shot, two stops. Flowers darker than mid-tone are not often encountered, but in this case you would need to give one stop *less* light. For example, considering the same exposure as above (1/8 second at f/11), the corrected exposure for a dark subject would be 1/15 second at f/11 or 1/8 second at f/16. For a *very* dark subject you should add up to two extra stops of

Plates 395 and 396.
Orchis mascula
(Lammermoor Hills, East Lothian, 15 May 2004).
Plate 395 (left) was taken prior to 'gardening' and Plate 396 (right) afterwards.

light. With practice you will soon build up experience and come to know instinctively when to override your camera's exposure meter, and by how much. If in doubt take a few shots around the exposure you calculate to be correct, varying the exposure by about half a stop each time. Take careful note of what you have done so that you can make a meaningful assessment of your results once the film has been processed. The most difficult part of the procedure is recognising mid-toned subjects in the field.

Gardening

'Gardening' is the term for tidying up the area you wish to include in your photograph. This is especially relevant to the background of your shot. Competing herbage, twigs, dead grasses from the previous year, light-coloured stones or other debris will undoubtedly appear somewhere in the frame and may spoil your final composition. After the rigours of winter much of the old vegetation will be bleached to a pale colour and this can be highly distracting when out of focus in the background. By carefully removing offending items you can usually improve the overall result. Elements such as diagonal grasses crossing the corners of the composition, or the pale undersides of leaves – or grasses inadvertently bent over by you in the course of your gardening – can also detract from the final image.

For gardening to be successful it is important that you do not overdo it. Your policy should be to remove only what is really necessary. For extreme close-up work I carry tweezers and a small pair of scissors as my gardening tools. Where the offending element is living foliage it is better to tie it back, releasing it again once you have finished your photography. If considerable gardening is needed it would probably be better to forget that particular specimen and look for another plant to photograph.

And finally …

Recheck the composition within your viewfinder. Is it pleasing? Have you selected the best viewpoint? While looking through the camera, check that no offending items of foliage, etc., are *just* intruding into the edge of the frame. For this you will need to take a critical view of all four edges of your viewfinder image. Do you want to create a photograph where your orchid portrait stands out from an otherwise out-of-focus background or do you require great depth of field? If your aim is to produce the former you must be very careful to ensure that your camera is positioned precisely parallel to the orchid plant so that you can get it all in focus at a largish aperture. Using the depth-of-field preview to guide you, stop the lens down only as far as is required to ensure that the plant is fully sharp. Will a reflector be useful to lighten that dark corner? Try hand-holding one and moving it around to see if it improves the shot. If it does, prop it in position with three or four knitting needles. If your shot requires great depth of field you will have no alternative but to give it a longish exposure to compensate for the small aperture required. If it is windy you may be tempted to use a fast shutter-speed and large aperture – but don't. The depth of field will not be sufficient, even if the fast shutter-speed has 'frozen' the plant. It is better to set your camera controls to give you the depth of field you require and wait for a lull in the wind, releasing the shutter the instant that the plant stops moving. If your orchid is growing in a windy spot it may be worthwhile visiting it very early in the morning or last thing in the evening – times when the weather is often less windy. Alternatively, it may be possible to shelter the plant by erecting a wind-break.

Finally, take great care of your subjects and the surrounding vegetation, particularly when working in fragile terrain, and look out for seedlings that may be growing around your chosen specimen. These can be tiny and are easily crushed underfoot.

The photographs in this book

The majority of the photographs in this book were taken using a Nikon F3 camera body with 24 mm, 35 mm, 55 mm or 105 mm Nikon lenses, the latter two being macro lenses. From early 2002, however, I added to my field kit a Nikon F4 body and 200 mm Nikon macro lens, and these were used for nearly all of the orchid portraits and close-ups dated 2002 onwards. Prior to that I had used the F3 body and 105 mm macro for perhaps 75 per cent of all my photography, including plant portraits and close-ups. Most of the habitat shots were taken using the 35 mm wide-angle lens. The 24 mm wide-angle and 55 mm macro lens were only occasionally employed. A rigid tripod allowing a low camera position was used to support the camera for every photograph, regardless of whether it was a simple habitat shot or a tight close-up. I do not take any photographs without using a quality tripod. The film used for the majority of the photographs was Fujichrome Velvia 50 ISO.

Three species, namely *Cypripedium calceolus*, *Epipogium aphyllum* and *Spiranthes aestivalis*, were photographed in mainland Europe. Owing to a strict conservation regime it has not been possible recently to photograph the *Cypripedium* at its single native site in Yorkshire. The *Epipogium* has not been seen in Britain in any numbers since 1986. A single specimen did occur in the Chilterns in 1987, and single plants also appeared near Reading in 1994, 1998 and 1999, but unfortunately I did not receive information of these in time to visit the sites. The last record of *Spiranthes aestivalis* flowering in the New Forest was in 1959 and it is now regarded as being extinct in the British Isles. It is included in this book for the sake of completeness, and in case the species is ever reintroduced.

Further reading

Those of you who wish to pursue the photography of wild orchids, or any other plants for that matter, and achieve the highest standards of quality can do no better than read the following two books, which I recommend.

John Shaw's Nature Photography Field Guide
by John Shaw (2000), published by Amphoto Books, New York
(www.watsonguptill.com), ISBN 0-8174-4059-3 (paperback)

The Backpacker's Photography Handbook
by Charles Campbell (1994), published by Amphoto Books, New York
(www.watsonguptill.com), ISBN 0-8174-3609-X (paperback)

Plate 397 (opposite). This photograph of *Neotinea tridentata* subsp. *conica* was shot as a semi close-up (Serra dos Candeeiros, Portugal, 22 March 2003). It illustrates the type of background that you should strive to capture – quite a bit darker than the subject, but without any distracting objects or highlights. Having chosen the background carefully I was forced to shoot more or less straight into strong sunlight. This harsh lighting was diffused with white taffeta material, the near side of the orchid receiving additional illumination from two silver reflectors. A medium aperture was chosen, as a compromise, to achieve just sufficient depth of field on the flowers but limit the sharpness of the background. Careful use of the depth-of-field preview was essential in achieving this balance. The camera was a Nikon F4, with 200 mm Micro-Nikkor lens; exposure 1/15 second at f/11, on Fuji Velvia 50 ISO film.

Acknowledgements

We warmly acknowledge the financial support that has made this book possible, received from: the Royal Botanic Garden Edinburgh (a registered charity supported by the Scottish Executive Environment and Rural Affairs Department), the Members (formerly Friends) of the Royal Botanic Garden Edinburgh, and Mr Derek Prescott. We would like to thank the trustees of the Orcome Trust for their significant contribution towards the cost of producing the colour plates that appear on these pages. Michael Foley also thanks the Department of Biological Sciences, University of Lancaster, for provision of facilities.

We must record special thanks to the many botanists, landowners and friends who have helped us in one way or another to make this book so complete. Sincere apologies are extended to anyone we have inadvertently omitted from the following list: Phyll Abbott, Brian and Jenny Allan, Dr Crinan Alexander, Chris Badenoch, Margaret Baecker, Dr Bill Baker, Alex Barty, Prof. Richard Bateman, Allan Bennell, Ruth Berry, Iona Birchall, Günther Blaich, Tim Brain, the late Humphrey Bowen, the late Lady Anne Brewis, Dr Peter Brough, Andrew Buckholm, Ken Butler, Andy Byfield, Mike and Lauraine Chalk, Prof. Mark Chase, Winston Churchill, Les Colley, Peter Corkhill, Dr Yiannis Christophides, Dr Malcolm Coe, Rob Cooke, Dr Eva Crackles, Dr Phillip Cribb, Dr Adrian Davies, Rod D'Ayala, Dr Ian Denholm, Lois Duncan-Miller, Bill Elliot, the late David Ellis, Gwynn Ellis, Malcolm Emery, Dr Chris Ferreira, the late John Fisher, David Franklin, Peter Gahan, Fergus Garrett, Graham Giles, Graham Goodfellow, Donald Grant, Dave Green, Tom Grime, Dr Richard Gulliver, the late Kathleen Gunning, Dr Geoffrey Halliday, Mike Hallsworth, Dennis Harding, Ron and Trish Harrison, Bill and Primrose Helyar, Prof. Douglas Henderson, Leueen Hill, the late Kathleen Hollick, Dr Peter Hollingsworth, Dr Frank Horsman, Nigel Jee, Martin Jenkinson, Bo Göran Johansson, Mary Keane, Ronald Kell, the late Joy Ketchen, Paul Kirkland, Claire and Mark Kitchen, Karel Kreutz, Isobyl and Eric La Croix, Brian Laney, Peter Lambley, David Lang, Richard Laurence, Peter Lawson, the late Peter Le Brocq, John Leedal, Yvonne Leonard, Geoffrey Leader-Williams, the late Frances Le Sueur, Dr Rolf Lidberg, Margaret Lindop, Pat Livermore, Dr David Long, Mike Lowe, Phil Lusby, Maggie Maan, Dr. Murdo Macdonald, Andrew McBride, Douglas McKean, Richard Manuel, Patrick Marks, David Maylam, Tom Medd, the late Mary Mendum (née Bates), Deborah Millward, the late Mary Milne, Rose Murphy, Simon Nobes, Robert Northridge, Andrew and Valerie Oxford, Dr Caroline Pannell, Keith Payne, Rob Petely-Jones, Mary Pinn, Mike Porter, Sarah Priest, Dr Hans Reinhard, the late Eileen Rhone,

Plate 398 (opposite). Characters from both parents are easily seen in this *Gymnadenia borealis* × *Dactylorhiza fuchsii* subsp. *fuchsii*. Rough grassland, Fife, 2 July 2003.

Dr Tim Rich, Prof. John Richards, Dr Jimmy Robarts, the late Dick Roberts, Frank Robertson, Dr Francis Rose, Duncan Rothwell, Dr Fred Rumsey, Dr Alan Showler, the late Arthur Smith, Paul Stanley, Dr Wolfgang Stern, Kenny Stevenson, Tom Stevenson, Dr Lawrence Storer, Dr Jill Sutcliffe, Pip Tabor, Don Tag, Barry Tattersall, Ian Taylor, David Tennant, Michael Troy, Dr Leslie Tucker, the late Derek Turner Ettlinger, Jonathan P. Tyler, Robert Unwin, Chris Wain, Rene Weston, Felizitas and the late Herbert Weyler, Malcolm Wright, and Joe and Jean Zorzi.

Many people have helped in putting this book together. We are grateful to Professor Stephen Blackmore for his kind Foreword, and to all at the Royal Botanic Garden Edinburgh for their support. In particular we thank Ida Maspero, Publications Manager, who has done so much to facilitate the production of *Orchids of the British Isles*, and Frieda Christie, Microscopist, who captured the scanning electron microscope images (on p.10).

Our warm thanks are due to contributing authors Crinan Alexander, John Grimshaw, Barry Tattersall and Ian Taylor, who have ensured that this book presents a complete account of all aspects of British and Irish orchid biology, conservation and cultivation. Professor Richard Bateman of the Natural History Museum has freely advised throughout on taxonomic matters, and Dr John Rodwell of the University of Lancaster kindly provided data on NVC habitats. John Grimshaw at Griffin Press Publishing has tied all the loose ends together, edited the text and taken the book through to publication; we thank him and Sarah Cannon and Jenni Navratil, who have copy-edited, designed and produced *Orchids of the British Isles* so beautifully.

Michael Foley, Sidney Clarke
May 2005

Dactylorhiza fuchsii

New Taxonomic Combination

Dactylorhiza purpurella (T. & T.A. Steph.) Soó var. ***cambrensis***
(R.H. Roberts) R.M. Bateman & Denholm, **comb. et stat. nov.**

Plate 399. The ongoing
process of taxonomy:
the new combination
Dactylorhiza purpurella
var. *cambrensis* is
published here for the first
time. Marshy grassland,
Merioneth, 13 June 2002.

Basionym

Dactylorchis majalis (Reichenb.) Vermeul. subsp.
cambrensis R.H. Roberts, *Watsonia* 5: 41 (1961).

Synonyms

Dactylorhiza latifolia (L.) Soó subsp. *cambrensis*
(R.H. Roberts) Soó, *Nom. Nov. Gen. Dactylorhiza*: 5 (1962).

D. majalis (Reichb.) P.F. Hunt & Summerh. subsp.
cambrensis (R.H. Roberts) R.H. Roberts,
Watsonia 7: 104 (1969).

D. majalis (Reichb.) P.F. Hunt subsp. *occidentalis*
(Pugsley) P.D. Sell var. *cambrensis* R.M.
Bateman & Denholm, *Watsonia* 14: 368 (1983).

D. cambrensis (R.H. Roberts) Averyanov, *Bot. Zhurn.*
69: 874 (1984).

D. comosa (Scop.) P.D. Sell subsp. *cambrensis*
(R.H. Roberts) R.H. Roberts, in P.D. Sell &
G. Murrell, *Fl. Gr. Br. Ire.* 5: 365 (1996).

Possibly including

D. purpurella (T & T.A. Steph.) Soó subsp.
majaliformis Nelson, *Taxon* 28: 593 (1979),
ex Lojtnant, *Bot. Tidsskr.* 74: 176 (1979).

Glossary and Abbreviations

2n = Normal (diploid) chromosome number.

10-km square Unit used in recording occurrence of species across the British Isles; also known as a 'hectad'. It is 10 × 10 km (i.e. 100 km², not 10 km²). A dot on one of the distribution maps reproduced in this book indicates a record within the corresponding 10-km square (possibly only one population, or even a single specimen). For a key to the colours used for the dots, see Chapter 5 (p. 55) or below (p. 378).

aberrant Deviating from the normal.

achlorophyllous Lacking chlorophyll, therefore not green.

acidic (soil) Of pH less than 7; usually sour and relatively infertile.

aggregate/agg. A group or complex of similar, usually variable, taxa.

albino A plant lacking normal pigmentation, usually appearing white and green. Albinism is sometimes called 'hypochromism'.

alkaline (soil) Of pH greater than 7; usually fertile. In the British Isles, usually with a high calcium content.

allele One of pair of genes occupying homologous positions on pair of chromosomes; often slightly different through mutation.

allopolyploidy A state of increased ploidy resulting from the doubling of the two sets of chromosomes in a hybrid between two species. Such plants are usually 'allotetraploid', having four sets of chromosomes (instead of the usual two).

anther Male part of flower, producing pollen.

anthocyanins Pigments responsible for red, purple and blue colours of plants.

anthropogenic Caused by human activity.

anthropomorphic Shaped like human body.

autecology The ecology of a single species.

autopolyploidy A state of increased ploidy resulting from doubling of the normal two sets of chromosomes in a single species. Such plants are usually 'autotetraploid', having four sets of chromosomes.

autogamous Self-pollinating (flowers).

basic/base-rich (soil) Of pH greater than 7; usually fertile; not necessarily rich in calcium.

binomial Scientific name (for species), consisting of a genus and a species epithet.

bog Wet, acidic area overlying peat.

boreal Northern; (biogeographic region) characterised by long, cold winters.

bract Leaf-like organ subtending the flower.

bulbil Small bulb present on the leaf margin or between leaf and stem.

bursicle Flap or sac-like organ covering the viscidium, preventing drying out.

calcareous Lime-rich or chalk-rich (soils or water).

calcicole Plant occurring on lime-rich soil.

calcifuge Plant that avoids soil containing lime (i.e. usually occurring on acidic soil).

callosity, callus Crest or fleshy outgrowth on the labellum.

canaliculate Channelled.

capsule Structure at base of flower comprising several seed-containing carpels.

carpel Seed-containing division within the capsule.

caudicle Extension of the pollinium, sometimes connected to the viscidium.

cauline Borne on the stems.

chlorophyll Green pigment in plants, responsible for photosynthesis.

Plate 400 (opposite). Contemporary British artist Jonathan P. Tyler specialises in painting orchids: here he portrays the Fen Orchid *Liparis loeselii* var. *ovata* in its dune-slack habitat (×2 life-size, approximately). Painted in April 2002.

chlorotic Yellowish in colour (plants), usually from mineral deficiency preventing formation of chlorophyll.

chromosome Body within cell nucleus containing a thread of DNA. In the normal cell chromosomes occur in pairs (diploid state), but in gametes only one set is present (haploid state), combining on fertilisation to restore the diploid number in the zygote. Occasionally more than two sets of chromosomes occur in a cell, resulting in a polyploid state or 'level'.

circumboreal Occurring all around the northern part of northern hemisphere.

circumpolar Occurring in northern regions, especially within arctic circle.

cladistics The study of evolutionary relationships for taxonomic purposes through the comparison of data sets to generate a branching, tree-like diagram – a 'cladogram'. This is built up of 'clades', or lineages of species derived from a single ancestor.

cleistogamy Self-pollination and fertilisation within an unopened flower.

clinandrium The part of the column to which the anther is connected.

clitter Fragments of limestone.

clones Genetically identical individuals.

column Central organ in orchid flower, made up of the style and filaments of the anther(s), bearing both the stigmatic surface and the anther(s); also sometimes termed the 'gynostegium'.

connate Joined together.

connivent Coming into contact.

cordate Heart-shaped (i.e. having two equal lobes at the base).

crenate With rounded teeth at edge.

deflexed Bent or turned downwards.

Defra UK Government Department for Environment, Food and Rural Affairs.

deltate Triangular in shape, attached at the broad end.

depauperate Of smaller than normal size and stature, often because of adverse or harsh growing conditions.

diploid Having the normal number of chromosomes (occurring in two sets); written as '2n ='. For example, *Orchis mascula*, 2n = 42: two sets of 21 chromosomes.

distal At the further end.

divergent Spreading from the centre.

DNA Deoxyribonucleic acid: the genetic material of all cells.

dune slack Depression behind or between sand dunes; often caused by wind erosion, often moist or wet.

duplex Having twice the normal number of organs.

ellipsoid An elliptic solid.

elliptic Ellipse-shaped.

endemic Found only in a restricted geographical area.

endogenous Within plant body.

epichile The outer portion of a complex labellum (as e.g. in *Cephalanthera*, *Epipactis*).

epiphyte A plant growing on trees, but not parasitic on the host.

etiolated Pale in colour and sometimes weak (plants), as a result of growing in reduced or absent sunlight.

F1 First-generation hybrid.

F2 Second-generation hybrid, resulting from a cross between two F1 plants.

fen Wet area resulting from peat overlaid by alkaline water.

flexuous With stem bent in a zig-zag.

flora The plants of a geographical region; also, a work enumerating and describing these plants.

flush Wet area (usually sloping) formed by water issuing from a spring.

form / f. Lowest taxonomic rank (*forma*) into which a plant will normally be classified; usually showing minor differentiation in only one character, and not forming distinct populations.

friable Crumbling, readily broken into smaller pieces.

galea The 'hood' formed by connivent perianth segments above the column in some orchids.

garrigue Short Mediterranean scrub.

gene Unit of heritable information, on chromosome, encoded by DNA.

genome The full genetic complement of a set of chromosomes.

genotype The genetic make-up of an organism, not affected by environmental factors.

genus (pl. **genera**) A group of species more closely related to each other than to species in other genera.

geophyte A plant surviving an adverse period by means of underground storage organs.

glabrous Lacking hairs; smooth.

glaucous Grey-blue in colour, usually from a superficial layer of grey wax.

globose Rounded.

grikes The eroded crevices between the blocks of stone (or 'clints') in a limestone pavement.

gynostegium *See* column.

hanger Wood on steep hillside, especially on chalk in southern England.

hectad *See* 10-km square.

hood Loose structure formed by dorsal sepals/petals.

hybrid Plant originating from the fertilisation of one species by another.

hybrid swarm Group or population of hybrids that exhibit a range of characters between those of the parents.

hyperchromism Condition of having an excess of pigments, causing plant of darker than normal colours.

hyper-resupinate Rotated through 360° (flower) during development.

hypha (pl. **hyphae**) A strand of fungal tissue. Many hyphae make up the main fungal body or 'mycelium'.

hypochile The basal part of a complex labellum (as e.g. in *Cephalanthera*, *Epipactis*).

inflorescence The flower-bearing part of a plant.

infraspecific Within a species. Infraspecific variation can be recognised at the taxonomic ranks of 'subspecies', 'variety' and 'form'.

intergeneric Formed (hybrids) by fertilisation between two species of different genera.

interspecific Formed (hybrids) by fertilisation between two different species.

introgression Incorporation of genes from one species into the genotype of another; occurs through repeated hybridisation, or repetitive back-crossing between an F1 hybrid and one of its parents.

ITS/Internal transcribed spacer A region of nuclear ribosomal DNA.

IUCN The World Conservation Union (formerly International Union for the Conservation of Nature).

keeled Folded along the midrib (leaves) giving a sharply ridged appearance.

labellum The conspicuous, often complex, lowermost petal (inner perianth segment) of an orchid flower; also called the 'lip'.

lanceolate Shaped like a lance; broadest in the middle, and tapering to a pointed end.

lax Loose.

leached Having had soluble elements dissolved by water and washed away (soils), reducing fertility.

leucistic With reduced pigmentation (plants), but not completely albino; often rather yellowish.

ligulate Strap-shaped.

lingulate Tongue-shaped.

lip *See* labellum.

locules Chambers within ovary.

lobe Division of leaf, sepal or labellum.

machair Coastal short grassland over shell-sand; usually in Hebrides and other western areas.

maquis Tall, drought-resistant Mediterranean shrubland.

marsh Wet area where the soil does not contain peat.

meiosis The process by which chromosomes replicate and divide to create a haploid gamete.

mesotrophic Containing a moderate quantity of nutrients (water or soil).

microtopography Local variation in the landscape.

monocarpic Dying after flowering.

monophyletic Having a single ancestor (a group of taxa). A monophyletic group is a natural lineage, believed to be an accurate reflection of evolutionary relationships.

monospecific Containing only one species (genus).

montane Of mountains.

morphology The visible form of an organism.

morphometry The accurate measurement of plant parts.

mycoheterotroph A plant that obtains nutrients from a fungal partner. 'Obligate' mycoheterotrophs lack chlorophyll. 'Saprophyte', used formerly, indicates that a plant is itself gaining nutrients from dead material, while a mycoheterotroph is dependent on a fungal partner for nutrients; these may also be supplied through connections to another (living) plant.

mycorrhiza A beneficial fungus associated with the roots of a plant.

neutral (soil) Neither acidic nor basic, having a pH of 7.

notho- A prefix denoting hybrid origin; hence 'nothogenus', 'nothospecies'.

non auctt. A designation (in the authority for a plant name) meaning 'not as used by many authors': i.e. there has been widespread confusion about the identity of the taxon in question.

ovary Female part of a flower, containing ovules, and later seeds. In Orchidaceae, often acts as the pedicel.

ovoid Egg-shaped solid.

palmate With free segments originating from a basal point; shaped roughly like a hand.

pandurate Fiddle-shaped; apical portion widest, with a constriction in the middle and a smaller basal portion.

papillae Small protuberances on the surface of a petal or leaf, sometimes somewhat hair-like in appearance.

papillose Bearing papillae.

paraphyletic Artificially divided (group of taxa, monophyletic lineage) to accommodate perceived distinctions.

pedicel Stalk bearing a flower. In Orchidaceae the pedicel is often indistinguishable from the ovary, but it can sometimes be seen (e.g. in *Epipactis*).

peloric With inverted natural symmetry (flower). This is the strict definition, but the term is often used by orchid enthusiasts to indicate a plant with abnormally shaped flowers, more accurately termed 'semi-peloric'.

pendent Hanging.

perennial A plant that lives for a period of more than two years.

perianth Whorl(s) of floral parts; especially used when petals and calyx are not easily distinguished. In an orchid flower, the outer perianth segments are the sepals and the inner perianth segments are the petals.

petal *See* perianth.

phenotype The observable expression of the genotype; can be affected by environmental factors.

photosynthesis Process by which water and carbon dioxide are converted into glucose and oxygen, catalysed by the green pigment chlorophyll.

photosynthate The carbohydrate product of photosynthesis.

phrygana Type of Mediterranean scrub.

phylogeny History (i.e. 'family tree') of evolutionary relationships.

plastid An organelle, such as a chloroplast, found within a plant cell.

ploidy The number of chromosomes found within a cell nucleus.

pollinia The masses of pollen produced by the anther, sometimes crumbling into clumps but often detached entire as a single unit for dispersal.

polyphyletic Supposedly sharing close relationship (a group of taxa), but in fact being of several distinct (monophyletic) origins. Such a group is artificial in construction and does not accurately reflect the evolutionary origins of its members.

polyploid Having more than the normal (diploid) number of chromosomes.

porrect Directed out- and forwards.

proteranthous Producing leaves before flowers.

protocorm Whitish, rounded body with fine hairs protruding from it, formed after orchid seed germinates following infection by mycorrhizal fungus.

pseudobulb Thickened leaf-base, but not a true bulb.

pseudocopulation Attempt by male insect to mate with a flower it perceives to be a female insect, effecting in the process removal/transferral of pollen; occurs especially in *Ophrys*.

raceme An unbranched inflorescence with laterally produced flowers, usually with a pedicel.

rachis　Central axis of the inflorescence or of a pinnate leaf.

reclinate　Bent down into another part.

reflexed　Folded backwards.

reniform　Kidney-shaped.

resupinate　Rotated through 180° during development (flower), so upside-down to embryonic position.

reticulate　Arranged in net-like manner.

rhizome　A persistent horizontal subterranean stem bearing roots and shoots.

ribosome　Organelle within cell, mainly composed of RNA (ribonucleic acid), responsible for protein synthesis. Transmitted through the female line, ribosomes are considered to be a reliable source of genetic information.

rostellum　Area of upper edge of stigma, sometimes forming a projection, on column between stigmatic surface and anther; produces the viscidium.

rosulate　In rosette-form.

RSPB　Royal Society for the Protection of Birds.

saprophyte　*See* mycoheterotroph.

secund　With flowers all facing in one direction (inflorescence).

sensu lato/**s.l.**　In the broad sense.

sensu stricto/**s.s.**　In the narrow or restricted sense.

sepal　*See* perianth.

sessile　Lacking a stem or stalk.

simple　Unlobed or undivided (leaf).

slacks　Depressions among sand dunes, often moist or wet.

spathe　A large bract subtending the inflorescence.

species　Division of a genus comprising groups of plants with similar characters, all more closely related to each other than to any other similar group.

speculum　'Mirror patch' on labellum of an *Ophrys*.

spike　An inflorescence in which the flowers are sessile (lacking a pedicel) on the main axis.

spur　Hollow process or sac protruding from lower part of labellum at back of flower, usually containing nectar.

SSSI　Site of Special Scientific Interest: a designated area or habitat having some limited legal protection against harm or destruction.

stamens　The male reproductive organs, in most flowers comprising anthers and filaments but in orchids fused with the stigmas to form the column.

staminate　Bearing stamens, upper part of the column in an orchid flower.

staminode　A sterile stamen.

stigma　The part of the female organs in a flower that receives pollen and on which the pollen germinates. In orchids the stigma is usually in the form of a 'stigmatic surface', a slight depression at the base of the column.

stolon　Horizontal shoot growing away from its parent plant, which is therefore 'stoloniferous'.

subspecies/subsp.　Taxonomic rank for a group of plants that have the principal characters of a species but with significant definable morphological differentiation. Populations of a subspecies can occupy a distinct geographical range or habitat.

symbionts　Dissimilar organisms (usually of two different species) living together in prolonged and close association, not necessarily in a mutually beneficial manner.

synonym　An alternative or former name for a taxon, usually considered to be invalid. Synonyms arise when a taxon has been described more than once, in which case the prior name is usually the one accepted as correct; or when an article of the International Code of Botanical Nomenclature has been contravened, requiring the publication of a new name. The development of taxonomic thinking may be recorded by an increasing list of synonyms, as generic and specific concepts change over time.

talus　Scree.

taxon (pl. **taxa**)　A group of organisms that share the same taxonomic rank (families, genera, species, infraspecific variants).

taxonomy　The scientific classification of organisms.

terata　Mutants, or 'freaks' (from Greek *teras*, 'monster').

tetraploid　Having four sets of chromosomes in a normal cell instead of the usual (diploid) two.

trifoliate　Three-leaved.

tuber　Underground storage organ derived from roots or stem.

turloughs　Shallow lakes (in the Burren, Co. Clare) that fill up or dry out according to the balance between rainfall and seepage of water through the porous limestone of their beds. The marginal areas are therefore a 'difficult' habitat for plants.

variety/var.　Low taxonomic rank (*varietas*) encompassing a set of variants of a species showing comparatively minor differentiation in a few characters, but occurring as recognisable populations. Often loosely used for rare, minor variants that are more usefully ranked as 'forms'.

viscidium　A sticky area of the rostellum that assists in attaching the pollinia to a pollinator; in some cases it can be detached with the pollinia as a sticky pad at the base of the caudicle.

Key to distribution maps

- ● present as a native plant between 1987 and 1999
- ● present as a native plant between 1970 and 1986, but not recorded as either a native or an introduction since then
- ○ present as a native before 1970, but not recorded as either a native or an introduction since then; *or* records undated
- ● present as an introduction between 1987 and 1999
- ● present as an introduction between 1970 and 1986, but not recorded as either a native or an introduction since then
- ○ present as an introduction before 1970, but not recorded as either a native or an introduction since then; *or* records undated

Bibliography

Allan, B. & Woods, P. (1993). *Wild Orchids of Scotland*. Edinburgh: HMSO.

Anon., 'St Christopher's School, Burnham-on-Sea' (1978). Operation Orchid. *Watsonia* 12: 197.

Arber, A. (1986). *Herbals*. Third edition. Cambridge: Cambridge University Press.

Babington, C.C. (1860). *Flora of Cambridgeshire*. London: John van Voorst.

Bateman, R.M. (2001). Evolution and classification of European orchids: insights from molecular and morphological characters. *Journal Europäischer Orchideen* 33: 33–119.

— (2004). Burnt tips and bumbling bees: how many orchid species currently occur in the British Isles? *Journal of the Hardy Orchid Society* 1: 10–18.

— (2005, in press). How many orchid species are currently native to the British Isles? In: Bailey, J. (ed.), *Studies in the British Flora*. London: Botanical Society of the British Isles.

Bateman, R.M. & Denholm, I. (1983). A reappraisal of the British and Irish dactylorchids. 1. The tetraploid marsh-orchids. *Watsonia* 14: 347–376.

— (1985). A reappraisal of the British and Irish dactylorchids. 2. The diploid marsh-orchids. *Watsonia* 15: 321–355.

— (1989). A reappraisal of the British and Irish dactylorchids. 3. The spotted-orchids. *Watsonia* 17: 319–349.

— (1995). The 'Hebridean Marsh-orchid': nomenclatural and conceptual clarification of a biological enigma. *Edinburgh Journal of Botany* 52: 55–63.

— (2003). The Heath Spotted-orchid (*Dactylorhiza maculata* (L.) Soó) in the British Isles: a cautionary case study in delimiting infraspecific taxa and inferring their evolutionary relationships. *Journal Europäischer Orchideen* 35: 3–36.

Bateman, R.M. & Farrington, O.S. (1989). Morphometric comparison of populations of *Orchis simia* Lam. (Orchidaceae) from Oxfordshire and Kent. *Botanical Journal of the Linnean Society* 100: 205–218.

Bateman, R.M. & Hollingsworth, P.M. (2004). Morphological and molecular investigation of the parentage and maternity of *Anacamptis* ×*albuferensis* (*A. fragrans* × *A. robusta*), a new hybrid orchid from Mallorca, Spain. *Taxon* 53: 43–54.

Bateman, R.M., Hollingsworth, P.M., Preston, J., Yi-bo, L., Pridgeon, A.M. & Chase, M.W. (2003). Molecular phylogenetics and evolution of Orchidinae and selected Habenariinae (Orchidaceae). *Botanical Journal of the Linnean Society* 142: 1–40.

Bateman, R.M., Hollingsworth, P.M., Squirrell, J. & Hollingsworth, M.L. (2005, in press). Neottieae: phylogenetics. Account for *Genera Orchidacearum. 4*. Oxford: Oxford University Press.

Bateman, R.M., Pridgeon, A.M. & Chase, M.W. (1997). Phylogenetics of subtribe Orchidinae (Orchidoideae, Orchidaceae) based on nuclear ITS sequences. 2. Infrageneric relationships and reclassification to achieve monophyly of *Orchis sensu stricto*. *Lindleyana* 12 (3): 113–141.

Bateman, R.M. & Rudall, P.J. (2005, in press). The good, the bad, the ugly: using naturally occurring terata to distinguish the possible from the impossible in orchid floral evolution. In: Columbus, J.T., Friar, E.A., Porter, J.M., Prince, L.M. & Simpson, M.G. (eds.), *Monocots: Comparative Biology and Evolution* (*Aliso* special volume).

Baugen, T. (2003). Narrmarihand *Orchis morio* – en kresen øyboer. *Blyttia* 61: 164–170.

Bauhin, C. (1623). *Pinax theatri botanici*. Basle, Switzerland.

Blackmore, S. (1985). *Bee Orchids*. Princes Risborough: Shire Natural History.

Bournérias, M. (ed.) (1998). *Les Orchidées de France, Belgique et Luxembourg*. Paris: Collection Parthenope.

Brummitt, R.K. & Powell, C.E. (eds.) (1992). *Authors of Plant Names*. Kew: Royal Botanic Gardens, Kew.

Campbell, M.S. (1937). Three weeks botanising in the Outer Hebrides. *Botanical Exchange Club Report* 11: 304–318.

Cameron, C.K., Chase, M.W., Whitten, W.M., Kores, P.J., Jarrell, D.C., Albert, V.A., Yukawa, T., Hills, H.G. & Goldman, D.H. (1999). A phylogenetic analysis of the Orchidaceae: evidence from *rbc*L nucleotide sequences. *American Journal of Botany* 86: 208–244.

Carey, P.D. (1999). Changes in the distribution and abundance of *Himantoglossum hircinum* (L.) Sprengel (Orchidaceae) over the last 100 years. *Watsonia* 22: 353–364.

Carey, P.D. & Dines, T.D. (2002). [Species accounts] In: Preston, C.D., Pearman, D.A. & Dines, T.D. (eds.), *New Atlas of the British and Irish Flora*. Oxford: Oxford University Press.

Chase, M.W. (1999). Molecular systematics, parsimony, and orchid classification. In: Pridgeon, A.M., Cribb, P.J., Chase, M.W. & Rasmussen, F.N. (eds.), *Genera Orchidacearum. 1. General Introduction, Apostasioideae, Cypripedioideae*, pp. 81–88. Oxford: Oxford University Press.

Cheffings, C.M. & Farrell, L. (eds.) (2005). *The Vascular Plant Red Data List for Great Britain*. Online at www.jncc.gov.uk: Joint Nature Conservation Committee.

Church, J.M. & Farrell, L. (1999). *Orchis simia* Lam. (Orchidaceae). In: Wigginton, M.J. (ed.), *British Red Data Books. 1. Vascular Plants*. Third edition. Peterborough: Joint Nature Conservation Committee.

Clarke, D., Iveson, D. & Roberts, J. (2003). A new Cumbrian site for the 'Dune Helleborine' *Epipactis dunensis* (T. & T.A. Stephenson) Godfery. *Botanical Society of the British Isles News* 93: 17–18.

Clarke, W.A. (1900). *First Records of British Flowering Plants*. London: West, Newman & Co.

Clements, M.A., Muir, H. & Cribb, P.J. (1985). A preliminary report on the symbiotic germination of European terrestrial orchids. *Kew Bulletin* 41: 437–445.

Cox, A.V., Pridgeon, A.M., Albert, V.A. & Chase, M.W. (1997). Phylogenetics of the slipper orchids (Cypripedioideae: Orchidaceae): nuclear rDNA sequences. *Plant Systematics and Evolution* 208: 197–223.

Crackles, E. (1990). *Flora of the East Riding of Yorkshire*. Hull: Hull University Press.

Cribb, P. (1997). *The Genus Cypripedium*. Kew: Royal Botanic Gardens, Kew.

Cribb, P. & Bailes, C. (1989). *Hardy Orchids*. London: Christopher Helm.

Curtis, T.G.F. & McGough, H.N. (1988). *The Irish Red Data Book*. Dublin: Wild Life Service Ireland.

Curtis, W. (1775–1787). *Flora Londinensis*. London.

Curtis, W.H. (1941). *William Curtis 1746–1799*. Winchester: Warren & Son Ltd.

Darwin, C. (1862). *The Various Contrivancies by which British and Foreign Orchids are Fertilised by Insects* (second edition, 1877). London: Murray. Also known as *The Fertilisation of Orchids*.

Davies, P., Davies, J. & Huxley, A. (1983). *Wild Orchids of Britain and Europe*. London: Chatto & Windus.

Delforge, P. (1995). *Orchids of Britain and Europe*. London: HarperCollins.

— (2001). *Guide des Orchidées d' Europe (d' Afrique du Nord et du Proche-Orient)*. Lausanne/Paris: Delachaux et Niestle S.A.

Delforge, P. & Gévaudan, A. (2002). Contribution taxonomique et nomenclaturale au groupe d'*Epipactis leptochila*. *Les Naturalistes belges* 2002: 83; hors-série – spécial Orchidées no. 15: 19–35.

Dickson, J.H., MacPherson, P., Watson, K., Hammerston, D., Jardine, W.G. & Jarvis, M.C. (2000). *The Changing Flora of Glasgow: Urban and Rural Plants through the Centuries*. Edinburgh: Edinburgh University Press.

Dines, T.D. (2002). [Species accounts] In: Preston, C.D., Pearman, D.A. & Dines, T.D. (eds.), *New Atlas of the British and Irish Flora*. Oxford: Oxford University Press.

Dressler, R.L. (1990). *The Orchids: Natural History and Classification*. Cambridge, Massachusetts/London: Harvard University Press.

— (1993). *Phylogeny and Classification of the Orchid Family*. Portland, Oregon: Timber Press.

Ettlinger, D.M.T. (1987). Peloric and duplex examples of *Orchis purpurea* Hudson in Kent. *Watsonia* 16: 432.

— (1997). *Notes on British and Irish Orchids*. Dorking: privately published.

— (1998a). A new variety of *Ophrys apifera* Hudson (Orchidaceae). *Watsonia* 22: 105–107.

— (1998b). *Illustrations of British and Irish Orchids*. Dorking: privately published.

Fay, M.F., Qamaruz-Zaman, F., Chase, M.W. & Samuel, R. (2004). Military and Monkey Orchids – what do we have in England? *English Nature Research Reports, No. 607. Proceedings of a Conservation Genetics Workshop held at the Royal Botanic Gardens, Kew, 27 November 2001*. Peterborough: English Nature.

Fisher, J. (1987). *Wild Flowers in Danger*. London: Gollancz.

Foley, M.J.Y. (1986). Plant records. *Watsonia* 16: 195.

— (1987). The current distribution and abundance of *Orchis ustulata* in northern England.*Watsonia* 16: 409–415.

— (1990a). An assessment of populations of *Dactylorhiza traunsteineri* (Sauter) Soó in the British Isles and a comparison with others from continental Europe. *Watsonia* 18: 153–172.

— (1990b). The current distribution and abundance of *Orchis ustulata* in southern England. *Watsonia* 18: 37–48.

— (1992). The current distribution and abundance of *Orchis ustulata* in the British Isles – an updated summary. *Watsonia* 19: 121–126.

— (1993). *Orobanche reticulata* Wallr. populations in Yorkshire (north-east England). *Watsonia* 19: 247–257.

— (2000). *Dactylorhiza incarnata* (L.) Soó subsp. *ochroleuca* (Wüstnei ex Boll) P.F. Hunt and Summerh. (Orchidaceae): a comparison of British and European plants. *Watsonia* 23: 299–303.

— (2004). A summary of the past and present status of *Spiranthes aestivalis* (Poir.) Rich. (Orchidaceae) (Summer Lady's-tresses) in north-west Europe. *Watsonia* 25: 193–201.

Forrest, A. (2001). Genetic structure within and among populations of *Spiranthes romanzoffiana* Cham. in Scotland. M.Sc. thesis. Royal Botanic Garden Edinburgh and University of Edinburgh.

Forrest, A.D., Hollingsworth, M.L., Hollingsworth, P.M, Sydes, C. & Bateman, R.M. (2004). Population genetic structure in European populations of *Spiranthes romanzoffiana* set in the context of other genetic studies on orchids. *Heredity* 92: 218–227.

Freudenstein, J.V. & Rasmussen, F.N. (1999). What does morphology tell us about orchid relationships? A cladistic analysis. *American Journal of Botany* 86: 225–248.

Frosch, W. (1980). Asymbiotische Vermehrung von *Orchis morio* mit der ersten Blüte nach 23 Monaten. *Die Orchidee* 31: 101–104.

Genera Orchidacearum. See Pridgeon *et al.* (1999), *Vol. 1*; (2001), *Vol. 2*; *Vols. 3, 4*, in prep.

Gerard, J. (1597/1633). *The Herball, or Generall Historie of Plantes* (first edition, 1597; second edition, 1633). London: John Norton.

Godfery, M. (1933). *Monograph and Iconograph of Native British Orchidaceae.* Cambridge: Cambridge University Press.

Good, R. (1931). A theory of plant geography. *New Phytologist* 30: 149–171.

Grigson, G. (1955). *The Englishman's Flora.* London: Phoenix House.

Gulliver, R., Grant, E., Robarts, J., Keirnen, M., Jønch Møller, S., Beare, A. & Sydes, C. (2005, in press). Conservation of *Spiranthes romanzoffiana* Cham. (Irish Lady's-tresses) in Scotland – the role of twin lateral bud production. In: Leach, S. & Page, C. (eds.), *Botanical Links in the Atlantic Arc. Symposium held by the Botanical Society of the British Isles.*

Gunther, R.T. (1922). *Early British Botanists and their Gardens.* Oxford: Oxford University Press.

Hall, P.M. (1935). Plant Records. *The Botanical Society and Exchange Club of the British Isles – Report for 1935* 11: 41.

Harron, J. (1986). *Flora of Lough Neagh.* Belfast: Irish Naturalists' Journal Committee; Coleraine: University of Ulster.

Hédren, M. (1996a). Genetic differentiation, polyploidization and hybridization in northern European *Dactylorhiza* (Orchidaceae): evidence from allozyme markers. *Plant Systematics and Evolution* 201: 31–55.

— (1996b). Electrophoretic evidence for allotetraploid origin of *Dactylorhiza purpurella* (Orchidaceae). *Nordic Journal of Botany* 16: 127–134.

— (1996c). The allotetraploid nature of *Dactylorhiza praetermissa* (Druce) Soó (Orchidaceae) confirmed. *Watsonia* 21: 113–118.

Hédren, M., Fay, M.F. & Chase, M.W. (2001). Amplified fragment length polymorphisms (AFLP) reveal details of polyploid evolution in *Dactylorhiza* (Orchidaceae). *American Journal of Botany* 88: 1868–1880.

Heslop-Harrison, J. (1953). Microsporogenesis in some triploid *Dactylorhiza* hybrids. *Annals of Botany* 17: 539–549.

Hollingsworth, P.M. (2001). British orchids, taxonomic complexity, molecular markers and conservation. *NERC News*, Spring Issue: 14–15.

— (2003). Taxonomic complexity, population genetics, and plant conservation in Scotland. *Botanical Journal of Scotland* 55 (1): 55–63.

Hollingsworth, P.M., Squirrell, J., Hollingsworth, M.L., Richards, A.J. & Bateman, R.M. (2005, in press). Taxonomic complexity, conservation and recurrent origins of self-pollination in *Epipactis* (Orchidaceae). In: Bailey, J. (ed.), *Studies in the British Flora.* London: Botanical Society of the British Isles.

How, W. (1650). *Phytologia Britannica.* London.

Hutchings, M.J. (1987). The population biology of the early spider orchid, *Ophrys sphegodes* Mill. I. A demographic study from 1973 to 1984. *Journal of Ecology* 75: 711–742.

IUCN (2001). *IUCN Red List Categories and Criteria: Version 3.1.* Gland, Switzerland: IUCN (Species Survival Commission).

Johnson, T. (1634). *Mercurius Botanicus: sive Plantarum gratia suscepti itineris, anno 1634 descriptio.* London.

Kemp, R.J. (1987). Reappearance of *Orchis purpurea* Hudson in Oxfordshire. *Watsonia* 16: 435–436.

Kitching, I.J., Forey, P.L., Humphries, C.J. & Williams, D.M. (1998). *Cladistics, The Theory and Practice of Parsimony Analysis.* Second edition. Systematics Association Publication No. 11. Oxford: Oxford University Press.

Kullenberg, B. (1961). Studies in *Ophrys* pollination. *Zoologiska Bidrag Fran Uppsala* 34: 1–40.

Laney, B. & Stanley, P. (2004). Bee Orchid (*Ophrys apifera*) in Ayrshire (v.c. 75). *Botanical Society of the British Isles News* 95: 30.

Lang, D.C. (1980). *Orchids of Britain.* Oxford: Oxford University Press.

— (1989). *A Guide to the Wild Orchids of Great Britain and Ireland.* Oxford: Oxford University Press.

— (1998). [*Serapias* account] In: Rich, T.C.G. & Jermy, A.C. (eds.), *Plant Crib 1998.* London: Botanical Society of the British Isles.

— (2001). *Wild Orchids of Sussex.* Lewes: Pomegranate Press.

— (2004). *Britain's Orchids.* Old Basing, Hampshire: WildGuides Ltd.

Lees, F.A. (1888). *Flora of West Yorkshire.* London: Lovell Reeve.

Leighton, W.A. (1841). *Flora of Shropshire.* Shrewsbury: Van Voorst.

Lester-Garland, L.V. (1903). *A Flora of the Island of Jersey.* London: West, Newman & Co.

Lewis, L. & Spencer, E.J. (2005). *Epipactis phyllanthes* var. *cambrensis* (C.A.Thomas) P.D. Sell and other unusual *Epipactis* at Kenfig National Nature Reserve. *Watsonia* 25: 290–295.

Lindop, M. (1996). *Cypripedium* conservation report 1995. *Botanical Society of the British Isles News* 72: 45.

Linnaeus, C. (1753). *Species Plantarum*. Stockholm: Laurentii Salvii.

Linton, W.H. (1903). *Flora of Derbyshire*. London: Bemrose & Son.

Lloyd, C. (2004). *Meadows*. London: Cassell Illustrated.

Lousley, J.E. (1969). *Wild Flowers of Chalk and Limestone*. The New Naturalist. London: Collins.

Lowe, M.R. (2003). *Dactylorhiza majalis* in Scotland. *Eurorchis* 15: 77–86.

Lyte, H. (1578). *The Niewe Herbal, or Historie of Plantes*. London.

Mabey, R. (1997). *Flora Britannica*. London: Chatto & Windus.

McClintock, D. (1975). *The Wild Flowers of Guernsey*. London: Collins.

Meikle, R.D. (1985). *Flora of Cyprus, Volume 2*. Kew: Bentham-Moxon Trust.

Merrett, C. (1666). *Pinax Rerum naturalium Britannicarum*. London.

Miller, P. (1758). *Gardeners Dictionary*. London.

— (1758). *Figures of the most Beautiful, Useful and Uncommon Plants figured in the Gardeners Dictionary*. London.

Mitchell, R.B. (1989). Growing hardy orchids from seeds at Kew. *The Plantsman* 11: 152–169.

Möller, O. (1985). Die Mineralsalze der Standortböden der europäischer Orchideen. *Die Orchidee* 36: 118–121.

Morison, R. (1680–1699). Bobart, J. (ed.), *Plantarum Historiae Universalis Oxoniensis pars secunda (–tertia)*. Oxford.

Neiland, M.R.M. & Wilcock, C.C. (1998). Fruit set, nectar reward, and rarity in the Orchidaceae. *American Journal of Botany* 85: 1567–1571.

New Atlas of the British and Irish Flora. See Preston *et al.* (2002).

Nilsson, L.A. (1979). Anthecological studies on the lady's slipper, *Cypripedium calceolus* (Orchidaceae). *Botanisker Notiser* 132: 329–347.

— (1983). Mimesis of bellflower (*Campanula*) and the red helleborine orchid *Cephalanthera rubra*. *Nature* 305: 799–800.

— (1984). Anthecology of *Orchis morio* (Orchidaceae) at its outpost in the north. *Nova Acta Regiae Societatis Scientiarum Upsaliensis, Serie V* C3: 167–179.

O'Mahony, T. (1974). *Neotinea intacta* (Link) Reichb. frat. in Co. Cork. *The Irish Naturalists' Journal* 18 (2): 48–49.

Parkinson, J. (1640). *Theatrum Botanicum: The Theater of Plants. Or, an Herball of a Large Extent …* London.

Petty, L. (1898). The constituents of the North Lancashire Flora 1597(?)–1893. *The Naturalist*: 42.

Pillon, Y., Fay, M.F., Hedrén, M., Bateman, R.M., Devey, D.S., Shipunov, A., van der Bank, M. & Chase, M.W. (submitted). Insights into the evolution and biogeography of western European species complexes in *Dactylorhiza* (Orchidaceae). *Taxon*.

Pouyanne, A. (1917). La fécondation des *Ophrys* par les insectes. *Bulletin de la Société d'Histoire naturelle de l'Afrique du Nord* 8: 6–7.

Preston, C.D., Pearman, D.A. & Dines, T.D. (eds.) (2002). *New Atlas of the British and Irish Flora*. Oxford: Oxford University Press.

Pridgeon, A.M., Bateman, R.M., Cox, A.V., Hapeman, J.R. & Chase, M.W. (1997). Phylogenetics of the subtribe Orchidinae (Orchidoideae, Orchidaceae) based on nuclear ITS sequences. 1. Intergeneric relationships and polyphyly of *Orchis sensu lato*. *Lindleyana* 12: 89–109.

Pridgeon, A.M., Cribb, P.J., Chase, M.W. & Rasmussen, F.N. (eds.) (1999). *Genera Orchidacearum. 1. General Introduction, Apostasioideae, Cypripedioideae*. Oxford: Oxford University Press.

— (2001). *Genera Orchidacearum. 2. Orchidoideae, 1*. Oxford: Oxford University Press.

Proctor, M. & Yeo, P. (1973). *The Pollination of Flowers*. London: Collins.

Qamaruz-Zaman, F., Chase, M.W., Parker, J.S. & Fay, M.W. (2002). *Genetic Fingerprinting Studies of Orchis simia and O. militaris*. Report from the Royal Botanic Gardens, Kew to English Nature.

Ramsay, M.M. & Stewart, J. (1998). Re-establishment of the lady's slipper orchid (*Cypripedium calceolus* L.) in Britain. *Botanical Journal of the Linnean Society* 126: 173–181.

Rasmussen, H.N. (1995). *Terrestrial Orchids: From Seed to Mycotrophic Plant*. Cambridge: Cambridge Univ. Press.

Ray, J. (1660). *Catalogus Plantarum circa Cantabrigium nascentium*. Cambridge.

— (1663). *Appendix ad Catalogus Plantarum circa Cantabrigium nascentium*. Cambridge.

— (1670). *Catalogus Plantarum Angliae*. London.

— (1690/1696/1724). *Synopsis methodica Stirpium Britannicarum* (second edition, 1696; third edition, 1724). London.

Red Data Books (British, Irish). See Wigginton (1999); Curtis & McGough (1988).

Reinhardt, H.R., Gölz, P., Peter, R. & Wildermuth, H. (1991). *Orchideen der Schweiz und angrenzender Gebiete*. Egg, Switzerland: Fotorotar AG.

Richards, A.J. & Porter, A.F. (1982). On the identity of a Northumberland *Epipactis*. *Watsonia* 14: 121–128.

Roberts, R.H. (1988). The occurrence of *Dactylorhiza traunsteineri* (Sauter) Soó in Britain and Ireland. *Watsonia* 17: 43–47.

Rodwell, J.S. (ed.) (1991–2000). *British Plant Communities, Volumes 1–5*. Cambridge: Cambridge University Press.

Rose, F. (1948). *Orchis purpurea* Hudson. Biological Flora of the British Isles, No. 26. *Journal of Ecology* 36: 366–377.

Rose, F. & Brewis, A. (1988). *Cephalanthera rubra* (L.) Rich. in Hampshire. *Watsonia* 17: 176–177.

Salazar, G.A., Chase, M.W., Soto Arenas, M.A. & Ingrouille, M. (2003). Phylogenetics of Cranichideae with emphasis on Spiranthinae (Orchidaceae: Orchidoideae): evidence from plastid and nuclear DNA sequences. *American Journal of Botany* 90: 777–795.

Salisbury, E.J. (1942). *The Reproductive Capacity of Plants.* London: G. Bell & Sons.

Scacchi, R. & de Angelis, G. (1989). Isoenzyme polymorphisms in *Gymnadenia conopsea* and its inferences for systematics within this species. *Biochemical Systematics and Ecology* 17: 25–33.

Sell, P.[D.] & Murrell, G. (1996). *Flora of Great Britain and Ireland, Volume 5 (Butomaceae – Orchidaceae).* Cambridge: Cambridge University Press.

Skelton, P. & Smith, A. (2002). *Cladistics. A Practical Primer on CD-ROM.* Cambridge: Cambridge University Press.

Smith, J.E. (1828). *The English Flora.* London.

Soliva, M., Kocyan, A. & Widmer, A. (2001). Molecular phylogenetics of the sexually deceptive orchid genus *Ophrys* (Orchidaceae) based on nuclear and chloroplast DNA sequences. *Molecular Phylogenetics and Evolution* 20: 78–88.

Sowerby, J. (1790–1814). [Illustrations for] J.E. Smith, *English Botany* [usually referred to as 'Sowerby's *English Botany*']. London: J. Davis.

Sowerby, J. de C. (1829–1866). [Illustrations for] *Supplement to English Botany.* London.

Squirrell, J., Hollingsworth, P.M., Bateman, R.M., Tebitt, M.C. & Hollingsworth, M.L. (2002). Taxonomic complexity and breeding system transitions: conservation genetics of the *Epipactis leptochila* complex (Orchidaceae). *Molecular Ecology* 11: 1957–1964.

Stace, C.A. (1997). *New Flora of the British Isles.* Second edition. Cambridge: Cambridge University Press.

Stewart, A., Pearman, D.A. & Preston, C.D. (eds.) (1994). *Scarce Plants in Britain.* Peterborough: Joint Nature Conservation Committee.

Stewart, J. & Stearn, W.T. (1993). *The Orchid Paintings of Franz Bauer.* London: Herbert Press.

Stone, D.A. & Russell R.V. (2000). Population biology of the late spider orchid *Ophrys fuciflora* – a study of Wye National Nature Reserve 1987–9. *English Nature Research Report,* 389.

Summerhayes, V.S. (1951/1968). *Wild Orchids of Britain* (second edition, 1968). The New Naturalist. London: Collins.

Sumpter, J.P., D'Ayala, R., Parfitt, A.J., Pratt, P. & Raper, C. (2004). The current status of Military (*Orchis militaris*) and Monkey (*Orchis simia*) Orchids in the Chilterns. *Watsonia* 25: 175–183.

Tali, K., Foley, M.J.Y. & Kull, T. (2004). Biological Flora of the British Isles, No. 232: *Orchis ustulata* L. *Journal of Ecology* 92: 174–184.

Turner, W. (1548). *The Names of Herbes in Greke, Latin, Englishe, Duche and Frenche wyth the commune names that Herbaries and Apotecaries use.* London.

— (1551/1562/1568). *A New Herball.* [*The first and seconde partes of the Herbal of William Turner, with the Third parte, lately gathered.*] Cologne (Part 1, London, 1551; Part 2, Cologne, 1562).

UK Biodiversity Group (1995). *Biodiversity: The UK Action Plan.* London: HMSO.

Wallis, J. (1769). *The Natural History and Antiquities of Northumberland: and much of the County of Durham, Volume 1,* p.231. London.

Webb, D.A. & Scannell, M.J.P. (1983). *Flora of Connemara and the Burren.* Cambridge: Cambridge University Press.

Wells, T.C.E. (1981). Population ecology of terrestrial orchids. In: Synge, H. (ed.), *The Biological Aspects of Rare Plant Conservation.* New York: John Wiley & Sons.

Wells, T.C.E., Rothey, P., Cox, R. & Bamford, S. (1998). Flowering dynamics of *Orchis morio* L. and *Herminium monorchis* (L.) R. Br. at two sites in eastern England. *Botanical Journal of the Linnean Society* 126: 39–48.

Wigginton, M.J. (ed.) (1999). *British Red Data Books. 1. Vascular Plants.* Peterborough: Joint Nature Conservation Cttee.

Williams, J.G., Williams, A.E. & Arlott, N. (1978). *A Field Guide to the Orchids of Britain and Europe with North Africa and the Middle East.* London: Collins.

Willems, J.H. (1992). Establishment and development of a population of *Orchis simia* Lamk. in the Netherlands, 1972 to 1981. *New Phytologist* 91: 757–765.

Willems, J.H. & Bik, L. (1991). Long-term dynamics in a population of *Orchis simia* in the Netherlands. In: Wells, T.C.E. & Willems, J.H. (eds.), *Population Ecology of Terrestrial Orchids,* pp. 33–45. The Hague: SPB Academic Publishing.

Willems, J.H. & Melser, C. (1998). Population dynamics and life-history of *Coeloglossum viride* (L.) Hartm.: an endangered orchid species in the Netherlands. *Botanical Journal of the Linnean Society* 126: 83–93.

Willis, A.J., Martin, M.H. & Taylor, K.B. (1991). *Orchis purpurea* Hudson in the Avon Gorge, Bristol. *Watsonia* 18: 387–390.

Wood, J. & Ramsay, M. (2004). *Anacamptis laxiflora* Orchidaceae. *Curtis's Botanical Magazine* 21: 26–33.

Index

Page numbers of principal references are printed in bold and illustrations are indicated by italic type. English names are indexed separately (pp. 388–389), as also are general terms (p. 390).

Plate 401 (opposite).
Orchis purpurea at the base of a beech tree. These ladies have much fuller figures than those in Plate 165 (p. 166). East Kent, 23 May 1994.

Index of English names

General index